Bluet

To mary

love Jane Hogger
x

Bluebell Girl

by

Jane Hoggar

YOUCAXTON
PUBLICATIONS

ISBN 978-1-913425-97-5
Published by YouCaxton Publications 2021
YCBN: 01

YouCaxton Publications
www.youcaxton.co.uk

Disclaimer

The contents of this book are based on events that occurred, and people that the author encountered during her dance career. One or two characters have been combined therefore, some names have been changed.

For Miss Shipton

Contents

Like giant exotic moths

Feathered and bejewelled

Showgirls come out at night

Nocturnal creatures

Drawn to the spotlight

Flitting from place to place

Living for the moment

Fleeting, transient

Elegant, delicate

Likely to escape your grasp

Stop her mid flight

She may turn to dust ...

PROLOGUE

OUR LEADING LADY is poised, gracefully perched on the glittering *Panache* sign as it rises up out of the floor. A vision of elegance in diamonds and white plumes, she unfolds a delicate arm to present Miss Bluebell's immaculate lines of dashing Kelly Boys, dapper in white sequinned suits and trilby's, as they sashay in perfect unison onto the stage. The Bluebell Girls are on their way, creating a flurry of excitement amongst the audience. The orchestra gathers pace as this breath-taking spectacle opens the first of two sensational, nightly shows at Le Lido de Paris on Avenue des Champs-Élysées.

> "Le Show! Le Lido!
> Avec Panache!
> Ce Soir!
> Au Lido de Paris!"

The audience blink in astonishment at the dazzling scene before them, assuming that this exquisite leading lady in white, is a Parisian Belle.

Little do they know, she is Sherri-Lee from Wigan.

Miss Bluebell has been recruiting tall dancers of sophistication and beauty for her glamorous shows, for over

xiii

fifty years. Insisting on a minimum height of five feet and ten inches tall, Bluebell travels far and wide in search of such ladies. At six-feet tall, Sherri-Lee was whisked to Paris within days of attending an audition in London, transformed from secretary to showgirl in a flash. She was the talk of Wigan and surrounding areas for years, much to the immense joy of her proud mother. When Mrs Griggs had seen Miss Bluebell's London auditions advertised in The Stage newspaper, she hadn't been able to get Sherri-Lee on that train quick enough. After years of sewing costumes for dance competitions late into the night and waiting for her daughter in changing rooms during endless dance classes, she'd felt it was pay-back time.

Sherri-Lee hadn't let her down.

Our Master of Ceremonies, Romain, steps into the central spotlight, to sing,

"You are just, too marvellous, too marvellous for words!"

As he strolls across the stage, I'm inclined to agree with Romain wholeheartedly, after the rollercoaster journey I've endured in recent years. Glancing with pride at Sherri-Lee, the Kelly Boys and the rows of dazzling Bluebell Girls, I feel thrilled to be part of the cogs in the wheel that make Paris the most romantic city in the world.

A Bluebell Girl at last, I am where I've always wanted to be. But getting here has been, shall we say, eventful?

Arriving at this prestigious point of my career, at the Lido, I acknowledge that my journey hasn't been quite as straight forward as Sherri-Lee's.

Shimmering under the lights, we glide onto the stage. Taking our places, poised, radiant, tiaras glistening with diamantes and lustrous plumes soaring high, we prepare to be presented to almost a thousand guests of Miss Bluebell.

Since the beginning of my career, I'd been angling towards Miss Bluebell's girls, when the boys at my ballet class had confessed that they couldn't lift me anymore due to my rapidly increasing height. It had taken me longer than I'd anticipated, to seek her out though. There had been endless distractions along the way.

At last, my dream had become a reality, and my debut at the Lido would have felt 'too marvellous for words' if it hadn't been for the unexpected message brought to my dressing room just minutes before curtain up.

1

IPSWICH - 1960'S/70's

I WOULDN'T CHOOSE to wear fur now, but at the age of four, nothing felt more thrilling. I didn't know that Granny's coat was made of innocent creatures as I paraded down her elegant stairs in it. The cool silk lining caressed my skin as I strode along, what seemed then, a vast expanse of Axminster carpet. Arriving at the umbrella stand by the front door, I would take a bow. The thrill of my procession was heightened if I could persuade a passing relative or visitor to applaud. This was definitely where my love of performing began. My earliest memory is rummaging uncomfortably on top of all of the ballroom dancing shoes, at the back of Granny's wardrobe and discovering a furry stole with a fox head on the end of it. He looked very angry to have been disturbed and I remember screaming, a real scream, as we stared at each other in the semi-darkness until Granny dragged me out and held me to her ample bosom. I never went into that wardrobe again, choosing instead, to stay by the dressing table, exploring the costume jewellery from her Japanese treasure box.

Granny and Mum used to pass my brother and I back and forth to each other, enabling them to work as short-hand typists, at a time when most mothers were happy, or obliged, to stay at home as housewives.

"You have to have your running away money," Granny would explain with a frown as she sprayed hair lacquer furiously over her wash and set.

As she skilfully applied a quick slick of Risky Rouge to her lips, I would sit, transfixed, waiting in eager anticipation for her pout at the end. With a final glance of approval, she would smooth down her silk blouse and tweed skirt, before brushing passed me with her familiar waft of Players N°6, mingled with Charlie perfume. I never quite understood what she meant by running away money, until years later. Her words came back to me when my parents argued one afternoon. I convinced myself that Mum was going to run away, with her typing money.

Our parents and grandparents took it in turns to walk us to school in the mornings throughout our early years. I looked forward to Granny's turn because I loved the clip clop of her high heels on the pavement as my brother and I scurried along, trying to keep up.

Mum and Granny had insatiable appetites for reading and escapism. They never missed an episode of Crossroads and always had a Catherine Cookson on the go. Every week we went to make our choices from the library, a grand, elegant building that introduced me to Enid Blyton, Noel Streatfield, Dodie Smith and later, Jane Austen. These authors brought calm to my worried mind. The uplifting stories of confident girls, with such gung-ho, give-it-a-go approaches to life, were an inspiration to my own. Their innovative solutions to tricky situations were impressive, teaching me many a cunning wheeze to outwit the bullies of the classroom. Such knowledge proved most useful in later years. The heroines of Enid Blyton's *St. Clare's* and Winifred Norling's *The Testing of Tansy* really were a force to be reckoned with. Teaching me to stay calm in a crisis, I think these gals should take the credit for my tireless optimism, that naturally springs into action whenever I'm faced with a dilemma. When plans go pear shaped, I naturally find tempting, alternative solutions, looking on the bright side and finding a sunny outlook on most predicaments.

My first experience of this approach was the nativity play. It was my stage debut and Granny was on the front row with Mum when I clearly remember having to be a true professional and look delighted as my best friend Jayne played the role of Mary. While the audience admired the beautiful stable scene, I was stuck at the back on a bench, having been cast as a little angel. This was to be the only time in my life that I was ever to be cast as something little. As I watched Jayne from my bench in the shadows, she lowered her eyes and prayed importantly. Clad in her satin blue scarf, she watched over her brand-new Tiny Tears doll that returned her gaze from the straw. It stared vacantly back at her from the manger, reminding me of the fox in the wardrobe. Jayne really did steal the show that day. Fortunately, my natural ability for making the best of a situation kicked in, pulling me through the performance with flare. I donned my white pillowcase and tin foil star, tackling the job in hand without a screaming tantrum and managed to enjoy myself after all. At the tender age of four, I had rallied around, discovering that being a little angel could be fun. You didn't *have* to be the star of the show. Being a supporting role is hugely rewarding and vital to the success of the final production, in any walk of life.

The nativity proved very good training for the future, when I was to find myself performing with all sorts of demanding personalities. I would regularly have to tackle many a tricky scenario with a smile, realising early on, that very little is ever achieved by pessimism.

Having grown up during the glamorous thirties and forties, my Granny had enjoyed endless trips to picture houses and music halls with her friends during her youth. Noticing my interest in song and dance very early on, she hoped that maybe one day, I would 'tread the boards'. Constantly encouraging me to sing or 'do a turn' at family gatherings, Granny was extremely proud of my recitals, which had usually been devised in her hallway. She *always* called me through to watch the dancers on Seaside Special as they strut their stuff in bright, white shorts. They even had their names printed on their T-shirts, so I got in huge trouble from Mum, for writing my name in felt pen on my C&A shirt.

My parents, brother and I lived in close proximity to most of our relatives in the town of Ipswich. There were frequent family gatherings, especially at weekends, when aunties, uncles and grandparents lit up cigarettes, drinking endless cups of tea, as they chatted for hours on end while the children were expected to entertain themselves. We would sit patiently colouring in our picture books and building enormous LEGO houses, while the adults put the world to rights in the smoke-filled lounge. Whenever I see plumes of smoke or dust floating across a room full of sunlight, it immediately takes me back to that time. After an hour or so, we children would feel strangely nauseous. Granted permission to go outside, we would burst into the fresh air and freedom of the glorious garden, where I would sit at the top of Grandad's apple trees, singing my heart out. Grandad's pale blue shed was down at the end of the garden, with a concrete path that led from its door, through the centre of the endless rows of tall runner bean plants and dahlia's, all the way to the lawn. I would sing and dance gracefully down the path, the fruit and veg as my audience, nodding as I went.

Growing up during the sixties and seventies, we had no electronic gadgets to while away the hours so my books, Twinkle comics, music and imagination were my best friends. The book that I treasured most amongst my collection was, remarkably, an illustrated Bible. My maternal instincts have always been strong, inspired by the nativity scene, so I used to re-enact it constantly. Inviting neighbours, the milkman, the coalman or Jehovah's Witnesses, to bring Gold, Frankincense and Myrrh to my imaginary baby Jesus on the manger (Mum's paisley pouffe in the lounge) the game would last for hours. It was that same year that I asked Father Christmas for a blue satin head scarf like Mother Mary's, and Mum really started to worry about my obsession with the Bible, especially when I screamed "Jesus!" at the top of my voice, when her friend, Sue, went to sit on the pouffe manger during one of Mum's Tupperware parties.

During my early years, I had a tendency to feel isolated during meal times, struggling to be heard by a family who were often engrossed in highly spirited conversations. I couldn't keep up with them, so I tended to switch off. Instead, I developed an imaginary friend to connect with, called Madeleine. Every day, I would set a place for her at the dining table. When I started school, I was horrified that the teacher, Miss Phillips, refused to allow Madeleine to sit next to me in the classroom. Understandably, Miss Phillips could foresee that the whole class, after being introduced to Madeleine, would discover imaginary friends of their own. There just wouldn't have been enough chairs. Miss Phillips was smart, wasting no time in distracting me from Madeleine, with her wonderful Music and Movement lessons, using the record player in the hall. My spirits soared as she taught us an exciting dance to Little Eva's, *Do the Locomotion*. Madeleine was quickly replaced by real friends and things improved rapidly.

Mum's typing speed had hit a record high, giving her the confidence to apply for a full-time job as personal assistant to our local member of Parliament. Girl power was continuing to flourish during the early seventies, as mothers all over Britain, tied front door keys around their children's necks, discovering the freedom of the working world. Conveniently, with this excitement came entertainment in the form of children's television programmes, introducing us to Blue Peter, Jackanory, Crackerjack and Playschool. Valerie Singleton kept us busy with arts and crafts, creating wonderful, pink Barbie houses fashioned from cornflake packets, poster paints and sticky-backed plastic. John Noakes showed us how to build magnificent cakes in the shape of daleks and caterpillars. His lashings of blue and green food colouring would bring such a transformation to a Swiss roll with great dollops of icing and generous sprinklings of hundreds and thousands. We would chip away at the remnants of these cakes, left on a plate near the kettle, for weeks. I loved my Barbie house. I had always wanted one since my friend Cheryl, whose father worked on the American airbase, had invited me to tea. Cheryl had the coolest family I had ever met. They ate exciting food, like French Toast swamped in maple syrup, and Cheerios cereal, with marshmallow bits in it. This highly commercial type of food was imported from the States, so wasn't available at our local supermarkets in Britain at that time. It was so exotic to my young taste buds. The most enchanting part of my visit to Cheryl though, was when we went up to her bedroom to look at the Barbie house. It was a real plastic one, bought from a shop. It wasn't made with cornflake boxes like mine. It had real furniture, a wardrobe full of clothes and a garage with a pink car in it. Rather than sulk that I didn't own one like her, I rushed home and built an extension for mine out of a shoe box, with great pride. Cheryl nodded politely when I showed it to her on her next visit.

"You don't need a Barbie!" Mum would remark scathingly as she served up the fish fingers and beans after school. "Barbie sits around all day, trying on clothes and waiting for Ken to get home. I have bigger and better plans for you, young lady."

There was one night of the week though, where our family did see eye to eye, and that was Top of the Pops on a Thursday evening. After tea, my brother and I would make sure we had finished our homework, ready for the big night of the week. Diving onto the sofa in the lounge with a large Tupperware bowl of Angel Delight and two spoons, we prepared to watch all the best bands, miming their latest hits, 'live' in the studio. If I ever taste butterscotch Angel Delight, it takes me back to those nights immediately. It wasn't just *my* family either. Thursday night was Top of the Pops night for everyone, the pop charts being the main topic of conversation in the playground at school. Watched by families all over Britain, the nation would grind to halt, to wonder at the magnificent glamour of T. Rex, David Bowie, Mud, The Sweet and The Bay City Rollers, as they battled for a place at the top of the pop charts. You couldn't be late, or you missed the moment when the DJ would announce,

"It's Thursday night. It's Top of the Pops."

CCS's *Whole Lotta Love*, would send us into raptures of excitement. My brother would roll about on the floor with his air guitar and I would shake my long hair wildly, as I stamped around the lounge.

When a fast song came on, Mum and Dad would leap up from their armchairs, jiving to songs like *Tiger Feet* by Mud, igniting something within them, that I never saw at any other time. My brother and I would gaze in awe at their skill. Not taking their eyes off each other, Mum and Dad danced as one unit, in an almost private world of their own. There was such a connection between them that I sometimes wonder whether, if they had continued to dance regularly, their marriage would not have failed in later years. My parents had learnt to dance during their courting years in the fifties and sixties. For Mum and Dad, the Friday night dance was the only place that young people could socialise. All young couples of that time learnt to jive to Rock Around the Clock, when Bill Hayley and The Comets hit the music scene with enormous impact. Bill started a new dance sensation that has never, in my view, been rivalled.

The highlight of Top of the Pops, for me was a group of female dancers called Pan's People. In perfect unison, these feisty women took to the stage, strutting their stuff with lots of jazzy hands, hip thrusting and leg kicking. Their tantalising attire consisted of either risqué, floaty frocks of immense femininity, or brightly coloured, funky hot pants, cropped T-shirts and knee-high boots, displaying a more girl power approach as they kicked and punched the air. Their bodies were so finely tuned and perfect that you couldn't help gazing in adoration. Added to this, apparently, they only ever had one day to learn the routine. The role of Pans People was to dance to the song of whichever band wasn't available to appear that night. This was simply heroic in my opinion. Polished to perfection, they took to the stage as one beautiful group of loveliness. They had cool names like Dee-Dee and Babs, and I would rush up close to the screen, as would my Dad and brother. Not having recording facilities, I would carefully memorise each step of their dance, later on working hard to recreate my own version in my bedroom. I was constantly adding new moves to my ever-expanding repertoire, planning to change my name, one day, from Jane to Lulu.

Top of the Pops was filmed in London, clearly the place to be, and so much more exciting than Ipswich. As far as I was aware, at that time, the highest achievement for a girl in Ipswich, was to be chosen as the carnival queen. Carnival queens didn't excite me at all. They never seemed to have an opinion about anything. I was convinced that Pan's People had more substance and attitude, living an exciting life that I craved to be a part of.

The audience on Top of the Pops were just as entertaining as the bands, because the general public hadn't yet mastered the art of free-style dancing. The jive had disappeared, as disco crept in, so people often weren't sure what to do with themselves on the dance floor. There were lots of slightly nervous girls, treading on each other's patent clad toes, in their crimplene tunics and American Tan tights. They shuffled about grinning at each other with shifty, excited embarrassment. At the end of each song, the lucky ones would be shown, live to the nation, standing next to the DJ of the moment. As he introduced the next hit, he often held his arm around one of them, and this, in my opinion, was the coolest thing that could ever happen to a girl. When Mum sent us up to bed at the end of the show, I would sit in my room, unable to consider sleeping. Instead, I would put on a record and dance, wearing very fetching outfits rustled up from her wardrobe where there was an abundance of chiffon scarves, high heels and costume jewellery. I'd also complete the look by dabbing on plenty of blue eye-shadow and orange lipstick, borrowed from her handbag.

My babysitter, Deborah, was cool. I loved her. She even had a T. Rex song written all about her. She made the mistake one night though, of arriving to look after us in a suede mini skirt with poppers up the front. I was completely transfixed and when she refused to let me try it on, I made her 'dance like Pan's People' in it, to *Remember You're a Womble*. She wasn't at all keen.

As time went by, we listened to more and more pop music at home, mainly on our transistor radios and fortunately my music tastes developed rapidly. My favourite station was Radio Caroline, an independent, offshore station based off the port of Felixstowe. My brother had explained to me that it was a pirate station. Of course, I immediately imagined an old galleon moored in an exotic, forbidden lagoon somewhere in the English Channel, with swashbuckling DJs and rock chick mermaids on the deck. Mum would often find me fast asleep with my radio still playing under my pillow when she went up to bed, and there would be hell to pay. We also enjoyed Ed Stewart's Junior Choice on a Saturday morning too, but it was really designed for younger children. *Sparky's Magic Piano* or *The Candy Man* were not really suitable for Pan's People dancing. The best radio programme had to be the Top Twenty on Sunday nights. It seemed to lift the depressing 'school tomorrow' feeling, as we listened in. The chart hits caused great excitement because, to realise that your favourite band had reached number one was such a thrilling start to the week. We used to buy single vinyl records cheaply with our pocket money from Woolworths department store, choosing from the top twenty hit singles, listed on a black and white chart on the wall. I was lucky enough to have a record player in my bedroom called a Dansette and bringing my new record home from the shops with pride, I would play it endlessly. This was where my love of music and dance really began.

As well as my selection of top twenty singles, I owned two treasured LPs. One was called *Your Waltz and Ballet Favourites*, and the other was called *Top of the Pops*. I was given *The Wombles Greatest Hits* by a well-meaning aunt, but I only played that when I was extremely bored. On the front cover of my *Waltz and Ballet Favourites* LP was a delightful couple, dancing a Pas de Deux in beautiful pink costumes. I had been taken to see *The Nutcracker* at The Royal Festival Hall in London one Christmas, and it had left quite an impression on me. I had a warm affection for the dancers on my LP cover. I wanted to be that girl so much with her fluffy tutu, satin clad, pointing feet and silky hair, slicked back into a neat ballet bun. I imagined the thrill of a man being in love with me, just like the ballerina's handsome partner was, so obviously, in love with her. He wore no trousers. Just pale soft tights with a curious lump at the front. My friend from ballet class came for tea once and calmly explained to my family that, this appendage was for the lady to put her foot on, to help her during the lifts. This charming man gazed down at the ballerina lovingly, holding her effortlessly in his arms as she stretched her leg up, high above his head. I imagined that life was trouble free and truly beautiful in the ballet world.

There is a song called *At the Ballet*, written by Edward Kleben, from the musical *A Chorus Line*. It always reminds me of this time. It goes

"Everything, was beautiful, at the ballet,
Graceful men, lift lovely girls, in white,
Yes, everything was beautiful at the ballet
I was happy, at the ballet."

On the front of my *Top of the Pops* LP, there was a girl wearing a red T-shirt and a saucy smile. Her hair was dark and glossy and as I grew up, I had to admit that I probably looked more like her than the ballerina. There was a selection of songs on that LP, ranging from Alice Cooper's *Schools Out Forever*, to The Sweet's *Wig Wam Bam*. Every spare moment I had, I would set up a stage in my bedroom, adding raunchy dance moves that I'd learnt from Pan's People, to my growing portfolio of choreographies. A particular favourite song was Alvin Stardust's *My Coo Ca Choo*. When my brother was out, I'd steal his T. Rex record and sing along to the curious words of *Get It On*, desperate to know what they meant.

"You're built like a car,
You've got a hub cap diamond star halo,
You're dirty, sweet and you're my girl
Get it on, bang a gong, get it on ..."

I would sing to my reflection in the mirror and stick my tongue out, feeling strange.

Choreographing dances for hours and hours, I wafted around in my world of dancing bliss, but my dancing didn't feel complete. I yearned to go back to the ballet school up the road. You see, I'd fled years before, in terror, when the teacher had announced to the class that I would be taking an exam. I was petrified at the thought of the formality of it all, persuading my mother to write a note to the teacher, explaining that I had decided to join the Brownie Guides and would not be returning to ballet classes. After several years of dancing alone in my room though, I'd become bored with my LPs and I had begun to wear the carpet away. My Dad complained that there were cracks appearing in the lounge ceiling where I had been hurling myself around with gusto, in my bedroom above. I decided that there was nothing for it, but to find the courage to return to the ballet school. The simple fact was, that I had run out of ideas for my choreographies and needed guidance from a professional. I still so desperately wanted to be in Pan's People.

As soon as I arrived at the elegant ballet school, my love of the place came rushing back to me. I climbed the steep, stone steps and rang the Victorian brass bell before entering the gracious hallway, where I was greeted by the pleasurable smell of ballet shoe leather and floor polish. I could hear the inviting plonk-plonk of the piano, and the distant voice of the teacher, Miss Linda Shipton, as she counted the students through their exercises. It felt like coming home. I loved the way that all the girls walked with their feet turned out, and I started to copy them immediately. It made me feel a little bit important.

When I walked into the studio and saw the smiling face of Miss Shipton, standing at the front of the class in her flared skirt and matching leotard, I knew everything was going to be alright. This was my future. My feelings of elation were dampened slightly however, when Miss Shipton explained that I was going to have to start classes with the younger children in order to learn all the exercises for each grade. I was even going to have to wear the uniform, a hideous turquoise leotard with a childish skirt attached and matching hairband.

"No! That is not meant to happen," I thought, aghast, thinking of Pan's People as I watched the older girls trailing out to their lesson in a different studio. Those girls were wearing grown up, shiny, navy leotards. They hadn't chickened out and left years before, to start Brownies instead, like I had. Thankfully, as I reviewed the situation, my optimistic streak kicked in. I realised there was only one option. I was just going to have to battle it out.

"How bad can it be?" I pondered positively, as I pedalled furiously up the hill the next day to my first class.

"If it's really terrible, I can always go back to Brownies and work towards my Hostess badge," I thought, reassuring myself that I was very skilled at making Butterfly Buns and Cornflake Cakes. I managed to convince myself that it was a win-win situation, overcoming the humiliation of starting at the lowest grade in a baby costume, and buckling down to work. I was learning that if you wanted something badly enough in life, then you just had to get yourself out there, lose the fear of failure, and throw yourself into it. Something told me that it was better to have a go and see what happened, rather than spend the rest of your life wondering what could have been. This approach became ingrained within. My parents must have appreciated my efforts because they never let on that the lessons were costing them a fortune in fees. I thought the teacher taught us for fun.

The years went by and I biked up that hill to ballet class on most evenings after school, existing only for each lesson and, of course, Top of the Pops on Thursdays.

In no time at all I was moved up to the navy shiny class and things really took off.

2

GROWING UP

SEVENTIES BRITAIN WAS full of angst, strikes and industrial action but I was blissfully unaware of any of the political problems that were going on. The miner's strike over pit closures was causing coal supplies to run low, resulting in power cuts. It didn't occur to me to ask my parents why the power cuts were happening. I just enjoyed arranging candle-lit games of Murder in the Dark with my friends. If it wasn't in my *Jackie* comic, then I wasn't hugely interested. *Jackie* was a must-read for every teenage girl. The Cathy and Claire problem page and the pin-up posters, of David Cassidy and Donny Osmond, were an essential part of life. I could only get to sleep if I had the reassuring face of Donny looking down at me from the back of my bedroom door.

My parents were quite groovy. I remember being rather proud of them at school fetes and events. They would arrive in our camper van, sporting whacky sunglasses and an air of liveliness. Dad looked elegant, towering over us in his funky cheesecloth shirts and flared cords. Mum was pretty and so smiley in her dungarees. She even wore clogs. Most of the other mums were tucked in and tidy in their woolly skirts and gingham blouses, seeming older.

Our VW camper van had brown patterned curtains. There were stickers on the back window, displaying all the places we had been to. We really were the height of cool during this Bohemian phase of our family life, as we cruised around Europe on mystery tours during the long summer holidays. We never needed to plan the route as we pootled along the coastline, surviving on baguettes stuffed with tomatoes, smothered in copious amounts of Heinz salad cream. My parents probably drank copious amounts of wine with this while my brother and I enjoyed Tupperware beakers of orange squash.

In those days, with fewer laws against camping on beaches or in fields, we had complete freedom to pack up at the end of the school term, hop on the ferry to France at the port of Felixstowe, and just see where the road took us. I don't remember washing. Mum stashed essentials like beans and ketchup in the secret cupboard under the back seats. On the way home, she would fill the same cupboard with bottles of cheap wine hoping we weren't pulled over on our way through customs. She always insisted that one of us laid on the back seat, pretending to be fast asleep on the way through. Only the most cruel of customs officers would insist on waking a child.

Our trusty old van was a big part of our lives, not just for holidays but at weekends too, when we would spend hours on end in it with our two cousins, in the pub car park. Our parents, aunts, uncles and grandparents would sit drinking and smoking all afternoon in the lounge bar of the pub. We would wait obediently for them in the van, sipping our little bottles of Coca-Cola through paper straws until we were quite giddy. There was a packet of cheese and onion crisps to share between the four of us, as we contentedly played I Spy. If the car park wasn't too busy, my brother would give us driving lessons. We discussed many subjects during these times, and it was on one of these occasions that it was explained to us, by a friend who had joined us for the day, that grown-ups actually had sex for fun, not just to make a baby. We were horrified at this ridiculous suggestion, refusing to believe her. However, it did explain a few scenarios I had inadvertently walked into in the past. I remember telling my parents at breakfast time once, that I thought our house must be too warm. I explained to them that the previous night, I'd had a bad dream and gone down the stairs to tell Deborah, the baby-sitter and her boyfriend about it, only to find when I entered the lounge, they had taken most of their clothes off.

I swear that those long afternoons in the car park of the pub were where my entertainment skills became finely honed. I would rally the troops and get us all out onto the wide expanse of tarmac where I would choreograph dance routines, weather permitting. There would always be an enthusiastic audience because other children were also waiting in cars, for their parents to come out of the pub, like us. The naughty ones would get out of the car and learn my dance routine. The obedient ones would stay in the car, as they'd been told, watching eagerly, with their noses squashed up against the steamed-up windows.

When the adults eventually drove us home, and slumped on the sofa, Mum would prepare ham sandwiches and crisps for us all to enjoy in front of the wrestling on TV. During half-time we would perform our well-rehearsed dance routines to them, and I would feel proud as punch.

When we hit puberty my brother and I found that, although we had loved our childhood holidays, the novelty of the camper van was starting to wear off. Our teenage hormones were kicking in and we ceased to be quite so enamoured with playing *London's Burning* on our descant recorders for hundreds of miles, in the stifling heat of the van. Both measuring almost six feet tall, we had outgrown the tiny bunk beds, expertly fitted into the van roof, obviously designed for younger children.

Starting secondary school brought with it a welcome independence that I loved. Catching the bus and meeting up with friends on the way, opened up a whole new social world that was exciting. If we walked home, we could spend our five pence bus fare on a Traffic Light lolly and some fizz bombs. The walk home took an hour, but it was worth it for the heady rush of sugar after such a long day at school. It also explains why I have so many huge mercury fillings in all my back teeth.

As I reached my early teens, I grew taller than many of my schoolteachers, let alone my peers, and by the age of fourteen I'd begun to resent my ever-increasing height. I was hugely self-conscious, just wanting to be the same as all the other girls. Fortunately, my dance classes began to develop a welcome confidence within, that had been lacking in my early years. I had also begun to find my voice and so thrilled was I, with my new-found skill of conversation, that I was often scolded for distracting my classmates during lessons. I entertained my friends constantly with funny stories and, as I beamed down at my teachers, like a big, friendly ostrich, it must have been challenging for them, to say the least.

The other girls in my class seemed so dainty as they filed into assembly with their delicate little feet and pretty shoes. I felt rather envious that they could wear fashionable platform heels called Wedges, without towering over everyone, like I did. My feet were so long by the time I was a young teenager, that I had to wear whatever we could find to fit me at the shoe shops. My mother, angry that ladies' shoes didn't go up to a size 9, would traipse around with me for hours asking for size 8's, hoping that I would be able to cram my toes into something appropriate for school. The shop assistants would bring us dusty boxes of whatever they could dig out, from the back of the stock room, watching my mother sympathetically, as she sat nodding helplessly at me, gazing in horror at my awkwardness. Mum would insist that I walk up and down the shop to see if the shoes fitted properly. They never did.

"At least you'll be a good swimmer! You'll have to just wear the boxes," she jested, trying to lighten the mood.

Trying to laugh with her I would complicate matters, announcing uneasily, that I didn't want any sort of heel on my shoes. I already towered above all the boys at school, even in my bare feet. Looking in the mirror at home in my bedroom, I felt quite pretty, but I knew that boys would never dare to ask me to be their girlfriend. It wasn't acceptable for a girl to be taller than a boy, for snogging reasons. It looked all wrong at the disco to be smooching with a boy, if he had to look up lovingly at you. It looked as though he were dancing with one of the teachers, or someone's mum. Girls were supposed to be dainty and acquiescent, while boys were supposed to be tall and protective. This proved to be a very unreliable assumption years later, when divorce rates hit the roof. Women soon learnt that, more often than not, they were the ones left, having to be tall and protective.

However, there were a few boys in my class with whom, if I was careful with my posture, we could at least be the same height. I found that if I had completely flat shoes on, I was at least in with a slight chance of a goodnight kiss at the bus stop or a dance at the disco. I became amorous with a boy called Dylan at this time and we spent blissful days together kissing and lolling in each other's arms on the park. I was so happy, convinced that I had found true love. Unfortunately, I was wrong. Dylan turned up to meet me at Woolworths one Saturday morning with a strange scarf around his neck. I giggled when I saw it and complimented him for his new dapper appearance, until later in the morning, as we browsed the Pick 'n' Mix, the scarf slipped, revealing a love bite on his neck. I knew it wasn't from me because I would never have done such a disgusting act. My heart was shocked and broken but I held my head high, baffled and hurt. I explained that I couldn't be his girlfriend anymore and ran home. Shortly after this incident, I received a phone call from the girl responsible for the love bite. She was in a phone box.

"Hi, it's me, Angela. You can't chuck Dylan, please don't chuck Dylan, you two are so good together. It didn't mean anything, and we were drunk."

I stood in the hall, astonished at her words as they cascaded down the line. How could Dylan and I be good together if he had to have another girlfriend sucking his neck on the quiet? I was very polite.

"Oh no, it's fine Angela. I really don't mind. You can have him. Thanks for ringing though." I chirruped bravely.

Despite my calm response to Angela, the disappointment really knocked my confidence, making it more apparent to me that I still hadn't grown breasts. I was forced to nod admiringly at my friend's white frilly bras when they showed them off in the changing rooms during PE. I was an open invitation to the bullies, and they would scream with laughter as I hurriedly put on my PE kit, hiding my vest and wishing my boobs would grow. I was envious of girls that were allowed to buy a Teen

Bra, even though some of them, like me, had no boobs yet either.

"Don't be silly! There's nothing to hold up darling!" my mother chuckled when I bravely broached the subject one tea-time.

Women's Liberation was growing rapidly, so Mum had burnt all her bras. She certainly wasn't going to buy one for me. Fortunately, misery caused my entrepreneurial skills to go into overdrive, tackling the predicament with one of my extraordinary coping mechanisms. So desperate was I, to own a Cross Your Heart Bra, that one rainy, Sunday afternoon, accepting that Mum was not going to let me order a bra from the Kays catalogue, I knitted two squares and attached them with crocheted straps. It was a masterpiece, all created with my Knitting Nancy set.

I'm glad, in hindsight, that I didn't quite have the confidence to wear my masterpiece to school. Instead, I just wore it secretly at weekends, feeling hugely mature and a little bit like the girl on the front of my Top of the Pops LP.

Once I'd made a bra, there was no stopping me. My confidence soared and sent me rushing to the fabric shop in town. There I'd discovered a newfound freedom, amongst the endless rows of shelves that heaved with bolts of fabric. Laura Ashley had hit the fashion world hard, with her floral prints and feminine loveliness. It was normal for women to make their own clothes then, much more so than today. At school during needlework, we made smocks in a fabric of our choice. I immediately imagined what Dee Dee or Babs from Pans People would have chosen, opting for denim. Everyone else brought in flowered prints or Broderie Anglaise, a very popular, lady-like material of the moment. It had horrified me to learn we were making smocks at school, recoiling in distaste as people took their neatly folded pretty fabrics out of the pristine paper bags on the first day of term. It made me think it was anticipated that the next stage, expected in life for us, was to have a baby.

Pan's People didn't have babies.

To cheer myself up and make a point, I saved up enough pocket money to buy a metre of sequinned, fuchsia pink, stretchy material from an exciting area of the fabric store, designated to the rapidly emerging disco scene. I very quickly fashioned a boob tube, much to my Mum's amazement, and proceeded to wear it proudly on Thursdays for Top of the Pops. I didn't know at the time, but that boob tube was to accompany me on many trips, later in my life, for various performances around the world. Eventually, it became a piece of vintage history in my daughter's dressing-up box. I still own it to this day, although, sadly, it doesn't get worn that often. I'm considering making it into a knitting bag for when I'm sent to the old people's home.

My height predicament was accentuated at school by my best friend Hannah. She was as petite and dainty, as I was tall and awkward. My saving grace was that Hannah and I were both blessed with a wickedly pleasing sense of humour. Our laughter and cheeky comments resonated throughout the school at break-times, until eventually, we were offered roles in the school musicals as a way of channelling our energy. This was a new lease of life and we decided to abandon the idea of boyfriends. I was developing sloping shoulders from attempting to chat up boys and as for Hannah, well, she'd been having trouble fighting them all off. We threw ourselves instead, into singing and dancing for school performances with the music and drama department, causing quite a stir, demonstrating that personality played quite a large part in the dating game. It wasn't all about tits and height after all.

My newly discovered distraction of performing song-and-dance routines on the stage, pleased my father hugely. He wasn't ready to consider the possibility of his daughter having a boyfriend. He treated any boy that dared to knock at our door, as though they were a bailiff or a double-glazing salesman. The dread of a pregnant daughter was a fear worse than death in those days and my mother often reminded me in hushed tones that there would be plenty of time for love when I was older. Sex before marriage was seen as shocking and sinful at that time and Mum, having married at eighteen so she could get on down with Dad, reassured me that I would find a tall, handsome man when I got out into the real world. I can assure you that I proved her right there, making up for lost time when I eventually set off on my travels. I tested out quite a few actually, tall, short, thin and plump.

There were interesting situations that presented themselves at school due to my extremely long arms and legs. Mr Sanderson, my PE teacher, had high hopes for me as he tried enthusiastically, to encourage me to enter into the world of sport.

"She really has the potential to be quite an athlete," he would explain at parents evening.

Little did he know; I possessed not an ounce of competitive spirit. I felt quite a strong affection for Mr Sanderson, but he only came up to my hip, so I couldn't enjoy any romantic thoughts about him. The only time I was popular and felt confident was in netball when the cool girls wanted me on their team so that I could be goalkeeper.

"Just stand by the net and wave your arms around if the ball comes this way," they would instruct with a titter, in their bossy little voices, before sprinting off to score loads of goals up at the other end of the court.

Mr Sanderson would give me the thumbs up and punch the air, causing the little whistle around his neck to bounce about as he jogged along the side-line. I would wander reluctantly across to my lonely spot.

Whenever it rains now, on warm tarmac, there is a smell that reminds me of this time.

I didn't want to disappoint Mr Sanderson because he was such a sweet man. I had a feeling he fancied me a bit, but I knew he had a girlfriend because I'd seen her helping him on the tombola stall at the school fete, so I didn't flirt. At netball matches, I was supposed to pat the ball away from the net with my big hands whenever the opposition came charging towards me to shoot. The best teams always chose me for this purpose and so the ball never came over to me, because we were usually winning up at the other end. I would sway with boredom, as I stood waiting for the match to end, talking to the goal shooter from the opposite team. Goal shooters were usually tall like me and we would, at least, have some sort of camaraderie with our mutual stature problem while we waited for the game to finish. The trouble with this arrangement though, was that while we waited, I would be tempted to distract the goal shooter with jolly banter and cartwheels. Keeping us so entertained meant that we were slow to react when the ball suddenly shot up to our end. I was usually somewhere else doing the splits on the grass. One of the opposition would often score at these moments and boy, did I get into trouble from the bossy girls. Mr Sanderson always forgave me.

I loved acrobatics and one day, I found myself goal watching alongside a like-minded girl called Tracy King. Tracy was impressed with my demonstrations of cartwheels and splits and explained that she was a member of a gymnastics club. She proceeded to do a walk-over which left me speechless. A walk-over is a handstand that keeps going over, until you find the ground with your feet and stand up again. I had never been in such close proximity with someone who could do a walk-over. Being almost as tall as me, Tracy made it look fantastically elegant and her walk-over trick had started to draw large crowds in the playground at break-time. I swiftly invited Tracy to my house so that she could teach me how to do it.

I couldn't believe my luck. Life suddenly had a new glimmer of hope to it and on the next available Saturday morning, we turned my Dad's lovely lawn into mud as I battled away until my first walk-over happened. After succeeding once, there was no stopping me. It became my party trick, which I performed at every opportunity and little did I know then, but this trick was going to hold me in good stead for the future.

3

MIXED COMPANY

IT TURNED OUT that, unbeknownst to me, there had been a hive of glamorous activity going on in Ipswich after all. It wasn't just fetes and carnival queens. There were also night clubs and DJs in Suffolk and one day, out of the blue, I met someone who was to introduce me to a thrill that I'd thought only existed in London. The beauty of life is, that just when you think there is no hope of things ever going your way, if you persevere long enough, something completely new and unexpected appears, to spur you on. This happened for me one evening at my dancing class as Mrs Chisnall, the pianist, sat poised and ready to play our jolly warm up tune. Waiting for the nod from Miss Shipton, we'd organised ourselves into neat lines ready to begin, when suddenly there was a tap at the studio door.

We were delighted when a beautiful girl burst in, clad from head to toe in red lycra. We gazed in awe at her locks of red hair that tumbled over her shoulders, reminding me of Babs.

"I'd like to learn to dance," she announced, smiling politely.

Miss Shipton invited her to join us, to see how she got on in our class, making me rather aggravated that she wasn't sent to the baby class like I had once been, years before. I held my tongue. Besides, I wanted her to be in our class even if she was useless at dancing. After going religiously to rather repetitive lessons for so many years, we were all thrilled with this glamorous newcomer. We were flabbergasted and hugely impressed at how quickly she picked up the routines. The mundane choreography of the Imperial Society of Teachers of Dancing seemed to be transformed by her fresh approach. It soon became clear that her stylish attitude, delivered the steps in a much more upbeat fashion.

Mrs Chisnall, the pianist, hammered away at the traditional tunes as we danced. With fingers weighed down with large golden rings, her hands flew up and down the keys like a female version of Liberace, the brightly coloured sleeves of her chiffon blouse puffing out in the breeze as she played. She always put on her best performance and we loved her for it.

"Oh, my days," she chuckled, her music failing to match our newly discovered approach to the choreography.

As we set off home at the end of our class, still chatting excitedly about the mystery visitor, Hannah dived into a doorway, eyes wide as she pointed down the street. Strolling along in her red leotard was the new girl from the class. In true teenage style, we decided that the best thing to do, rather than catch her up and introduce ourselves, was to follow her and see where she lived. We weren't very good at this discreet plan because when she stopped to throw her bag into the back of a green sports car, it was just too much for Hannah.

"Oh, my God is that yours?" she exclaimed from across the road.

"Hi girls! I'm Lynn. Need a lift?" the girl offered, jumping into her car with practised ease.

In a split second, we'd squashed ourselves into the back seat, ready to pose through the town centre with our new best friend.

"I'm going to rehearsals with my dance group if you want to join me," she shouted above the roar of the engine.

I believe we just nodded with opened mouths. Tinkling with laughter, she accelerated away like Penelope Pitstop.

We'd not travelled more than a few streets away before we pulled into the car park of a large arts centre that we knew from school concerts and events. It was fortunate that the journey was short because I learnt that evening, that I don't fit easily into the back of tiny sports cars. My legs were bent up to my ears like a grasshopper, so I didn't look hugely cool. However, it had all been worth it because it turned out that Lynn ran a cool dance group called Mixed Company. These dancers were famous for their tours of the night-clubs of Suffolk and the nearest thing to Pans People that I had ever seen.

Fortunately, having failed our eleven plus, Hannah and I never had too much homework to do. Our parents didn't seem hugely worried about it, the pressure of academic excellence having faded. Everyone was now hoping that we would excel at vocational skills. Our teenage lives improved rapidly as, every Saturday evening we would tell our parents the old chestnut that we were going to each other's houses to do homework. In hindsight, this should have caused huge suspicion but conveniently, my parents were going through a phase of holding fancy dinner parties, involving Cheese Fondues and After Eights. They would entertain friends from their pottery class and bird watching society, quite glad that I was occupied for the evening.

After hearty swigs of cherry brandy from Mum's cocktail cabinet, Hannah and I would sneak out to the bus stop, where we would change into our sexiest dance gear and head out to wow the crowds with our raunchy routines, having been booked to perform with Lynn's dance group in night clubs or at corporate events. Strutting our stuff with Mixed Company, the most glamorous group of people in town, we couldn't believe our luck. The dancers of Mixed Company were a range of carpenters, secretaries and car mechanics who danced for fun and fitness. We were in awe of these new mature friends and didn't let slip that we were only fifteen, although nobody seemed to really care about our age. They were so keen to learn new choreography and incorporate it into their show, all seeming to think Hannah and I were hugely talented and knowledgeable. Bursting onto the stage, clad in miniscule leotards and shiny hot pants, we would throw ourselves about with great gusto, to songs like *Funky Town* by Lipps Inc. and *The Beat Goes On* by The Whispers. When the clock struck ten, Hannah and I would slip out to catch the bus home before our parents started wondering where we had got to. The rest of the group, no doubt, partied into the night.

Hannah often came back to my house after our night club forays. We would change out of our dance gear in the front garden and slip in the back door and up the stairs, with a quick yell that we were back from Girl Guides. When the last of Mum's dinner party guests had left and the house was quiet, we would sneak down to polish off the posh leftovers from the fridge. We would begin with the remainder of the prawn cocktail starter mixture, a seventies classic, plunging our spoons into the cut glass bowl, devouring the creamy sweet and sour softness with the occasional thrill of a plump little prawn. There were always a few soft bread rolls left in a basket, to go with this, laden with Stork margarine. Next, we would bring out the silver tray displaying the last piece of Mum's Ginger Cream dessert. Basically, this was a packet of ginger nut biscuits sandwiched together with whipped cream and left to go mushy, a perfect example of the culinary skills of the time, no doubt taken from an article in Good Housekeeping magazine. If we weren't feeling too sick, we'd nibble at Quality Streets from the tall glasses that stood elegantly in the middle of the table. As we discussed our night out in tired whispers, our giddiness would subside as exhaustion set in. Staggering up to my room we'd collapse amongst the make-up and disco attire that was strewn over the bed from the earlier preparations.

Of course, my parents eventually discovered our little arrangement with the nightclubs of the area and there was hell to pay.

I knew then that this was the career for me.

4

THE PURPLE SHOP

MUM'S TYPING SKILLS had gone from strength to strength so when she started working as personal assistant to our local member of parliament, his daughter, Tracey, became a good friend of mine. We spent frequent days together over the holidays when our parents were busy campaigning for the Labour Party, and I admired Tracey's eagerness to experience the delights of the Ipswich social scene. The American soap, Dallas, was huge at that time and we likened ourselves to Sue Ellen and Pamela Ewing with great pride in our bright, shoulder padded jackets and roll-on lip gloss.

At that time, people didn't really drink much alcohol and a glass of lager would last all evening. Without the dangerous drinking culture of today, there were never the demands for ID that there are now, so it was easy to be admitted to night clubs and pubs. At fifteen years-old though, our parents wouldn't allow us to go out at night unless it was for something

31

wholesome like fund-raising and helping people. I convinced myself we were helping people to have a good time, by dancing with Mixed Company, and Tracey, also quite a rebel, had a similar approach. One night however, when Tracey's father received a phone call from another parent informing him that she had been spotted strutting her stuff at a club in my sequinned boob tube, it all came to a disappointing end. Arriving at The First Floor Nightclub in his dressing gown and slippers under his mackintosh, her father frog-marched Tracey across the dance floor to the waiting car outside. Of course, Mum heard about this story at work, leading her to make more precise enquiries of *my* whereabouts on Saturday nights. The truth was soon revealed, and I was immediately banned from going out after eight o'clock, as was Hannah, resulting in a curfew that I felt would never, ever, be lifted. I was convinced that I would be doomed to a life of knitting bras by the fire.

It was around this time though, that I started to notice an optimistic view of situations that seems to simmer within me. I will always be grateful for this part of my character that has constantly seen me through endless challenges and tricky situations in my life so far. During my curfew, as I pottered around my bedroom, I knew that there would be a time one day soon, when I would be let loose again. I just had to wait and as I'd predicted, the doom and gloom was eventually lifted with a new and exciting proposition.

Some friends in Ipswich had invited me to help at their fashion boutique in the town centre, so out of the blue, I managed to land myself a very trendy Saturday job. Mum loved the thought that I would be occupied for an entire day, learning the skills of retail at The Purple Shop which still thrives to this day, although now with different owners. I'm proud to have been a part of this Ipswich landmark when it first opened during the late seventies. At that time in my life, I would probably have paid *them*, to let me work there and this was just as well because I was paid an absolute pittance. I never missed a shift though, arriving in my white grandad shirt tucked into my Lee Cooper jeans, tucked into my cowboy boots. With my dark glossy hair tumbling down my back, I felt a frisson of fabulousness developing, and I loved it.

The shop sold incense sticks, patchouli oil, coloured strings of tiny beads, bangles, hippy bags, jewellery and trendy clothes from India. There were other imported home decorations too, that were very upbeat for the time, bringing a bit of London's exciting Carnaby Street to our town. The Purple Shop was such a novelty that everyone wanted a bit of the groovy vibe, so to actually work there, was the coolest thing you could do. I would sit poised behind the counter, the envy of all my friends.

After a few months, to add to the excitement, a new member of staff called Mark arrived to work alongside me. He was the most handsome man that I had ever seen. He was very tall with sparkling green eyes, a black beard and long legs, enhanced by faded denim jeans and scuffed boots. We instantly hit it off, having such fun and giggles as we sat for hours flirting, sharing jokes and drinking coffee in the shop. We developed such a rapport with the customers that the owners often left us to manage the shop, allowing them to travel to London to buy new stock.

At twenty-five years old, Mark was a fair bit older than me, but not wanting to spoil the growing feelings of attraction that were developing rapidly between us, I fibbed a bit by telling him that I was nearly eighteen. I didn't think that saying this could really do any harm to anyone. Seeing as it was the first time that my height had been an advantage, I was excited beyond belief.

Whenever there were no customers around, Mark would choose a tape and turn the cassette player up loud. Catching my eye, from where I sat behind the counter, he would slowly approach. Holding out his hand, he would lead me out for a dance on the shop floor, to songs such as Exile's, *I Wanna Kiss You All Over*. It was the first time that I had ever looked up adoringly into a man's eyes. Pulling me close to his chest, my heart would leap as he shimmied me around the shop. Laughing, he would gaze into my eyes, our faces close. I longed to kiss him, and felt it wouldn't be long before we collapsed amorously into a rail of kaftans. When the song by Exile first came out in 1978, I remember wondering what the singer meant by kissing someone all over.

"Why would you want to kiss someone *all over?*" I would ask my parents in a disgusted tone.

Years later, after my dances with Mark, I gained a better idea of the meaning of these lyrics and would think about our beautiful moments together throughout the week, waiting for Saturday to come around again.

So, it was a shock to both of us one Monday morning, when he arrived at my school as the new geography teacher. For a few seconds longer than was appropriate, we stared at each other with a mixture of horror and delight, as he sat with the other teachers at the front of the assembly hall. I'm not sure which one of us was more surprised. My mind raced and my knees turned to jelly as I was forced to accept that the secret of my real age was out, and things would never be the same again.

Sitting on the bus home, later that day, stunned and miserable, I recalled that he'd once told me he had just finished teacher training, but I hadn't for a moment thought that he planned to work at *my* school.

The next Saturday, he didn't appear at the shop. I spent an awful day, trying not to cry as I served the customers, realising that his job had just been until the start of his new teaching post. For a while, my Saturday afternoons became long and tedious, but all was not lost. Mark was to prove to be my hero a few months later during my last term at school.

It was one afternoon, as I waited to catch the bus home on the main road, when a group of the worst bullies in the school approached. They were the girls that everyone avoided at all costs, as they were always picking fights and generally causing grief for teachers and pupils alike. My heart sank when I saw them and I urged the bus to hurry up as they crowded around me, lighting fags and staring up at me in mischievous glee, deciding how best to upset me.

"Look Tanya, it's the giraffe!" one of them shouted. They all collapsed in forced laughter. This only encouraged the ringleader of their little gang.

"Nice shoes," sneered Tanya, narrowing her eyes at me as she lit a cigarette. They all sniggered at my ugly lace ups, before demanding that I open my Family Circle biscuit tin and then helping themselves to all of my beautiful butterfly buns from cookery class.

I felt terrified, but knew that if I walked away, then they would just follow me. It had started to rain, so I stayed in the bus shelter, desperately surveying the horizon and willing the bus to arrive.

It was at this moment, that through the half-light and annoying drizzle, I saw headlights flash and a beautiful, bronze Ford Cortina pull over to where we were all standing. The girls fell silent as we all squinted to see through the windscreen. My heart leapt into my mouth as the window went down and there he was, looking sexier than ever, having removed his tie and rolled up his sleeves, revealing his tanned arms.

"Jane! Get in."

Mark was Mark once more. Not Mr Wray the geography teacher, but *My Mark*.

The girls parted like the proverbial waves as I handed my empty cake tin to an open-mouthed Tanya. Making my way to the car door, I climbed in as elegantly as I could.

"Fuck me! It's Mr bloody Wray!" murmured Tanya.

I didn't dare look at the girls as Mark accelerated away. We dissolved into nervous laughter as he whisked me into town.

"You just saved my life," I explained.

"Oh, they won't give you trouble anymore," he reassured me as we sat in the traffic jam that I prayed would never clear.

"I miss you on Saturdays," I ventured, staring ahead, desperately wanting to reach out and hold his hand.

"Me too, love." He smiled over at me knowingly before adding, "We had fun didn't we?"

I desperately struggled not to cry as he delivered me to my house. There was no hint of anything further developing. He was a respectable man. I waved goodbye to him like a ten-year old, despite having the feelings of an amorous adult pounding in my chest. We both knew that we couldn't change the situation and I never really saw Mark at school much after that glorious day. I hadn't chosen geography as a subject, although it had been tempting and, to add to my misery, The Police had released a song called *Don't Stand So Close To Me*, all about a pupil's affair with a teacher. I had to tolerate it on the radio for months.

Immersing myself into school shows and concerts for my last term, as life continued to gallop ahead, I managed to feel grateful for the treasured times I had enjoyed with Mark, accepting reluctantly that I would never cross paths with him again when I left school.

Well, that's what I thought at the time anyway.

5

CHANCE OF A LIFETIME

MY PARENTS HAD developed a craving for sunshine and adventure during our camping holidays in France. During our last, family holiday together, they showed us various farmhouses and renovation projects, until it slowly dawned on my brother and I that Mum and Dad were considering moving the family home to France. Sure enough, after the holidays, our parents announced that our house in Ipswich was to be sold and they were planning to go in search of pastures new.

This was very exciting and extremely trendy of them at the time, and we were, of course, invited to join them. It caused rather a dilemma for my brother and I though, because at sixteen and eighteen we were making different plans. We didn't want to be builders or run a bed and breakfast company abroad. We wanted to secure government funded places at college, as was the way then in Britain, so to my parents' surprise, we were reluctant to leave England.

Despite Ipswich offering plenty of reliable career opportunities for girls in shops, salons and offices, these options hadn't appealed to me at all. I knew they weren't going to make me happy because Top of the Pops and the music industry had introduced me to another life that looked far more exciting. With the confidence gained from my fabulous stint with Lynn, Mixed Company and the glimpses of all the action I'd snatched from the television, I became desperate to be a part of the glamorous lifestyle that was being enjoyed up in London. Added to this, I was becoming convinced that my improving dance skills could very likely heighten my chances of success.

"It's now or never. I have to get to London," I whispered to my reflection in the mirror.

Gazing courageously at myself in my latest disco outfit, like a funky Dick Whittington, London seemed like a world away. Little did I know then, because no-one had pointed it out to me and I hadn't thought to ask, but London was actually only an hour away on the train.

John Travolta and *Saturday Night Fever* had introduced a new dance phenomenon to the disco scene. I had mastered the style effortlessly, developing a new confidence that grew as people crowded around, to watch me on the dance floor of the Girl Guides discos, in the dusty church hall. This was the only place my parents allowed me to frequent after banning me from dancing with Mixed Company. We were entering the *Fame* era of the eighties, making it very cool to walk about with legwarmers over the outside of our jeans, towelling sweat bands around our heads and sweatshirts with the collar cut off, exposing our bony shoulders. I embraced this all wholeheartedly.

On hearing that my parents were planning to move abroad, Miss Shipton arranged an audition for me at a professional performing arts college. Noticing my commitment to dance, she feared that all my efforts in class would be wasted if I went to rural France, adamant that my height and newly discovered singing voice, could possibly bring choreographers knocking from the world of cabaret if I was given the chance to train professionally.

An audition was arranged, and we were all ecstatic when a letter of acceptance arrived from Betty Laine of Laine Theatre Arts, but not as pleased as Mrs Chisnall, the pianist at dancing class. We both agreed that I'd outgrown the little ballet studio. Flinching in anticipation as I careered across the floor in her direction, Mrs Chisnall would play on courageously until my inevitable crash landing. After only one leap, I would often run out of space, joining her at the piano, hitting the high notes or worse still, landing in her lap.

As we examined the letter from Betty Laine, I dared to believe that I was in with a chance of success after all. It proved that however useless you were feeling, if you kept brushing yourself down and getting out there again, eventually something would happen to bring new hope and confidence banging at your door.

Added to this excitement Miss Shipton explained that, apparently, there was a lady called Miss Bluebell in Paris, managing a world-famous cabaret show. Miss Bluebell's dancers were exceptionally tall, meaning she was often in London looking for dancers for her show, the French girls being very petite.

"If you worked hard enough, there would be a chance that you could join the show in Paris. Miss Bluebell only accepts dancers with a strong ballet training and a minimum height of five feet and ten inches tall," she reassured me.

~

As ambition kicked in, I hadn't felt at all bereft as we'd waved the old family camper van off to France. Mum and Dad had trundled down our street on their way to the ferry in Felixtowe, Mum's hand waving out of the window as my brother and I had stood there on the pavement, awkwardly waving back as though they were just popping to Sainsbury's. The reality of the situation at the tender age of sixteen had not quite sunk in as we'd watched our parents, having been rather strict throughout our childhoods, gradually becoming a speck on the horizon. When the silence was broken by the sound of removal lorries roaring down our leafy lane, the new owners of our family home arrived. Stopping to buy cola cubes and sherbet lemons, we'd walked to Granny's house where we were to stay until the arrangements for our further education courses could be confirmed. My brother went straight to art school and never looked back. For me, being catapulted out there, was probably the only way of going about my particular career choice, because it was not an ordinary one by any means at that time. There are performing arts colleges everywhere these days, but back then, there were very few. I was thrilled to have gained a place, but I knew I still had to audition, to qualify for a government grant to pay for it, so alot of praying went on in Granny's spare bedroom.

Granny was very impressed when I mentioned The Bluebell Girls one afternoon, as she prepared a pot of tea and a plate of Custard Creams. The Bluebell Girls of Paris, and The Tiller Girls of Manchester, had been the stars of her youth during the thirties and forties. I followed Granny out of the kitchen as she reassured me that Miss Bluebell was still going strong in Paris. Grandad was sat in his chair in the lounge, engrossed in the afternoon western on full volume as he puffed on his pipe. Granny put the tray down on the coffee table amongst the Football pool charts and TV Times.

"I know you can do it," she announced with a smile.

She passed Grandad his tea before lighting a fag and going to peer through the net curtains, to keep her usual vigil on the neighbours.

"Of course, your father was a natural on the dance floor until he went into the building trade."

She turned and glared at me, remembering proudly, "He won trophies. And your Auntie Joan should have been a model. She's a stunner! It's in the genes you see."

She pursed her lips and folded her arms, looking over at Grandad as he joined in the discussion.

"Bright girl Joan. Sat at a desk all day in the bank though, with those long legs hidden away like that," he murmured, staring into space for a moment.

Granny's eyes sparkled at him across the smoky fug of the lounge as he turned the television off and re-lit his pipe. Granny seemed to have lost her spirit slightly since Mum and Dad had left for France. The family was dispersing as we all chased our dreams. She took a deep breath and nodded.

"You are going to do us proud my darlin' but you will have to be careful up there near London. And what with Mum and Dad off in France," she welled up with tears, clutching my hand.

"Granny, I'm proud of Mum and Dad and I like these adventures we're all having. It's time to set off!" then I hated myself for saying, "I'm bored in Ipswich, there's nothing for me here now."

~

The Imperial Society of Teachers of Dancing in London is an organisation formed of highly qualified teachers and choreographers usually better known as the ISTD. These experts were relied upon, at that time, to watch dance classes on behalf of the many county councils of the UK. Putting ticks and crosses against reams and reams of names of hopeful dancers from all over the country, they would determine whether they felt that it was worth the government funding their training, or not.

Since turning sixteen, I'd wasted no time in going up to London with friends to explore the city. Discovering Carnaby Street, we perused the fashion boutiques of Mary Quant and Chelsea Girl with great excitement. His Master's Voice record store on Oxford Street offered a whole new musical experience, compared to the limited supplies available at Woolworths in Ipswich. Standing over and above all of these wonderful new places though, was Covent Garden, the home of Pineapple Dance Studios. Lynn, Hannah and I quickly learnt that if we hung around in the coffee bar at Pineapple, we could spot stars like Sarah Brightman from Hot Gossip, the latest dance group, on her way to ballet class. Sarah's dancers had taken raunchy to a whole new level, leaving Pan's People in the shadows, taking the world by storm with their performance of *Star Ship Trooper*. These trips to London made me determined to go to the dance college but I needed to be awarded the grant from the government to pay my fees and accommodation. The fees were astronomical, and I knew my parents would not be able to pay them. I had applied for the grant, essential if I was to succeed, and was waiting to hear back.

When, at last, the date for my audition for funding arrived, I set off on the train to London. In my ankle-length, rainbow cardigan, ballet leotard and red leg warmers, I strutted along the streets feeling optimistic, the John Travolta beat thumping into my head from my Sony Walkman. Arriving at the ISTD headquarters was a bit like when Maria arrived at the abbey in The Sound of Music.

"Oh help!" I thought as I approached the receptionist at the front desk. I switched off John Travolta which seemed to change the mood somewhat.

"Name?"

She didn't even look up from her list at first, as she sat, poised importantly with her biro, waiting to tick her register.

"Jane Hoggar," I announced proudly with a grin.

She looked up, glaring over her glasses at my colourful attire. I flashed her a smile and lifted my striped cardigan up to display formal ballet leotard and tights underneath. It was slightly scuffed from the journey, but ready for action and fortunately I'd scraped my hair up into a tight ballet bun before I'd left home.

If I'd thought the reception area was daunting, I was in for a shock in the changing rooms. Government grants were obviously gold dust, and the pushy mothers were out in force, the air hung with equal amounts of determination and hair lacquer. I sensed a hush as I entered, every ballet bun and their mother turning to stare, checking out the competition. I was relieved and grateful to think of my own mother in France, leaving me to get on with this bit on my own.

"Hi!" I smiled as I took off my headphones, coming down to earth with a bump. It hadn't really occurred to me until this moment, that I might not get the funding. My stomach flipped slightly at the thought that I wouldn't succeed and would have to give up on my career plans after all. I didn't let myself dwell on the thought and very soon there was a tap at the door and a spritely teacher strode in clutching a clip board.

"Come along ladies, time for class."

With much fussing and twittering we made our way to the door, the mothers furious that they weren't allowed to come in with us. I removed my cardigan and legwarmers, doing my best to fall in with it all. I even performed a little tiny ballet leap on my way out.

"Project darling. And lift your chin!" called out one mother to her daughter.

"Don't forget to smile Tallulah, and remember what I told you," snapped another.

Thankfully, the mothers' voices faded away as we took our positions on the pristine white floor of the studio, ready to start the class. As we forced our toes out into the most perfect first positions we could manage, and sucked our stomachs in as far as possible, you could have heard a pin drop. The waiting was agony as the teacher took her position at the front, ready to begin. The pianist shuffled her music about, and I took a deep breath knowing that I had to give it my all because this was the chance of a lifetime.

The panel of examiners were a real mixture. There were two elderly ballet teachers in Chanel suits and pearls, sternly peering over their glasses at us. Next to them sat a dainty man, gesticulating theatrically with his long, elegant hands. He muttered to his colleagues in hushed tones, holding his manicured fingers up to his face as he analysed each and every one of us. Next to him sat a really funky looking woman in a purple Shell Suit, the latest fashion. She also had the fabulous, big hair and bright make-up of the eighties so there was clearly going to be a good variety of opinions, which was reassuring.

The class was hard work, with exercises at the barre before moving into the centre for a long and arduous ballet combination. We all sweated profusely, determined to show off our potential and impress these experts. I became conscious of my exceptional height though and as we neared the end of the class; I grew concerned that I hadn't been given the opportunity to show them all of my talents. Feeling that there were not many grants to go around, I became nervous. At the end of any ballet performance, dancers perform a customary reverence which is a traditional moment to curtsy or bow, thanking the audience and orchestra. In theatres, it's the time for bouquets to be thrown, amidst deafening applause. In class, it is a moment to thank the teacher and pianist. My heart felt heavy with dread as, after our reverence, the teacher dismissed us all with a curt,

"Thank you everybody, that will be all."

It was with a wave of emotional desperation as we all started to leave, that I took a deep breath and stepped out of the line.

"Excuse me, I would like to sing to you because I need to show you that I am more of an all-rounder."

An unbearable hush descended but I continued,

"I'm not just a ballerina. The college I have been accepted at specialises in performing arts, rather than just ballet. I don't feel that I have shown you everything that I can do. Would you allow me to sing please?"

My words tumbled out breathlessly and there followed a stunned silence amongst the panel as four baffled faces looked up at me from their clipboards, and then at each other. This had clearly never happened before. Turning to avoid the glare of the twenty horrified students as they filed out of the studio,

I spotted all their mothers watching through the glass panels of the swing door. They were all frowning as they peered in with astonishment, balancing on their tip toes, desperately trying to hear what I was saying. As the last dancer made her exit and the door swung closed, I knew I had no choice but to go through with my daring suggestion.

One of the elderly examiners removed her glasses, gave a little nervous cough and smiled politely at me,

"Well, we don't really ... I mean, the pianist doesn't have your music dear, for a start."

The man with the elegant hands slammed his pen down and beamed at me.

"Let her sing Irene, for goodness sake! This is wonderful! We need kids with a bit of pluckiness in this business. You'll have to sing *a cappella* darling, if that's ok."

Before any more discussion could waste the afternoon or spoil my chance, I threw myself into a Barbara Streisand ballad.

"Love ... soft as an easy chair, ... love fresh as the morning air."

I had to admit the acoustics were pretty good underneath the high ceilings of the dance studio. They all sat up, mesmerised. I think they'd had a long boring morning of endless ballet classes and this was just what they needed to perk up their day. When I'd finished, I was thrilled to see one of the old ladies remove her glasses and wipe away a tear. I didn't stop there. I was on a roll and knew I would probably never see these people again in my life. It was now or never.

"And now, I will be Sally Bowles from Cabaret."

Before they could stop me, I threw myself into a monologue from my favourite film until I was eventually stopped by a beaming Mr Hands.

"Darling that was tremendous! You can go now. But, well done," he punched the air. "We can see you are really ready for the course. Bravo sweetie."

Even Irene chipped in, "Yes, I quite agree, and there is always Miss Bluebell of course," she added, allowing herself a smile.

That name again. There were so many thoughts rushing through my head. Proud of myself as they nodded and smiled at me, I bobbed and bowed my way out of the studio. Walking on air, I marched straight into the path of one of the mothers. She had stepped across the corridor to block my way.

"So, young lady, you think you can go that one step further do you?" she forced a little laugh, but her eyes sparked with rage at me in the dark corridor. She had been spying on my performance.

"Little singer, little actress, little Miss Everything. I knew you were going to cause trouble as soon as I saw you arriving ... unaccompanied."

I stopped in my tracks, my heart pounding, feeling momentarily intimidated. As she glared accusingly at me, I started to answer as politely and bravely as I could, until a flash of anger overwhelmed me after her comment about being unaccompanied. How dare she suggest that I had an uncaring mother. Feeling rather pumped up from my performance, protective of my wonderful Mum, and confident since my audition, I took a step closer to her powdery face.

"That's show business. You need to get used to it and so does your daughter."

I paused for effect, waiting to be slapped. Fortunately, just at that moment, the judging panel came out of the studio on their way to their tea break before the next session began. The frightful mother immediately transformed into sweetness and light and I was able to scurry past her and get away. I decided it wouldn't be wise to stop for a matey chat with the other girls in the changing rooms. I grabbed my bag and made a hasty exit. I was so glad my mother wasn't there. All hell may have broken loose. Some of those mothers were capable of fisticuffs, I'd seen it before, at dance festivals.

∾

A few weeks later I was walking into my dance class back at home when Miss Shipton came bustling through the door. She thrust a letter into my hand.

"You've done it my darling!! They're awarding you a grant. Well done!"

I was on my way.

6

COLLEGE

TO BE ACCEPTED into performing arts college was the
stuff that dreams were made of and students arrived at Laine
Theatre Arts feeling full of ambition for their first term.
Fame and Saturday Night Fever were causing a new dance
craze, so our hopes and dreams became a reality as we dared
to believe, arriving from towns nationwide, that we were in
with a chance of a piece of the action. We had been given
the greatest opportunity that we could have ever hoped for.
Dance and drama weren't on the school curriculum then, so
to be offered a government funded place, in higher education
for this exciting profession was extremely rare. Before I left
home, our local paper printed a lovely photograph of Miss
Shipton and I, both beaming with pride, above descriptions
of my future plans, causing huge excitement for my relatives
and friends.

Students arrived at their new accommodation in Epsom, full of anticipation. Confident in legwarmers, we hugged each other theatrically each morning, carrying large shoulder bags full of dance shoes and leotards. We arrived for class, just brimming with enthusiasm, the pressure to succeed beginning to brew, beneath the surface. Admiring our latest hair and make-up ideas and calling each other Darling was the usual start to the day. This didn't go down quite so well when we all went home for the holidays. Calling the man at the corner shop or your grandad Darling, to most people in Suffolk, was weird. My family tittered as my theatrical side continued to reveal itself during the first few visits home.

Domestic arrangements had changed dramatically for most of the students since leaving home. Many of them shared flats and cooked for themselves. This introduced new eating habits, with endless bowls of breakfast cereal, chocolate, and the exciting discovery of wine. After one or two terms, the common worry of weight gain, every dancer's worst fear, took off. For many of the girls, this was to become a life-long obsession as they developed eating disorders from calorie counting and diet plans. Each morning, everyone in class rushed to the large mirrors on the walls of the studio, anxiously turning around to inspect their hips and thighs.

I was lodging with a family called the Ashfields, so when my friends were heading out to the supermarket for sweets and goodies in the evenings, I was sat by the television watching Coronation Street with Mrs Ashfield and her husband after enjoying a well-balanced meal together. Although I didn't like this arrangement, it certainly kept me away from the temptations of junk food.

The principal of the college, Betty Laine, was a powerful figure in our lives. Having given us all the opportunity to follow our dream, she was highly revered. We were eternally grateful to her for accepting us onto the course, as were our parents. She made it very clear from the start of the course that training as dancers, she would be disappointed in us, understandably, if we gained weight. Most of us, despite managing to keep up with the work, were beginning to lose the spritely dancer figures we'd had on audition day. This broke the deal with Miss Laine, swiftly hindering our progress and reminding us for the first time, of the discipline required to achieve the career we craved.

Within only a few months of arriving, we started to miss the support and encouragement of our families. Terrified by the demands of excellence expected of us, many of us felt a debilitating lack of self-esteem when compliments failed to appear. Some girls were as young as sixteen years old, so started comfort eating, miserably losing belief in themselves without the reassurance from loved ones at home.

Miss Laine had a huge responsibility to attain exceptional results from her students, on a professional level. Her merciless approach succeeded if one was committed and talented enough. The rest of us had to lurch along behind, attempting to join in where we could. The memory of these relentless, failed attempts to please Miss Laine, stayed with most of us, throughout our lives. My teaching years, much later on in my life, were a hugely rewarding time for me when drama and dance brought confidence and courage to so many children and their families, because I chose to lavish them with praise. In her defence though, Miss Laine's school wasn't about happy families. Her goal was to push naturally talented students to the top of the competitive, professional world of show business, with its rejections and pitfalls lurking around every corner. Many of her pupils made names for themselves in show business, and still do to this day. She made it clear to us all from the start, that the entertainment industry was not for the faint hearted. You had to toughen up and commit, if you wanted to be part of the professional world, outside the security of our college. I have to give her credit for my obsession with punctuality and immaculate grooming whenever I work now. Miss Laine drummed it into us all that we had to look our best at all times, and that lateness was unforgivable and could cost you your job.

"You never know who you will meet when you step out of that door each day," she would insist, encouraging us to walk around wearing thick make-up and perfectly coiffed hair at all times.

The underlying truth was, that even if you had all the criteria to be successful in the business, naturally pointed feet, exquisite looks and physical proportions, beautiful singing voice, if you had no *discipline*, it wouldn't happen.

Many students suffered irreparable emotional damage from the constant feeling of failure and this insecurity was still prevalent one afternoon, thirty-five years later, at a champagne reception held at Epsom Racecourse to celebrate Miss Laines eightieth birthday. More than thirty-five years after completing our training, having all grown into successful adults with rewarding careers and families, it was quite staggering to see grown men and women gathering around this lady, like wasps to a jam pot, waiting for their turn to describe their achievements since leaving college. It was fascinating to realise, that the need to please her was still tormenting us all, still desperate as we were for her approval. I never managed to engage with Miss Laine, accepting over time that you can't please everybody. I realised eventually, that it doesn't matter, especially when I think of all the wonderful things, that I do have to be thankful for.

A close friend from my college days, Stephanie, had joined me for Miss Laine's eightieth birthday party in Epsom. Stephanie and I were kindred spirits. Both measuring six feet tall, we had literally seen eye to eye throughout our years with Miss Laine, and then later when we set off around the globe as showgirls. As we sat chatting to old friends, I was completely amazed to notice Colin, a most charming pianist, whom I had been fortunate enough to study singing with, during my time at the college. He was sitting alone at the piano, working his way through all the standard musical theatre numbers that he used to play for us, thirty-five years earlier. My heart soared. Colin had an extraordinary knack of playing any song that you asked for, even writing out the music for you to take to auditions, in whichever key you wanted. This is every singer's dream, and he had helped me on many occasions throughout my college years. I was keen to go over to thank him, feeling gratitude for his unfailing support, that had contributed to my eventual success. I pointed him out to Stephanie.

"Go and sing a song with Colin," she grinned across at me, a glint of mischief and amusement in her eyes.

After a few glasses of chilled white wine, although we had no reason to, we felt like the naughty girls in the class again. Watching all the guests waiting for their turn to present themselves to Miss Laine, in a queue, as though we were at Buckingham Palace, we became rather giggly. I had been disappointed that the current third year students, who were also attending this important event, weren't being encouraged to use the afternoon as an opportunity to perform. I felt frustrated that this hadn't been arranged. After chatting to them, I realised it was just another example of the confidence problem, that was still present, all these years later.

"No way!" they chorused, terrified when I asked if they were going to provide some entertainment at some point.

We gazed at the empty stage. Colin looked lonely up there playing his piano and singing *Girl from Ipanema*. He hadn't changed a bit and was tickled when I introduced myself to him. I sang *Come to the Cabaret* with him and it was just like old times but, although Stephanie was delighted, Miss Laine wasn't impressed at all.

7

THE WORKING WORLD

SINCE GOING TO see Cats and A Chorus Line, the popular shows of the time, I had become rather keen to set my sights on musical theatre as a career. Managing to pass drama and singing competitions during the first year of college, I decided to audition for a role as one of the Kit-Kat Girls in the musical, Cabaret, at a repertory theatre in Ipswich over the Easter holidays. Although this work overlapped with term time, Miss Laine allowed me to take the job. The lead role of Sally Bowles was played by Imogen Stubbs, a budding actress, freshly graduated from RADA. Kit Kat Girls are tall and brash, so I seemed to fit the role rather well, along with five other raucous dancers. We had a ball, singing and dancing every night for three weeks with Imogen. The show was a huge success, and we even achieved a mention in The Stage newspaper, a weekly publication for those in the entertainment industry. The skilful choreography really brought the atmosphere of the nightclubs of pre-war Berlin to life, with kick-lines, energetic acrobatics and tap dancing. My walk-over trick was even included, albeit in a rather vulgar move, halted halfway over, by the Master of Ceremonies as he regarded my velvet clad shorts, with repulsion. It brought the house down every night though, so I went along with it. The only night that it was slightly awkward was when I spotted the captain of my Girl Guide group, Mrs Leckemby, on the front row, just inches away from me as I slid down into the splits at her feet.

The entertainment world was rapidly changing and to my dismay, Pan's People and Hot Gossip seemed to have disappeared from the scene as the pop world brought Madonna and Glam Rock to our attention instead. I loved this new style, but I missed Dee-Dee and Babs on a Thursday night, wondering what had become of them. I experienced weak moments when I felt that there was nothing for me to aim for anymore. There had been no more suggestions of musical theatre work and I decided that working for Miss Bluebell might be the best way forward after all. The showgirls in Paris, at the world-famous Lido de Paris gave me continued hope, sending my grandmother into raptures at the thought that there could be a Bluebell Girl in the family. The descriptions of the show sounded intriguing, although nothing like the musical theatre of the West End that I loved. I had started to feel more and more like the girl on the front of my Top of the Pops LP and I quite liked it.

During the 1980's, the only way that dancers could find out about auditions for dancing work was from the classified advertisements in The Stage newspaper. This hive of information arrived every Thursday and we would eagerly pass it around the changing rooms at college, lusting after the adverts for dance contracts in venues all over the world and in the West End. I was secretly thrilled to notice that, usually, the criteria for dancers in cabaret shows abroad, included a minimum height requirement of five feet and eight inches tall. These jobs, glamorous and exciting as they were, involved travelling to hotels in far flung places. I began to feel that the glamorous world of showgirls around the globe was rather tempting and the adverts certainly gave me a little boost of hope.

Despite this yearning for far off places, my heart leapt one morning, when I spotted an advert in The Stage for an open audition for Cats, the long running musical by Andrew Lloyd Webber. I decided that there was nothing for it but to pretend to be ill, telephone college to report I was sick, and go to the audition secretly. Fed up with all the speculation, the time had come to see for myself what it was really like in the West End and check out the competition.

On the morning of the audition, as soon as my landlady, Mrs Ashfield, had left the house to take her children to school, I called the office. Using her telephone in the hall, I felt my cheeks burn as I dialled. The phone was a luxury in those days as we had no mobiles. Landlines were expensive so it was rather naughty of me.

After preparing a perfect impersonation of Mrs Ashfield in my head, my voice seemed to come out unexpectedly squeaky in reality.

"Good morning, this is Mrs Ashfield," I announced, cringing as I spoke. "I'm just calling to let you know that Jane Hoggar won't be in college today. She's not well."

The call proved to be more challenging than I'd anticipated. As I put the phone down, I felt rather sweaty and uncomfortable from the thorough interrogation from the very experienced

Rose, head secretary at college. I had been naive to think that she wasn't used to these calls.

As I hurtled into London on the train, I soon forgot about this awkward little exchange on the phone. My big moment at the audition was approaching fast. I arrived at the theatre early, having spent most of the morning in a quiet coffee shop near Drury Lane, humming my Barbara Streisand *Evergreen* tune. This had been my lucky song so far, and I felt confident as I stretched my limbs discretely under the table in preparation for my debut. I began to feel really optimistic that my career was, at last, building momentum. I had a good feeling and noticed a definite spring in my step as I set off to impress the directors of the most famous musical in the West End.

I thought back to the panel at the audition for my government grant and how they had loved me, and all the applause we'd received as Kit Kat Girls in Ipswich. I fantasised about returning to college to announce my latest success to all the teachers and students later that day. The job was mine. I could feel it. I was actually smiling slightly manically with these thoughts as I arrived at the theatre and was thrilled to see such a long line of people queuing to buy tickets. It went right down the road and around the corner.

"It must be a great show," I thought, as I hurried to the entrance of the theatre. Beginning to feel quite important, I took care to turn out my feet impressively as I walked along in first position. It was just then, that I noticed with horror, that all the queueing customers were wearing leg warmers. It slowly dawned on me that all these people were also auditioning, like me, for the same measly role. Some of them were even from my college, on the same sneaky day trip! No-one was hugging and calling each other Darling today, as the smell of battle hung in the air, making us all very uncomfortable. I wondered how many calls the secretaries, Enid and Rose, had received that morning. I recognised girls from my college and nodded knowingly.

Smiling and cringing my way through the day, with all of the other hopefuls, I queued like a sheep waiting to be sheared. Standing out, like a graceful lamp post, I immediately started sloping my shoulders and feeling self-conscious. I felt that the dance routine likened me to Gulliver on his travels as I lurched around amongst all the tiny ballerinas. There then followed a group workshop where we had to make the best of a song, sung in an excruciatingly high key. The panel of directors smiled at us, one by one, as we were thanked and asked to leave. I joined the stream of rejected participants, filing out of the auditorium.

Just as I was crossing the road, wearily making my way to the tube, I heard a loud whistle.

"Jane! Over here darling!"

I glared stroppily over the road to see who was shouting at me. It wasn't Andrew Lloyd-Webber, I knew that much.

Sprawled elegantly at a bistro table, sipping lager and smoking a long slim cigarette, sat the beautiful Roz from college. She was with her flat mate Björn, the devilishly handsome Swede from Stockholm that all my college mates adored. These two were so tall and glamorous and my heart skipped a beat when I realised they were calling to *me*. I wandered over, doing my best to look casual and relaxed. Once there, I felt awkward, until Björn pulled out a seat for me as he ordered three more lagers from a passing waiter.

"So, your first time at Cats, right? We get thrown out every time honey. Don't be pissed off. OK?"

I plonked myself down next to him, not even bothering to look cool anymore. I accepted one of his cigarettes, glad that my brother had taught me how to smoke in the pub car park, for moments like these.

I took a huge slug of lager, realising that if Roz and Björn couldn't get a part in Cats, then I certainly didn't stand a chance. The lager felt amazing after the hot sweaty audition, going straight to my head. I settled down and listened, while they put me in the grim picture of how hard it was to get a job in the West End theatres. They went on to explain that they had recently decided to work for a man called Guy Stranger. I tried not to smile as they explained that his name was pronounced Ghee Stron-jeur, because he was from Paris. Apparently, Guy offered work for tall dancers on the cabaret circuit, on cruise ships and in hotels all over the world. Celebrating their last rejection from a West End audition, Roz and Björn had decided to go out to Paris at the end of their training. Guy had contracts lined up for the following year that would take them all over the world.

Roz checked her lipstick in a tiny mirror as she chatted to me, "Anyway darling, why would anyone choose to work in cold grey England if they could be cruising or relaxing on the beach?"

I saw her point, watching in awe as she popped her little mirror back into her handbag and drew on her cigarette. Inhaling deeply, she relaxed into her seat and winked at me as she blew out smoky hoops with a grin. It was at this precise moment that I decided to pursue my plans of being a glamorous showgirl with nothing but gratitude. Luxury travel with the comfort of a secure future beckoned and I was ready for it. Several lagers later I was fully informed of the state of play for tall dancers and weaving my way through the crowds to catch my train back to my digs, I started to feel that the day hadn't been a waste of time after all. I just wanted to earn a living as a dancer, and it looked like it wasn't going to be so impossible after all.

8

SHOWGIRLS

BACK AT OUR college studios the next morning, things cheered up even further when I was greeted with gossip that there were open auditions being held at college that very morning. Despite the intrigue though, my enlightening visit to the audition for Cats had left me feeling weary. I rummaged in my locker for ballet shoes, feeling glad, that at last, I knew the state of play with regards to auditions for the West End. The conversation with Roz and Björn about shows abroad was making more and more sense. I mulled it over, accepting the fact that I wasn't going to simply walk into a job in the theatres of London after all. I was jolted out of my reverie when the changing room door opened, and Enid popped her head in.

"Girls listen!" she was bristling with excitement, "Miss Laine says to put on your brightest leotards and a pair of character shoes. There will be no ballet this morning because there is an audition in studio 4. It's all high kicks and smiles today!"

Everyone initially gazed in amazement as she disappeared, until suddenly the silence was broken by a stampede over to the mirrors. Vying for space, makeup and hair alterations began in earnest with much pushing and shoving. Then, just to add to the hysteria, Enid returned, adding, "They also mentioned that it's an equity contract so you would get your card!!!"

Everyone screamed.

The Actors Equity Association is a union for live theatre performers, and, at that time, it was useful, if not vital to be a member, especially in British television work. To gain membership you had to have been contracted for employment in the entertainment industry for a certain number of weeks, so this audition was a golden opportunity. I believe it's easier to become an Equity member nowadays but when I was training, if an audition in The Stage newspaper stated, Equity Members Only, it was *not* worth applying if you didn't have an equity card. You knew you wouldn't get in. It was a huge advantage to have your membership by the time you finished training. This was one of the reasons that the college allowed students to take dance contracts over the holidays, to obtain their precious card, even if it over-lapped, occasionally, with term time.

I was overjoyed that the ballet lesson had been replaced with an audition. I knew I needed the daily strengthening of ballet but, being so tall, I was finding it really hard to keep up. I often wished I could join the boys' lessons where the syllabus was designed for larger frames with the graceful sweeping movements that I loved. However, boys work was not an option and I had to accept that fact and battle it out with the girls. The hardest part of ballet class for me was pointe work, a ghastly business that I really struggled with. My pointe shoes cost me a fortune because I had to have them made for me in a size 9. Fortunately, there was a lovely Italian ballet shoe specialist near Leicester Square, that provided made-to-measure ballet shoes to fit perfectly. Founded in 1919, Eugenio Porselli had opened his first shop in Milan. Each term I would visit the delightful London branch where the elderly owner, Sinora Porselli, who I assumed was a relative of Eugenio's, would spend a long time measuring and studying my feet, before smiling up at me as she marvelled at their size. I still have a pair of these shoes in my cupboard, that I treasure. Despite my challenging attempts at ballet, the classes gave me the vital, core strength required to be a showgirl. They are a part of my training that I hold close to my heart.

At the audition that morning in college, there was excitement in the air as the students lined up outside the studio, ready to learn the routine. I thought about my discussion with Roz and Björn the previous day as, discreetly, I pulled the clips out of my hair and shook out my ballet bun.

"I need to look more like Dee-Dee or Babs this morning," I thought as the sound of Michael Jackson's *Beat It* burst out of the speakers.

We were off!

Our beaming smiles reached extraordinary levels during the audition, before turning to tears as people were asked to leave. However, my height seemed to be lending itself perfectly to the high kicks and elegant turns of the choreography. The fiddly steps of the jazz and ballet routines that we usually learnt, were replaced by long graceful turns and kicks that came so naturally to me. It was the first time that a dance style had ever made me feel that I really owned it. Eventually, with just one other dancer remaining in the studio, we were asked our names and asked to leave.

Enid was busy consoling girls in the corridor outside, offering tissues and sympathy.

"It's all part of the tough world of showbiz darling. You did really well. Not this time though," she cooed to them, just loving the drama of it all.

The next day I was making my way to class when out of the office stepped Betty Laine.

My heart skipped a beat when it became clear she had been waiting for me. I could see the secretaries spying on the scene from their desks. Whenever word got around the college that Miss Laine's silver Mercedes was in the driveway, we knew that she was in the building and all hell broke loose.

"Good morning Miss Laine," I squeaked, sounding but not looking, like a little mouse as I smiled bravely down at her. I envied her dainty stature. With the power of a lioness, she scared the living daylights out of me in her brightly coloured jumpsuit and slash of fuchsia lipstick. I studied the crown of her head as she walked around me on a little inspection tour. I noticed that her roots were going to be in need of attention before long but decided not to mention it.

"Yes, I can see, you seem to be getting rid of some of that weight. Guy Stranger wants you and Samantha to go to his Damascus show for the winter season."

"The audition, of course," I thought.

I kept calm, although the excitement was overwhelming as I felt my dream becoming a reality. It wasn't quite Cats, but hey, it was a job. Someone wanted me in their professional show, and it felt wonderful! I resisted the temptation to grab Miss Laine by the hands and do a Ring-a-Ring-a-Roses dance in the narrow corridor. I just wished she would hug me with pride, but it wasn't her style. She had just managed to arrange work for me as a showgirl in the Middle East, so that I could obtain my equity card. She was hardly going to put that in her prospectus for the college. I dared to look at her with a timid attempt at seeking a little sign of approval. I hoped that she would, at least, agree that my success was some form of progress, surely.

"That's ... splendid!" I stammered allowing myself a smile, "Thank you very much Miss Laine," I muttered looking down at my shoes.

"Rose will give you the contract to sign when it arrives."

She returned to her office and closed the door.

I was about to make a face at the closed door when I spotted Rose, the secretary, peering over her typewriter at me from the office. She waved enthusiastically and carried on with her work.

I wished for a moment, that Rose was the principal.

∼

After the initial excitement of being offered employment though, an unexpected fly in the ointment reared its head, in the form of the ghastly political situation in the Middle East at that time. It turned out that the show we were destined for, was in a large hotel in Damascus, Syria, close to where there was ongoing unrest. I didn't allow this fact to spoil my initial euphoria because, since the audition, Samantha and I had become the talk of the changing rooms. I was thoroughly enjoying the fame, determined not to let the problems in the Middle East spoil it all. One of the boys, however, advised me not to go.

"You know that's in Syria don't you Jane?" Tony, the heartthrob of the college quizzed me after class, one afternoon.

"Yeah, it's OK though, it's all safe," I retorted confidently, as I pushed my leg above my head with a glare.

As I cycled frantically back to my digs, I mulled the situation over nervously.

"How dare Tony try to burst my career bubble, I'm sure he's just jealous," I muttered, amazed at how quickly you can go off a boy at college after fancying him for a whole term. The plan was that Samantha and I were going to be sent to the rehearsal studios of Guy, the man of the moment that Roz and Björn had told me about. Guy hadn't been at the audition, instead, sending over some of his dance captains to choose the new recruits on his behalf. We were to rehearse the show at his studios on the outskirts of Paris, before going out to a five-star hotel in Damascus over the winter. I was so keen to work, that after my exchange with Tony, I decided not to mention the precise location of the contract to my parents. Besides, Miss Laine wasn't bothered so why should I be? Rehearsals in Paris and then on to the Middle East would keep Mum and Dad happy. However, I became a little nervous when, with great pride, I told my landlady, Mrs Ashfield, during dinner one evening.

Mrs Ashfield had three lively children under the age of ten. She was a very strict mother with tight schedules for all of their activities, holding very high expectations for their futures. She tried to be friendly with me each evening, as we sat eating our nutritious meals together at the table in the silent, neat little dining room. She always seemed nervous of the topic of conversation that I might come out with in front of the children though. Tonight, it was going to be the exotic location of my employment over the Christmas period. I knew that she disapproved of my dance career. I'd mentioned once that some of my friends were leaving college to become showgirls on a cruise ship. She looked horrified, casting a quick glance at her children as if I had announced that these friends were going to be porn stars. I eventually had to lie a bit, saying that it was the QE2, and that they would be entertaining celebrities. She seemed to accept this a bit better. On this particular night, we were just making small talk to be polite while her children ate in silence.

"Now your parents are back from France I expect you're looking forward to Christmas with them Jane, aren't you dear?"

She handed a napkin to her little boy with a frown, as he shot gravy up his arm. Mum and Dad had returned from France and were settling back in England after their experimental trip to sample the good life. It had turned out to be a disappointment for them. They were back in Ipswich, piecing their lives together again, finding new jobs and a new home.

"Well, actually I'm going to work abroad this year over Christmas, in Damascus. It'll be my first job so I'm really excited. Rehearsals are in Paris and I'll get my equity card from it," I declared proudly.

I beamed across at her and stuffed a forkful of chicken pie into my mouth, making a mental note to look on the globe in her husband's study when they were out. It dawned on me just then, that I should learn the precise location of Damascus at some point. I was feeling so proud of myself because all I had ever wanted was adventure in the glamorous world of show business and travel, but Mrs Ashfield had started choking on her tea.

"Damascus! Are you sure?"

Her voice went up several decibels and her children stopped eating their dinner to stare at me with delighted curiosity. What was this strange girl, that lived with them for some reason, up to this time they wondered?

Mrs Ashfield was staring at me, stunned, holding her napkin to her lips.

"No daughter of *mine* would be going there. Do your parents know dear?" she croaked.

Later that evening when I'd fibbed that my parents were fully aware of my trip, she called me down during the News at Ten to show me the political unrest at that time, in Beirut. The globe had been brought out of the study and I learnt, at this moment, that Beirut was not that far from Damascus. Being a war zone, I had to admit, as I stared at the TV screen, it didn't look like they needed a cabaret show in those dusty streets.

"Well, I'm sure I'm not going *there!*" I protested, laughing nervously.

Not wishing to burst my adventurous bubble, I decided that evening, that I would not divulge exactly where in the Middle East I was going, to my parents. In Paris, I would find out the plans, feeling sure that they would never send us anywhere dangerous, not Miss Laine and Equity surely? There were certainly no calls for sparkling showgirls in the bombsites on the TV, so I felt there had to be an explanation.

I mean, the Middle East was huge, wasn't it?

9

CHANGE OF PLAN

MUM AND DAD, having struggled to find their dream life in France, had reluctantly returned to England. When I was offered the job with Guy, they were so busy sorting their own lives out, that they were only too pleased to hear that I had some new opportunities developing. In fact, Mum was even more excited than me about my proposed work. She seemed to have become an adventure junkie since my brother and I had left school.

My rehearsals in Paris sounded exciting, giving them one less thing to worry about, so I allowed everyone to picture me in a ballet studio with a Rudolph Nureyev lookalike, being coached, just the two of us, by one of the masters, near the Eiffel Tower. I left out the detail of our final destination for the time being.

On my next visit home from college, Mum, excited about my job in Paris, insisted on taking me to Marks and Spencer to buy a decent coat to wear.

"You can't go to Paris looking like *Fame* darling. You're a professional dancer now, let me buy you something elegant."

We walked into town and I tried not to sulk as I admired my rainbow leg warmers and chopped up sweatshirt. Having eventually mentioned that the final show was to go to the Middle East, Mum had convinced me that I needed vaccinations. Being seventeen but still used to doing what I was told, I asked no questions and followed her into the doctor's surgery like a lamb. Now that I'm a Mum, if it had been my daughter booking trips near war zones in the back of beyond, I know I would probably have done the same. By the time we got to Marks and Spencer, the side effects of my jabs were starting to take effect. I felt decidedly ropey.

"Oh, you do look pale darling, this trip is getting to you, isn't it? Try this on, we need to get some colour near your face," she whispered as she stuffed me into a full length, blue ladies' mackintosh. She pulled the belt tight. Pushing me gently over to the mirror, she stood back, nodding.

"Nice," she declared.

I looked like a Tory M.P. but agreed that it was gorgeous just to get us out of there. As we queued up at the cash desk, I felt hot and saw a few stars floating past. The side effects were kicking in again and, losing my balance, I leant rather heavily on the cash desk.

"Are you alright darling?" Mum came up close and felt my forehead. Two ladies, in the queue with us, nodded at each other.

"Drugs," one of them mouthed to her friend.

Mum saw her.

"Do you mind!! My daughter is …"

I blacked out.

≈

When we got home, I was put into bed. The worst part of this fainting drama was that Mum had still managed to purchase the blue mac. I laid in bed gazing at it, where she had hung it proudly on the back of my door ready for my trip. I decided that Mum was right and this whole ordeal was getting the better of me. However, the weeks passed and before I knew it, Mum and Dad were driving me to Heathrow in their little red Ford. Sadly, they had sold the camper van.

"It's the end of an era," Mum had explained quietly.

There was no Eurostar in the eighties and on earlier trips I had always taken the coach and ferry to France because it was much cheaper. Samantha, my partner in crime for this trip, didn't fancy such a longwinded journey though. She insisted we booked expensive flights. I went along with it, because I didn't want to fall out with her before we had even left the country.

Mum and Dad sang Abba songs all the way to the airport. With great excitement, they waved me off, making me promise to let them know exactly where our show was going to be, and the name of the hotel when I got there. I loved their enthusiasm but wondered to myself whether I would be doing the reverse journey in a few days. I still feared that the show was, in fact, in a dangerous part of Syria. I was starting to suspect that, possibly, Samantha and I were to be an upbeat version of Vera Lynn and Gracie Fields, sent to cheer up the soldiers amid gunfire at a barracks in the desert.

The journey was quite exciting as I hadn't flown before. If I'd thought my Mum had been making a fuss with posh coats and travel jabs, I was soon to realise how chilled she was in comparison to Samantha's mum. On arriving at the check-in desk at departures I was greeted by Samantha and her entire family flapping and fussing. They stuffed great wads of cash into Samantha's pockets and crammed bottles of water and sweets into her case.

"You'll need this, Paris is expensive darling," gushed her Mum.

Samantha rolled her eyes and hugged her family like a robot. It was with great relief that we were called through to the departure lounge, where it all suddenly went delightfully quiet. The journey was really ours. I was about to laugh about her family making such a fuss and suggest we went for a beer in the bar, when she turned to me and blurted,

"Oh, my God this is so stressful. I don't know if I can handle it. My Mum doesn't even know about Damascus. She thinks we're staying in Paris."

My heart sank as I patted her arm patiently. She allowed me to lead her to a nice little café, that looked after us beautifully as I spent my last few pounds and we waited to board.

Before smoking was banned, the smell of coffee and cigarettes used to always hit you on arrival at French railway stations and airports and I loved it. Charles de Gaulle airport in Paris is a groovy sixties circular design with dozens of identical exits that are a nightmare if you can't read the signs or speak French. I sensed that Samantha was secretly impressed by my confident manner. I made a mental note to thank my mother for organising daring holidays with French families throughout my early teenage years, giving me a very relaxed approach to journeys and a good grasp of the language. We waltzed through customs and found the underground trains, leaping on the Métro with no trouble. I'd been on the Metro many times on French exchange trips with school, so felt very confident in finding my way around.

Arriving at Gare du Lyon, we boarded the train, as instructed, to our rehearsal studios. We'd been told to take a particular train from the centre of Paris to the town of Montereau. Rehearsals were taking place near there and we had a number to call from the train station phone box if there was no-one there to meet us on arrival. In the eighties, there were no mobile phones. We had to find phone boxes and be much more organised and aware of plans. These days, people seem to wait until they arrive at their destination before they reach for their mobiles to find out what they are supposed to do next. Studying our tickets, I reassured myself that we were on the correct train, with the address and phone number of Guy Stranger at the studio, in my bag. Feeling relieved, I settled into my seat as the train slid out of the station. I put my head back for a snooze as Samantha went off in search of the loo. I was quickly awoken by a shrill voice.

"No darling, no-one in that carriage, wait a minute, well, who do we have here?"

The shrill voice turned out to be a very tall slender boy wearing a trilby, very tight jeans and lip gloss. His companion was a breathtakingly, beautiful girl with a shock of blonde curls. She was carrying a huge holdall and balancing a tray of coffees. Wearing rainbow leg warmers and a *Fame* sweatshirt, she must have measured about six foot two.

"Hello! You must be one of us! Welcome to our company darling girl!" gushed the boy as he threw himself across the seats opposite me.

"We bought coffee!" his eyes shone with delight as he bounced on his seat, already preparing to grill me for information on my life so far.

"How do you do? I'm Martin and this is Tina."

He was clearly a 'people person'. Stretching out a beautifully manicured hand, he explained that our manager, Guy, had told him to look out for us on his way to rehearsals. Relief flooded through me. He continued to chat as his friend Tina slipped in next to him, fluffing up her hair and checking her long scarlet nails. She then passed around the coffees, letting Martin carry on his welcome speech.

"I have to say, darling, you threw me slightly with your clothes. I'm usually good at picking out the dancers on the train but that delightful coat, well ..."

I cringed and sipped my coffee as he gazed at me, fascinated.

"Very ... Woman's Weekly."

I stifled a snort of laughter, as I knew he was spot on.

"Jane," I offered my hand in a jaunty gesture.

Samantha appeared from the toilets and plonked herself down, huffily, beside me. She hardly acknowledged our new friends. Martin looked relieved.

"Oh, another one!! Thank God! I thought we'd lost one. So, you must be Samantha then?" his eyes darted briefly to me with one raised, perfectly plucked eyebrow and back to Samantha. He had already perceived that she was a little precious and, sure enough, she began to describe how smelly the toilets were.

Martin changed the subject thankfully, when I asked him for a brief history of his work with Guy, so far.

"I've been with Guy for years. I keep thinking of leaving and then another contract comes up in a country that I can't resist, and before you know it ten years have passed. It's the weather too, I mean how can you turn down a sunny climate when it's so cold and miserable here?" We all nodded in agreement, feeling smug as we looked out at the black clouds threatening to burst as the train flew out to the suburbs.

"Even Damascus is worth it when it's so grey and cold here. It's only for a few months. We're taking the same show to Guadeloupe in the spring, you should come."

Martin clocked my expression and detected my anxiety. "Look, I always find a little corner with a sun-lounger by the pool in Damascus. You'd never know all the troubles going on outside the hotel, apart from a bit of noise in the night. There may be a few bomb scares but, well ...," he eyed me cautiously as he spoke, definitely testing the water. Tina joined in,

"Oh God! Martin, do you remember last year when we had to stop the show and sit in the basement for the night in our sequins," she babbled, glancing over to Samantha whose mouth was slightly ajar in horror.

"Yes, that was something I wanted to ask about, actually," I stammered looking into my empty coffee cup before crushing it nervously. Martin had sussed me out straight away as I sat there smiling politely in my M&S coat, tension mounting rapidly.

He continued, "Look darling, don't panic. I'll sort it out. If you're not mad and dangerous like me and Tina here, then I'm sure we can send you down to Madrid instead. They always need girls there over Christmas, and it's virtually the same show. For some reason, English girls always want to go home to their relatives for the festive season, ugh! I feel sorry for all you young dancers having to tell Mummy and Daddy what you're up to all the time. My parents lost interest eventually, and it was a great weight off my shoulders being able to do what the fuck I wanted at last, I can tell you."

Martin stretched out on his seat and took his hat off, putting it over his eyes. There were a few quiet minutes before he started laughing.

"One Christmas morning I announced to the family that I was gay, as I opened yet another inappropriate present. Everyone was so relieved. At last, they could all buy me beauty products instead of socks."

Martin was so light-hearted that I felt optimistic that he would help us through the Middle Eastern muddle we'd got ourselves into. I could tell he was used to these dilemmas and wanted the least hassle possible when he was topping up his tan over the winter, on his Christmas excursion. My heart soared as I realised that he was on the case with regards to our concerns over the location of our first job.

"Thanks Martin, we were a bit worried. Hope we can work something out," I replied quietly.

"Leave it with me poppet but it doesn't mean you don't have to work your arses off in rehearsals. A Can-Can is the same in any country, OK?" He reached over and patted my arm. "As long as you keep starving yourself and working hard, Guy will always have a job for you somewhere sweetheart! I don't know why you all bother going to college."

With that, he rested his head on Tina's shoulder, and drifted off to sleep, snoring gently.

Martin was not one to hide his opinions and they were so entertaining that you couldn't take offence. We rested our eyes for the remainder of the journey, exhausted from laughing at his anecdotes and feeling better. When the train pulled into Montereau train station Tina woke him up. We all clambered out and lugged our cases to the parking area where there was just a filthy old van with a shaggy dog looking out of the window. I was hugely relieved that we had Martin and

Tina with us because I am sure, without them, we would have turned around and caught the next train back to the centre of Paris and home.

"Ooh this is very French!" I exclaimed, trying to enthuse a very horrified looking Samantha. She grabbed my arm as a large unshaven man leapt out of the front of the van and embraced Tina and Martin before coming towards us.

"Bien Venue! My name is Guy, and I am ...," he struck a Bruce Forsyth pose here, flexing rather impressive old muscles, "The Boss!"

Guy was so merry and pleased to see us that I shook his hand and helped to pass our luggage up to him as he clambered up into the back of the van.

There followed a white-knuckle ride through winding country roads with no seat belts on. Being from Suffolk, I was completely accustomed to this. Samantha, being from Surrey, immediately went into the crash position. Tina, the grubby dog and I, bumped around on the scruffy back seats nodding and laughing as we hurtled around the winding roads. Martin and Guy were in the front, speaking very quickly in a mixture of French and English, obviously discussing the plans for the show, until eventually, we arrived at our rehearsal home. The van collapsed onto a large stony driveway with a sigh of relief as a gang of unruly dogs surrounded us, barking enthusiastically. We climbed down into yet another unexpected scenario.

There, in all its glory, stood a shambolic farmhouse with a large swimming pool surrounded by a huge terrace. The pool water was dark green and there were dead plants in pots full of dog ends, around the edge. From the open, upstairs windows of the farmhouse, beautiful girls sat smoking and chatting. They dangled their long legs over the sills, enjoying the last of some unexpected evening sunshine. Loud music boomed out across the garden from a large, attached barn that was obviously a rehearsal studio as I could just see the silhouette of a man holding a girl in a perfect lift above his head.

Guy turned out to be a likeable chap, married to our wardrobe mistress, Regine. They made an extraordinary couple, having many exotic tales to tell of their past travels around the world. They had once toured with their very own, erotic, cabaret act during the sixties and seventies. Since retiring, Guy had accepted the role of manager for a dancer named Olivier Briac, known to the dancers as just Briac. After producing glamorous cabaret shows worldwide for many years, Briac had retired to Pape'ete in the French Polynesian Islands, on the proceeds of his success. Taking over the running of the shows from Paris, Regine created the costumes while Guy ensured that there was always a constant stream of dancers being rehearsed at this extraordinary studio before sending them all over the world. In later years, it was always reassuring to know that Guy would have a contract ready to sign if we turned up looking beautiful and slim, when there was nothing better on offer elsewhere, which usually, there wasn't.

Judging by the faded photographs of Guy and Regine's cabaret act, that were proudly displayed on the walls of the office, it had been quite a kinky show, involving whips, leather thongs and mahogany tans. They had been well known in many night-clubs and cabaret acts around the globe in their day, and they knew the business inside out, running a very tight ship for Briac. Looking at the largest faded poster of them, photographed in a very contorted position, one could appreciate that they had continued to work well into maturity. The poster was quite something to behold, rather like an upbeat wrinklies advert for health supplements for strong joints. During our rehearsals, Regine loved it when Guy would call her from the sewing room to demonstrate a lift for whoever was dancing the Pas de Deux in our show. She would flutter her eyelashes down at us, her mouth still full of pins from her sewing work, as she was transported back to the good old days. In a perfect swanlike position, weightless, above Guy's head, he would carry her effortlessly around the studio and the dancers would clap adoringly and shout out,

"Bravo Regine!" trying not to giggle when her wig slipped. They really were masters of their trade.

Guy loved animals and we had to share our accommodation with his smelly dogs, so it wasn't unusual to see a flea riddled mutt strolling through the studio, checking itself out on the large, mirrored walls when we were halfway through a rehearsal. We would just have to leap over them. If he could have got away with it, I'm sure Guy would have created an act that incorporated the dogs leaping through hoops so he could bring them on tour with us, but the thought of those dogs in the minibus did not bear thinking about. I became used to them jumping on the bed in the middle of the night but some of the girls were petrified. The dogs seemed to know this and would always follow those particular girls around, even into the shower. You could sometimes hear squeals of horror as girls went to their suitcase, only to find a grubby dog asleep in their beautifully packed luggage, having eaten all their supplies of sweets, bought especially for a tour.

Over the years, I came to love the familiarity of Guy, Regine and the moth-eaten farmhouse and it's one of the many treasured memories of my dance career. So, on this first evening, Samantha and I sat around the large kitchen table, with Martin and the ten or so other girls rehearsing the Damascus show. We ate stew from a large pot on the hob, with chunks of baguette, drinking red wine until quite late. Some of the girls were French but much to Samantha's relief they spoke in English to us and French to each other, so we were able to find out a bit more about the plans. As we chatted to the other dancers, it became clear that, sure enough, the show was booked at a hotel in Damascus. I wasn't the sort of teenager that followed the news and the other dancers, bearing in mind it was 1981, didn't seem in the slightest bit concerned about the political situation over there. In hindsight, they must have been completely fearless, naive or mad. When I spoke to my parents on the phone from the office, I could tell that I was causing them increasing concern when it was clear that we would be staying in the centre of Damascus. I decided that I should try to agree an alternative plan, as Martin had suggested on the train, or brace myself to go home. Surprisingly, Samantha had told her family that we were staying in Paris for the entire contract, little fibber. Fortunately, Martin had been very complimentary about our performance during our first day of rehearsals and when I explained that I'd had pressure from home not to travel to Syria, he spoke with Guy. They agreed to re-locate us immediately. Not wanting to lose us altogether, they insisted that we should become part of the show in Madrid that had been mentioned on the train.

"Grab your stuff girls, you're off to Spain," Martin announced as he came into the studio the next day as we were warming up for a rehearsal of the Can-Can. He threw an envelope of train tickets at us, collapsing onto the floor into the splits.

"You're lucky, Guy and Regine don't want to lose you," he explained as he rolled over onto his back and pushed his foot behind his head. "I don't blame them. I'll miss you in Damascus. Spain is lovely at Christmas, but you won't earn anything near as much as us. I'm sure you'll have a great time though, and fall in love with a local," he chuckled.

Samantha and I hugged Martin and sheepishly went to our rooms to gather our belongings. We were to catch the overnight sleeper train from Paris to Madrid that night, and Guy was waiting to take us back to Montereau station.

I had visions of the other girls working in Damascus and being evacuated every night from the theatre, amid gunfire in their sequinned bikinis, along with a journalist reporting at the front-line. I suspect it was probably not quite as ridiculous as that, but I had my parents to consider.

"Oh! darling I'm so glad, we were getting really worried," my Mum's anxious voice rang out in the phone box making me feel guilty.

It always made me come down to earth with a bump when I heard her distant voice and the familiar background noises of our kitchen.

"Ok Mum, I'll let you know where we end up but we're not going far. You could come down to see the show in Spain!" I called, as my money ran out and we were cut off, my last French franc clattering into the machine. I liked to keep them informed even if it was brief.

So, thanks to Martin and Guy, being so decent as to re-locate us to a new 'parent friendly' job, Samantha and I set off on the first showgirl contract of our careers.

10

MADRID

AS OUR TRAIN from Paris pulled into Madrid station in a glare of early morning sunshine, I scanned the platform for anyone that looked remotely like a sleepy dancer, sent to meet our train. We had naively assumed that we would be met by someone from the show to guide us into town. All we could see though, were commuters in immaculate suits, jostling for a position in the queues for the underground.

After a while, as no-one had turned up to greet us, we decided we would have to join the crowd and jolly well find the theatre ourselves, rather than sit and wait in hope for someone to magically appear. We had an address for the theatre so there was really no excuse.

"POOEY!" Samantha turned her nose up. A waft of eggy sewage smell floated up from the drains near the pavement as we looked up the street for a taxi. I'd experienced this before in Paris and couldn't help laughing, but she scowled at me, sticking her hand out for a taxi as I folded my metro map and put it in my bag. Unlike her, I had very limited funds but calling a cab was second nature to Samantha.

"Teeeatrooo MONUMENTAL," she shouted very loudly at the taxi driver from the back seat.

Fortunately, as he pulled out at breakneck speed, he nodded, seeming to know where the theatre was, which was hugely reassuring. After a short but exciting taxi ride from the station, it was rather disappointing on our arrival, to find the theatre looking rather scruffy and locked up. There was very little traffic noise at this time of day, so it was quiet enough to hear the gushing water of the elaborate fountains coming from the main avenue just around the corner. The sun glinted just above the rooftops of Madrid, promising another bright sunny day in the city. The street sweeper whistled a happy little tune to himself and smiled at us curiously, removing the evidence of the previous night's party goers with his broom. Old streamers swirled around his boots and empty bottles rolled along the gutter, as he worked his way towards the grimy steps of the old Teatro Monumental. I peered anxiously through the shabby art deco windows of the entrance hall.

"Well, I think this is it," I announced wearily, checking the slip of paper Guy had stuffed into my hand as he'd bundled us onto the overnight train in Paris the night before.

"I'm sure it looks much more beautiful at night when it's all lit up. Most things do," I added with my usual chirpy outlook.

It was only when I looked around for Samantha that I realised she was still making her way up the street, glaring at the new surroundings with distaste. I had a quick peek through the large, locked doors. It was dark inside the entrance of the theatre as I squinted through the glass, looking for some form of life. Just above a flickering night-light and dusty, red, velvet curtains, I could vaguely make out photographs of tanned showgirls with toothy grins and false eyelashes. These ladies were draped over a glistening motorbike on which was perched a voluptuous diva with golden curls tumbling around her shoulders, clearly the star of the show. Her shifty expression hinted that she was not an experienced biker and probably wouldn't even know how to start the thing. With a name like Tania Doris though, I decided she might be something special in Madrid. Sure enough, when I stepped back and looked up at the front of the building, I noticed that her name was spelt out in bold neon lights, flashing out to the public on the tall brick facade of the old art deco theatre. She was obviously the nation's darling, but the pretty terraced apartments that stood each side of the theatre, accentuated the shabbiness of the pink plastic lights and peeling paint. Despite this, not wanting to allow myself to feel disappointed yet, I decided it all looked rather jolly although probably not the type of show that Teatro Monumental had been originally built for. I felt a pang of sadness for the place, imagining opera singers, actors and Flamenco stars gracing the steps under the flashlights of the paparazzi, at glamorous film premiers of silent movies during the 30's.

I was also slightly concerned, after looking more carefully, that although the top half of Tania's crew were nicely covered up in studded leather biking jackets, they were all proudly displaying their bum cheeks at the back. I wasn't sure how Samantha, my classically trained companion would feel about performing in such a style of costume. I felt a sneaking suspicion that we had been sent to Madrid to replace two of these biker girls. I knew that Samantha would not be 'chafing at the bit' to get on Tania's bike. I cringed as I took another look at the costumes and didn't reckon that the choreography would be anything like that of the Royal Academy of Dance syllabus that we enjoyed back home. I reassured myself, as I gazed through the glass, that back at college, we had all been able to see Samantha's bum when she had danced a Pas de Deux dressed in a white tutu at the summer show. Theoretically it was no different. I wondered if I would be able to convince her of this theory. There were probably rather different sentiments behind the meaning of Tania's Hard Rock, compared to Giselle. I would just have to hope that I could sway her opinion, but it wasn't going to be easy.

I was jolted out of my reverie when Samantha joined me on the steps before pushing passed me.

"Eww! This can't possibly be it," she announced.

As I feared, she took one swift glance through the dusty glass and threw her hands up in despair.

"Fuck! I am *not* going in there!"

She grabbed the paper with the address out of my hand and sat on the grimy step.

"Oh, my God! This can't be it. We must have the wrong address!"

Realising that we were exactly where we were meant to be, she got up again, pacing impatiently, trying to think what to do. I knew she was already mentally composing something to tell her parents in a call box. This filled me with dread.

"I can't believe this. I knew this was a mistake Jane, oh shit! shit! fuck! What the hell have we done?" She swung round to stare at me in complete panic.

I was just pleased that she was saying *we* and not *you*, because since we'd left Paris, her tone of voice had been making me feel that I was the cause of our calamities.

Opening up his stall, the nearby newspaper seller looked worried, but intrigued, as Samantha's ranting reached quite impressive decibels.

"She'll calm down in a minute," I thought, as I sat down on the steps again, feeling exhausted.

Her trembling chin and wide eyes were a clear sign that, as she struggled with the posh suitcases which her granny had bought her for the trip, she was feeling cross. Samantha was out of her comfort zone.

"Oh my God I feel really let down," she cried, stifling a sob as she plonked herself on the steps with me. "This is not the classy show they described at the audition. In fact, it looks like a right old dive. It IS a dive! LIARS!!" she screamed, gaining momentum, her voice turning angry as she continued to talk herself through the situation.

"This is nothing like The Bluebell Girls and Betty Laine has no idea what this place is like." She stopped in her tracks as reality dawned on her.

"This can't be an Equity contract!!" she growled as she wrung her hands over her head, pausing to place her fingertips dramatically on her temples.

"Think! Samantha, think ...," she whispered to herself, realising I was being rather backward in coming forward with a solution. I was actually beginning to thoroughly enjoy myself.

"No! I will not be part of this," she carried on, taking a semi yoga pose. Bringing her hands together across her face, she contemplated our situation, litter swirling around her dainty ankles. Turning to the tall entrance door with its faded grandeur, she reassured herself that she hadn't imagined the horrific scene and that this wasn't some awful dream.

"Actually ... Jane," she looked through the glass again, taking in the situation, "it honestly looks to me like its closed down, right?" There was a glimmer of hope in her eyes now, as it dawned on her that we possibly had a feasible reason to travel back to England.

I wasn't anywhere near as upset as her though. I was feeling glad to have found the place and start the ball rolling. My only concern really, was Samantha.

She muttered softly to herself as she slumped on the step again, exhausted.

"It's all been a terrible mistake and we'll just have to go home."

After hunting in her bag for her tissues and having a loud blow of the nose, a bit of weeping, hand wringing and lip gloss application, Samantha started to perk up. Trundling back down the main road, she set off again, in search of a taxi. It was the eighties, so we didn't have mobile phones and credit cards, thankfully. This would have ruined everything, as it does today, putting a stop to any spontaneity or adventure that may come your way. I had very little money in my purse and this was quite an advantage in some respects because it gave me a good reason to do things that my mother may not have approved of. I could just imagine the phone conversation.

"I know Mum, I had to be a naked belly dancer because I needed to save up for my flight home. You would have done the same, I had no choice, trust me."

As I sat gazing at Samantha's dramatic performance in my bleary-eyed state of early morning, *sleepless-night-on-a-train-and-no-breakfast* exhaustion, I had to agree that the theatre was a little tired looking. In the glare of the winter sunshine, it was not quite as prestigious as we'd been led to believe when we'd signed the contracts back in Paris. However, although, at first, Tania's motor-biking photographs had been a huge disappointment to me, I decided that in the grand scheme of things, we were missing the point. We weren't in middle class London anymore, with our ballet exams and Waitrose. We were on an adventure in the real world, faced with a juicy decision. It would be so easy to hop back on the train and leave it all behind to spend Christmas with the family around the tree. I could imagine Mum saying, "Oh, never mind darling, I'm sure it would have been awful. Well done for coming home. Have another Quality Street."

Alternatively, we could face the fact that Tania Doris was somebody's daughter, and probably a right laugh to spend Christmas with. I had started to have visions of Tania and I, sitting around a big table with her family, eating paella and swigging Sangria out of carafes, as we roared with laughter at my stories of when we arrived in Madrid and saw the cheeky photographs through the window. I took a moment to digest these thoughts and the options that we were faced with. Watching Samantha's silhouette prancing huffily along the street towards the taxi rank, ponytail swinging, I chuckled as I realised, she was going to be really furious when she noticed I wasn't rushing after her. I felt we had plenty of time to think things over. It didn't look like anyone was exactly rushing to meet and greet us. Surely, we could allow ourselves a cup of coffee, Samantha paying of course. We needed some time to reflect, before we went racing home with our tails between our legs, with excuses of sleazy theatres and scantily clad women. Also, I had spotted a little bar near the stage door saying Artistes' Bar. A vision had flashed through my mind of us coming out of the stage door, in our Spanish shawls straight onto our bar stools, with all our friends from the show, joining us for our post show gin and tonic.

"Yeah, bring it on," came that little voice from the back of my mind.

I wondered if the bar was open now, knowing that a stiff one would calm Samantha down, and bring her swiftly round to my very mature way of thinking. I knew she wouldn't dare to travel home alone. She'd made such a fuss getting here. After a while, and when Samantha realised that I wasn't scuttling along behind her, she turned around to see that I was still sitting on the steps of the theatre.

With a lop-sided grin on my face, I had started to find the whole thing rather amusing.

"Well, are you coming or what?" she called out in a haughty voice.

She sounded really young.

I came to the conclusion that there was no way that I was going home, defeated. Samantha was on her own with her homeward plans. She was going to have to decide if she was up for the ride with me, or if she preferred to travel back to England like a coward at Daddy's expense. My Daddy would have probably agreed with Samantha, but I didn't dwell on that thought because something told me he wouldn't appreciate a call of this nature from me on this particular morning, as he got ready for work. Organising your kids was much trickier in the days of no internet. You couldn't just book an Airbnb for them and an EasyJet flight home at the touch of your screen. You had to make painstakingly long calls to travel agents and hotels, with a number obtained from the lady at Directory Enquiries. You couldn't choose the cheapest option from a list on a website, it involved major planning and inconvenience and took up most of the morning. Another thought making me guffaw rather, on those steps, was that I had no doubt that my Mum would be more than happy to step in for Samantha and don a leather jacket with no hesitation whatsoever.

The sights and sounds of Madrid from the window of our cab that morning, had whetted my appetite. There were wafts of roasting coffee beans, the clicking sounds from the man selling castanets, little, tiny boutiques with bijoux bay windows selling Flamenco dresses and red shoes. Thinking of the grand avenues full of art galleries, elaborate fountains graced with marble statues and markets heaving with local produce, I knew that this was an opportunity that was too good to miss. There was just too much to explore and my bum cheeks quivered in anticipation of donning my leathers and joining Tania on her motorbike. I was ready to shake my bootee, earning my keep in this exciting city of culture and history.

Our fatigue wasn't helping our mood. We were so tired that we could barely think. While Samantha had sat up cursing the shabby overnight train and bumpy night's sleep in our bunks, I had marvelled at the view as the sun rose over baron fields of dry land and the promise of Spanish sunshine, after the lush green vineyards of rainy southwest France. I was also feeling very relieved that we hadn't ended up in Damascus with its hotel casino shows so close to the bombs and unrest, as originally planned. The thought of my parents biting their nails at home would have been unbearable. Samantha had sat awake for the early part of the train journey from Paris, glaring out at the inky sky while I dozed fitfully, raising my head occasionally to offer calming words as she ranted away.

"I can't believe they just threw us on this train, I mean, anything could have happened to us overnight!" she moaned as though the company in Paris were some kind of kids' holiday company and we were twelve years old. It hadn't occurred to her yet that we had made this decision ourselves and I don't think she was appreciating either, just how lucky we were to have been dug out of trouble. Copping out of an equity contract in the Middle East because we were scared, wasn't something to be hugely proud of. I certainly didn't want to repeat the process here in Spain, just because I didn't like the look of the cheeky costumes in the show. They would never give us a second chance, and I was worried that we would get labelled as troublemakers within the company and never be offered a job again. I'd rather liked the sound of Guadeloupe at Easter that Martin had mentioned, even though I had no idea where it was.

After the dramatic outburst on the steps, I eventually managed to persuade Samantha to come back and find a café and drink that coffee together. This turned out to be a huge success and we'd settled at a little table in front of two large, frothy coffees in a corner café opposite the theatre. The hot drinks were hugely restorative and while Samantha counted out coins, preparing to call her mother from a phone box, have a good cry and spoil her Mum's morning, I just took in the local atmosphere. I was just getting close to suggesting that she should buy some cigarettes and that I would have one to be sociable, when the rays of sunshine at the door were blocked by a large figure of what looked like, possibly Zorro himself.

'Siñoritas! So soooorreee!,"

The snakeskin cowboy hat was huge, and from underneath I could just make out large, brown smouldering eyes glinting at us. His boots shone and, as they clicked across the café floor, Samantha stopped counting her coins and slowly raised her face up to take in the beautiful vision that was Fernando. He removed his hat, allowing dark glossy hair to spill over the silk scarf around his neck. He pointed his pointy Spanish boot in front of him, as he bowed to us in his poncho, casting a long shadow across the café floor.

"Forgeeeeeve me, I was sleeeeeping!" he purred.

"Please, follow me ladies."

Word had obviously got out locally that there were two hysterical English girls on the steps of the theatre. I imagined someone must have called to inform Fernando.

He spoke very gently and there was a kindly sparkle in his eyes. He signalled to us to follow him, before setting off, swaying up the sunny street in his poncho, creating a dancing shadow behind him. Delighted to be rescued, we obediently followed him like lambs along the avenue. Lugging our cases, we broke into a mild trot as Fernando started to take giant strides, obviously keen to go back to bed. Having no luggage, he was still clearly not prepared to break a nail by helping us.

I managed to spot a huge window of cakes as I hobbled along and made a note to self to go straight back there on pay day. I was flabbergasted to notice also, that Samantha hadn't protested at all. In her current mood, I wouldn't have been at all surprised if she'd laid into Fernando for being late, thrown his hat across the café and stamped on it. She seemed to be adjusting to the Spanish way immediately though. There she was, nodding and agreeing with everything he said as she trotted along, gazing up at him in adoration.

Fernando was mainly speaking to us in Spanish with the odd English word thrown in. Whatever he was saying sounded most alluring. I knew Samantha wasn't understanding any of it, which made me laugh out loud with amusement. Things were looking up and I was thrilled that something good was happening, finally, as it usually does, and I felt a wave of great joy. We were on the next leg of our adventure at last, and not in a taxi going back to the station, defeated. The situation had been helped immensely by the fact that Fernando was clearly Samantha's idea of a perfect man. The possibility of her donning that biker jacket as pillion to Tania Doris was becoming more and more likely.

"I think we should at least give it a day and see if we can organise our journey home tomorrow, don't you?" she whispered authoritatively to me, as Fernando stopped at a doorway.

He pointed high up to the rooftops.

"You 'ave a room to share 'ere on fiff floor. They are expecting you ladies. Please come to the theatre at two o' clock for rehearsals. We need you in the show tomorrow night. My name is Ferrrrnandoooo, welcome to my country."

Samantha beamed at him, nodding so hard that her blond curls bobbed up and down. He smiled at her, just a few seconds longer than was necessary, before turning dramatically on his heels and striding back down the street towards the café. I felt like a gooseberry.

We were so relieved to be found, that we didn't really care about the unnerving comment about our forthcoming appearance in the show. Added to that, we now had to face the mammoth task of hauling our cases up five flights of stairs. As we climbed the winding steps, I realised why Fernando had chosen not to accompany us to our room. By the time we reached the top with our cases, we were puffing and wheezing. The sweat had started to trickle down my face and back. We had come to a door that turned out to be a hostel or pension, as they call them in Madrid. These, we soon came to realise, varied in niceness and price. Despite the stunning marble staircase and bright green wall tiles that led up to it, ours seemed to be one of the less nice, budget varieties.

"The residents here must have amazingly toned thighs," rasped Samantha as we tackled the last flight of steps.

We stood panting and laughing after ringing the bell. It was the first time I had seen Samantha smile in a long time, and, for a few seconds, I felt optimistic. Our smiles faded though, as a shifty looking man, with his shirt half untucked, answered the door.

"Welcome." His mouth split into a wonky smile displaying black and gold teeth.

"Ugh!" Samantha reeled backwards as a waft of garlic breath, wine and yesterday's paella hit us in the face.

We reluctantly followed our landlord. He shuffled down a dark corridor, past a little panelled reception area, where there was an old phone and scruffy directory amongst a display of droopy pot plants. Eventually, we came to a door where he steered us into a decrepit, dark twin room. After showing us the cruddy bathroom and rickety beds, he lingered a little bit too long. Samantha glared at him with hatred, as he asked us how long we would be staying and what our reason was for being in Madrid. There was a language barrier, but I managed to communicate excellently with a bit of French, hand actions, and loud English in a Spanish accent.

I felt he was being quite reasonable in some respects. He smiled sympathetically as I explained that I wouldn't be able to pay him until the end of the week. I knew Samantha was loaded, and she nodded along as I spoke, obviously planning to check into the Hilton later that day. I had no choice but to accept the scuzzy room. Knowing that we could speak to some of the other dancers later at rehearsals, I suspected we would be able to move to somewhere nicer if we wanted. We agreed to bide our time and find out a little bit more about the area and the going rates.

Despite being tired and miserable, with the sound of someone bonking next door, we managed a morning siesta.

The shower, it turned out at least, was in reasonable working order, so by two o'clock, we felt ready to take on the Teatro Monumental, Tania Doris and the Bum Cheek Gang.

As we left, I packed a bag of some of my things and Samantha did the same. I couldn't help suspecting that our landlord would come and have a good snout through our stuff while we were out. Bracing ourselves before we left the safety of our little room we were completely taken by surprise when, on tentatively opening the door, a hugely unexpected scene greeted us.

Since the early morning, the shutters had been flung open in the reception area, letting in bright sunlight, revealing a spectacular view from the vast open window. Looking out at the city of Madrid made me want to weep with joy. Pretty rooftops, avenues of grandeur with sparkling fountains and deep blue sky, sent my spirits soaring. I could spy our landlord singing, as he walked up and down a pretty, little tiled kitchen in the back of reception. He was gently pushing a large pram with the most beautiful, smiling baby sitting up in it. As we approached, a pretty little señora, who I presumed was his wife, rushed out to greet us. Throwing her arms around Samantha and I, she spoke very fast Spanish that we didn't understand. The smell of sumptuous cooking made me drool. I was relieved to realise that, in our exhausted state earlier, we had completely misinterpreted the standard of this authentic little hostel, and the humility of our host. I felt a welcome wave of happiness as, yet again, another ray of hope appeared.

Retracing our steps to the theatre, we felt like we were in a completely different place. It seemed that the city had come to life since our early morning arrival. Cars were tooting and there was a delightful fizz in the air as people were chatting and embracing everywhere you looked. The cafés and restaurants were busy with waiters flashing past in their gleaming white aprons, with trays heaving with coffee, wine, plates of tapas and dishes of paella. There was an excitement in the air, filling me with hope that maybe, Samantha would cheer up and want to be part of this adventure after all, even when she saw the racy photographs of the show in the entrance hall again. That moment was imminent, and I was dreading her reaction as we approached the stage door, easy to find by following the dancers, as they arrived for the rehearsal. I guessed they were dancers because they all had the same familiar, pasty look achieved from working in the show at night. With ruffled hair and sleepy eyes, they arrived, ready to be transformed. They had tiny figures too, as one has to have if one is dancing with Tania, in next to nothing. I steered Samantha expertly past the main entrance of the theatre, aiming straight for the stage door, just as a group of startlingly handsome Spaniards burst out onto the street, laughing and singing. This was very good timing, and we were soon inside the building, making our way through long elegant corridors in search of the dressing rooms.

We hadn't long introduced ourselves to the dance captain, Judith, before we were being taught our opening number. This was demonstrated for us by a beautiful girl, clad in nothing but a sequinned leotard revealing perfectly toned buttocks. We followed her about on the enormous stage, learning a routine called The Air Hostesses or rather, Les Hôtesses, in French since, after all, it was Guy Stranger's French company. I later learnt that in Spanish, the word for Air Hostess is Azafata, which I personally thought would have been much more appropriate. I kept my jovial opinions to myself because there were more urgent matters to attend to. Judith, the dance captain, was frantically going through the complicated steps with us. There was an air of panic about her, as she attempted to smile while we showed her what we had learnt, so far, of the fiddly routine. She had a terrifying stare which was most off-putting. However, I understood her concern, aware that we were expected by the management to dance the following night. We needed to get the routines into our heads as soon as possible. Apparently, the management used to count all thirty girls on stage every night during the Air Hostess dance, to make sure no-one was skiving off. If everyone was present and correct in this part, then we got the all clear, everyone got paid, and the management retired to the Artistes' Bar. During the finale, they would come back to do the counting again. Crafty, but with, I later learned, good reason. I heard through the grapevine that afternoon, that two of the dancers had recently performed a midnight flit and left the show. This happened a lot in the profession. Little did I know then that I was to do the same myself on occasions, later in my career, when I felt it necessary.

Anyway, Teatro Monumental were two girls down and we were saving the day, meaning everyone was being really nice to us. This helped Samantha's mood immensely and it also explained why Guy had been so happy to send us straight down to Madrid. In Damascus, the management were just grateful to anyone for going, never complaining if there were a few missing.

The Air Hostess number turned out to be very exciting although quite challenging, and rehearsals were intense. Judith glared at us manically from the front as we pounded away, memorising the routine like robots. We, the thirty air hostesses, had to dance onto the stage in our royal blue sequinned jackets with matching berets and thongs. We were supposed to mime the Spanish words to the song on the playback tape, but I decided to just move my mouth up and down. I definitely wouldn't learn a Spanish song by the next day as well as all the dancing. Fortunately, Judith seemed to accept this. We all had little sparkling briefcases, also in royal blue. At a certain point in the choreography, we had to march in our line, to the front of the stage and kneel down elegantly. I knew here that I mustn't lose my balance and roll over, imagining it would *not* be a pretty sight in a G-string, even if it *was* sequinned. Turning our brief cases around, we revealed large capital letters stuck on them, positioned in order to spell out Tania Doris! Genius. We even had to call out her name in air hostess voices as we turned our cases around. This moment was crucial because while we were strutting our stuff, an impressive, real, pretend aeroplane descended onto the stage, complete with engine noise. It then shuddered to a halt, before who should emerge, but 'Our Tania', amid rapturous applause from her fans. The dashing Air Stewards, handsome in crisp suits and peaked caps, waited in line to escort her down the rather shaky, cardboard looking steps. It really was quite an entrance and I was starting to feel quite proud to be part of this Spanish extravaganza. I looked forward to watching the show that night with a wave of affection, knowing that soon it would be us out there, supporting Tania Doris.

We had a break after rehearsals, before meeting Judith backstage as instructed, just before curtain up. At rehearsals, Judith had seemed rather mousey looking with non-descript hair in a loose ponytail and a pallid complexion. I, therefore, almost didn't recognise her when she waved over to us back-stage. She seemed to have transformed into a breath-taking Air Hostess, although her expression looked as though she was about to supervise a crash landing. It was rather exciting though, with the buzz of a theatre full of people waiting excitedly for the show to begin. There seemed to be whole rows of families, of all generations, on a grand night out. As they settled down with great anticipation, we realised that Tania was a serious household name in Spain. We definitely shouldn't have joked about her motorbike. I was fascinated that these families were completely comfortable with the scantily clad dancers, thinking how prudish we are in Britain about body parts.

The orchestra finished playing the overture. Judith found us an inconspicuous spot in the wings, just inside the curtains, so we could watch and learn. Although we weren't dancing that night, it wouldn't be long before we were out there. This was a great way of learning our cues and seeing how it all worked, giving us a good idea of the timings, for our debut the following evening.

"Now I want you to watch the opening number tonight and don't take your eyes off me during 'Hostesses' because *I* am dancing *your* part this evening Jane, so you will have to do everything that I do. *Tonight*, I will be *you*, tomorrow. Do you get it?" her voice quavered slightly with stress as I nodded and smiled.

I was pleased to notice that Samantha was trying to put on a brave face, despite her returning feelings of dread. I marvelled as the girls filed past in their sequinned thongs, blazers and the highest of silver heels. Their little sparkling berets looked so chic, perched on their immaculately slicked back hair. Their false eyelashes made their eyes enormous and I was desperate to join them the following evening. I thought they looked absolutely stunning under the spotlights. I also couldn't believe how beautiful Judith had turned out with a bit of lippy on as well. We had all looked so pale that afternoon as we'd rehearsed. I began to look forward to my own transformation. I'd never worn false eyelashes before and the tan coloured fishnet tights seemed to make everyone's legs look amazingly long and toned, with not a sign of wobbly bits anywhere.

The orchestra burst into action and the girls leapt out to great applause from the audience. I watched Judith from the wings, without blinking, recognising the routine and memorising her positioning on the stage.

Unfortunately, as she danced, Judith caught her heel on the hem of a passing steward on his way out and fell flat on her face. One of the Air steward boys rushed gallantly to her aid, by marching in front of her while one of his comrades scooped her up and plopped her back on her feet. With a quick embarrassed glance in our direction, Judith carried on. What a pro and what a shitty week she'd had. I vowed then and there, to make it up to her with a stunning performance the next evening. She needed a night off. I was sure I wasn't meant to do that falling over bit, despite her strict instructions to do everything she did. I decided not to crack any jokes about it unless she brought it up, which of course she didn't. I think she thought we hadn't noticed, which avoided any awkward explanations later.

Our debut arrived quickly. Before we knew it, we were backstage again, waiting for our cue to go on. We had brushed up exceedingly well. Stage make-up for these shows is so dramatic that you change into a sort of Disney character of yourself. I couldn't stop peeping in the mirror and feeling ecstatic with my reflection. Samantha was the same. She looked absolutely beautiful and was enjoying the constant compliments from members of the cast. Judith joined us in line. She tried to smile encouragingly as she adjusted our berets and fussed over our blazers.

"Tonight's the night girls. Everything alright?" she asked nervously.

"Yes, don't worry Judith, we won't let you down," I answered reassuringly, feeling like a World War Two pilot, about to close the lid of the cockpit.

As we stood in our lines preparing to go on stage, I was amused how the other girls were announcing where they were going after work, with not a thought about the show. Apparently, there was a party at Pablo's apartment, and I was already desperate for an invite but thought I ought to concentrate on the job in hand, because Tania was on her way. I had started to notice that every time Samantha got in a panic about anything, Fernando would give her a little wave from the wings on the other side of the stage. She would blush and beam back at him with delight. Fernando, it turned out, was a very accomplished Flamenco dancer and part of a traditional cabaret, that performed in-between one of our dance numbers. Jaw droppingly handsome in his frilly black suit with his guitar slung on his back, he looked quite a vision of Spanish loveliness. I even saw him signing autographs one evening, realising he was a bit of a star.

"Beautiful Eeeenglish girls, you look so preeeeety!" he remarked as we made our way to the stage.

Samantha giggled, blushed and went all daft. I wasn't sure if he didn't scare me to death, but Samantha seemed smitten.

Taking my first few steps out into the spot-light that night was a memorable moment for me. I wasn't quite aware then, of how many times I was going to perform in the future. It was to be the first of many shows over the coming years. I did make one mistake on my opening night. I went to the front, feeling very pleased with myself, having remembered the air hostess routine without a hitch. I didn't lose my balance, but sadly Judith had forgotten to remind us that the lights would go out at that point, plunging us into complete darkness momentarily, while we took our positions for the turning of the briefcases. This threw me rather and I even heard Samantha's voice saying, "Oh my God!" rather too loudly in the orchestral pause. I was the letter *D* so I felt my way to where I thought I should be, at the beginning of the 'Doris' line. Unfortunately, though, I'd managed to find my way to the beginning of the first name, not the surname. Letter *T* was forced to go in my place. The lights glared back on, to a burst of music from the orchestra, revealing our line of sparkling hostess cases spelling Dania Toris! As we scuttled off stage, people in the audience checked their programmes to see the spelling of their favourite star, but luckily Tania had burst into song from her aeroplane steps before they could dwell on who Dania was. Letter *T* forgave my little *faux pas*, thankfully, and everyone found it hilariously funny backstage.

After a few weeks, when the show was rolling, I was delighted to be asked to dance Tania's Hard Rock. It was the motorbike dance from the photographs that we'd seen on our first day in Madrid. I was thrilled. It took a bit of getting used to. I couldn't see anything throughout the entire number, having to feel my way due to the dark glasses we wore. Looking back, it was hugely dangerous, and I heard many a tale of dancers falling off the stage. I'm pleased to say it didn't happen to me.

Samantha and I had a wonderful winter in Madrid. Martin had been right about the Spanish going crazy for New Year's Eve and they certainly knew how to party. Going back to college at the end of the season was going to be hard for me, but impossible for Samantha. After her dramatic arrival, a few months before, when she'd cursed Betty Laine for sending her to such a dive, she now didn't want to leave. Having fallen head-over-heels in love with Fernando, she had slipped effortlessly into the relaxed Spanish way of life, all in just a few months.

"I can't bear it, I can't leave. I'm staying here," she announced as we walked to work one evening. Settling into our favourite street café along one of the elaborate avenues of the city, we ordered our pre-show café con leche. Samantha was like a different girl to the one that had sat crying on the theatre steps, just a few months earlier.

"Judith wants me to renew my contract. There's a new show starting rehearsals in a few months, for a whole year!"

I agreed completely that the life in Madrid suited her well, and I tried not to smile too much as she sat fanning herself, her hair scraped back into a Spanish chignon. Apart from keeping her blonde hair, she'd fully embraced the whole Spanish look. This drove the Spaniards wild. Fernando adored her and I was very happy for them, wishing I could find true love like that. No-one had compared to Mark from The Purple Shop yet. If I couldn't be with him, then I was happy to be single.

"Do you know what, darling," I reassured her, "I don't blame you. I think you should just grab this life and enjoy it. You'd probably end up coming back out here after college anyway."

I passed her a cigarette, secretly dreading the mayhem I would have to deal with at college when she didn't appear.

"Funny how things turn out isn't it?" I murmured.

She looked slightly sheepish and then we burst out laughing because she knew I was remembering that terrible morning, when she'd been foul to me and wanted to go home.

"I knew you'd understand, Janey. I'm going to miss you though. You must come back," she insisted.

"Maybe," I sighed, "We'll see what happens."

I really meant that, but of course, as it does, something far more thrilling came along.

11

DISCO DIVAS

Hi Girls!

As you will see, I'm not coming back.

Jane will explain. I have met the man of my dreams and you must all come to Madrid to meet him.

Fernando and I are starting our own show next year, and we want you all to audition!

Stay in touch!

Samantha x

Samantha had given me a letter to read out to all the girls in the changing rooms on my return to college. Never before had anyone performed such a daring feat of bravery. There were gasps of shock and disbelief as I described Fernando, life in Madrid, and the fact that Samantha had left college, just like that.

"That … is true love," someone swooned.

On my way out later that day, I was stopped by one of the girls on the street.

"Samantha's mum and dad are in Clarkes and want to speak to you," she said, nodding to the window of our favourite coffee shop.

I recognised Samantha's parents immediately, having seen them briefly at the airport on our departure for Madrid. Noticing how similar Samantha and her mother were, I went through and joined them. Mrs Thomas was sat, bolt upright, in a smart suit with her Gucci bag perched on her lap. She was looking distastefully around her at the homely, but slightly scruffy watering hole favoured by the students.

"Good morning," I smiled curiously, wiggling into the booth to join them.

I could see they were in no mood for niceties, clearly looking for someone to blame for the fact that their daughter had gone AWOL. It also dawned on me that this situation, really had nothing to do with me. Feeling virtuous that I had resisted the urge to elope with a Spaniard, I was rather frustrated when Mrs Thomas attempted to start a row. She reminded me instantly of Samantha when we'd arrived in Madrid.

"So, I have the right to know, what's going on young lady?" she hissed, extremely cross, her mouth set in a straight line of contempt.

I looked briefly around the café, noticing Samantha's Dad twiddling his thumbs awkwardly.

"Well!" I enthused, "looks like Samantha's found her calling in life, she *loves* it over there!" I offered, hoping to brighten the mood, even attempting a light smile.

I was delighted to see Mr Thomas smiling nervously back at me. He was obviously relieved to think that, at least one of his many daughters had launched herself into the world of work. There would be one less set of fees for him to pay. He looked quietly proud as punch.

"How dare you joke and laugh when my daughter is missing!" Mrs Thomas yelled, spoiling my little moment with her husband. People were starting to turn their heads.

"Oh no! She's not missing," I explained, "I have her address. Would you like it?"

After a lecture from Mrs Thomas on the worry and stress caused to her nerves over Samantha's behaviour, I started to feel rather angry. I let her finish her rant, horrified at the fury in her voice. It was becoming more and more apparent why Samantha had stayed in Madrid. Eventually, she stopped her tirade. She rummaged in her bag, took out a tissue, before sitting back expectantly, awaiting my reply. She reminded me of her daughter on the steps of the Teatro Monumental.

I had their full attention.

"Did it not occur to you to go and visit her maybe?" I gently smiled over at their stunned faces. "The show is fantastic, and Fernando is absolutely charming."

I never saw them again.

≈

As I scuttled down the corridor to my ballet class one morning later that term, Miss Laine's voice pierced the air. Even a passing teacher flinched with fear as we stopped in our tracks.

"Jane! Come in darling I need to speak to you for a moment," she ordered.

From the adjoining office, I could hear the clattering of manual typewriters grinding to a halt. Enid and Rose never liked to miss anything. Miss Laine's door was open, and she was clearly on the look-out for passing students for one of her latest projects. Despite putting the fear of God into me, her voice softened, and I wondered whether it was possible, that she was considering me as one of her favourites, but I didn't get my hopes up. I hovered awkwardly in the doorway, feeling annoyed at myself, my cheeks burning beetroot with embarrassment and insecurity. I didn't dare to appear all matey by stepping right inside the office, despite the fact that she was sporting a convincing smile. Instead, I waited, cautiously, taking the opportunity to glance around. Her office was usually forbidden territory. As she rustled some papers on her desk, I studied a glass bowl of fruit and chocolates. Frames of past pupils and huge vases of flowers with gushing thank you notes were on display. Miss Laine looked powerful, a vision in coral as she peered over her glasses at me across her desk, a vast expanse of leatherette. I shuffled from one foot to the other on the threshold as I awaited my fate.

"I'd like you to take yourself up to Studio Five and audition for the Cairo show darling. They're having trouble finding someone. It's all that disco diva stuff."

She removed her glasses, flicking back her auburn hair as she sat back, to look at me with penetrating eyes.

"You'll love it, and it will be good experience. Let's keep the ball rolling shall we Sweetie?" She really was smiling, probably thinking of all the commission coming her way.

"Thank you, yes! I'll go up right away!" I agreed with enthusiasm, wondering whether or not I should mention that she had lipstick on her teeth.

I was just feeling that it was a good time to take my leave when she popped up from her leather chair and scurried around from behind her desk. Then began, what I can only describe, as a thorough assessment, as though I were a racehorse. I prepared to have my mouth forced open for a tooth and gum inspection. Smiling awkwardly, I tried to look elegant as I sucked my stomach in, jutted my chin out and stood in first position. As I endured the inspection, it had started to dawn on me that there was, possibly, a chance of another adventure brewing. Like all of the students and teachers at the college, I was desperately hoping that one day I would be smiling out from a frame on the wall of her office. On this particular morning, though, I was slightly thrown, by her suggestion that I audition for another job. I hadn't been planning any immediate dance contracts abroad, still reeling as I was, from the last trip. I also had my training to consider. These contracts usually lasted several months, over-lapping the holidays and missing term time. I was starting to fall further behind in ballet class, struggling to keep up. However, Cairo sounded exotic and irresistible, so I knew I would be very easily swayed, with visions of pyramids, sunshine and camels springing to mind. I glanced out of the window at the buses passing through big puddles on the rainy street. How would I be able to resist it?

Enid and Rose both winked and 'thumbs upped' at me from behind their desks as they worked their way through a box of Milk Tray in between bursts of furious typing.

"Go for it!" mouthed Rose, as best as she could through a hazelnut whirl.

"Show 'em what ya made of sweetheart," boomed the fearless Enid.

"Thank you, ladies," cut in Miss Laine as she closed the office door.

When I was out of view, I scampered up the stairs, three at a time, to Studio Five. Wishing that I'd known beforehand about this audition, I scurried down the corridor. Having been on my way to ballet class, I looked rather more like Margot

Fonteyn than a Disco Diva. I adjusted my ballet dancer style walk to a John Travolta strut, deciding that I would go to see what was going on out of curiosity. If I didn't fancy the job, I could always tell Miss Laine that I had failed the audition miserably. She would never know any different.

Outside Studio Five all hell had broken lose. This job was obviously worth having because on turning the corner, I was greeted with a large group of very anxious students waiting for their audition. They were holding their ears against the studio door. The atmosphere was unbearable, and I immediately turned to leave. From inside the studio, I could hear The Bee Gees pumping away and as I reversed back to the stairs to make my escape, a voice bellowed from the far end of the corridor.

"Jane! Thank God!"

Shelly, the girl we all wanted to be, rushed over, grabbed my arm and started pulling the hairpins out of my ballet bun.

"You, my friend, are coming in with me. They want us in pairs," she explained. "You'll have to let me do your hair and make-up though, because you look like a nun. No offence."

I was very flattered to be Shelly's chosen one on this occasion, and I enjoyed the way the other girls were all watching me with interest. Glamorous Shelly was never in college because, with her ravishing blonde hair and film star bone structure, she was always working abroad or modelling for fashion magazines. This audition was clearly important to her. I decided that maybe I should pull myself together and see how I got on.

"Are you sure you want to go in with *me*?" I asked nervously looking down at my scruffy ballet shoes.

The studio door burst open and two hysterical girls came out. One of them was in tears and the other one looked furious.

"I've never been so humiliated in my life. It's so unprofessional. There's no set dance routine so you have to bloody improvise!" she blurted out to the growing crowd of wide-eyed hopefuls.

This actually sounded like my ideal job, seeing as I had a terrible habit of going blank in the middle of choreographed dance routines. I often forgot what to do next, when anyone watched me. Shelly steered me away from the group.

"Listen, I've worked for these people at a similar booking before. They're great. They just want you to dance free-style in their big, fuck off five-star hotel disco. This one's in Cairo for crying out loud!"

She was backcombing my permed hair furiously by now. My eyes were watering as I took in these tempting details.

"I tell you Jane, they treat you like royalty, you won't regret it I promise you. It's the easiest contract you will ever find, and the pay is always great in the Middle East."

"Mmm ... the Middle East again," I thought to myself as I gazed down at Shelly who was now on the floor, frantically emptying the contents of her make-up bag onto the grubby carpet.

I reminded myself to have a crafty look at Mrs Ashfield's globe again at some point, in case Cairo was anywhere near another war zone, but I didn't let my concern spoil things as I prepared to be transformed. Shelly started picking out lipstick and hair products from an impressive collection from the depths of her giant sports bag.

"I saw you dancing at Tony's party and you were amazing," she continued as she guided me over to the big mirror on the wall. She stood back to observe her work.

"We could have a ball this summer, what do you think?"

I thought back to the party, while Shelly enveloped me in hairspray, plastered my mouth with bright red lipstick and expertly slicked a black line over each eyelid. All I could remember of the Tony's party was waking up under a pile of coats in his kitchen, but I went along with Shelly's high opinion of me just the same. Before I'd had time to ponder, Shelly had pushed me through the door of Studio Five. I looked like something from The Rocky Horror Show. In no time at all, we were strutting our stuff for all we were worth. It didn't feel like Studio Five. With the blinds pulled down and disco lights flashing, it felt like Tony's party again. My best disco moves came flooding back instantly. I even managed a Moon Walk so it certainly made a change from the usual Monday morning ballet class. I decided to do as Rose and Enid had suggested, and 'Go for it' and 'Show 'em what I was made of,' rather than shuffle about nervously.

After a few seconds, I was whacking my legs past my head and boogying away with a beaming smile to *Jive Talking*. Shelly, catching my eye, whooped as she swayed to the beat. With her jaw dropping beauty she didn't really have to put much effort into the dancing. Eventually, the music stopped. We waited, panting and laughing, nervously. A spotlight went on at the desk in a dark corner, to reveal Eddy King, the agent for the disco show. Eddy had an impressive tan, gold medallion, and the customary open necked, satin shirt in kingfisher blue. His tanned, bald head shone beautifully under the spotlight and he looked very out of place in the cold, grey ballet studio on this overcast morning.

"Ladies … at last … welcome to my world," he purred, sitting back in his chair and folding his arms. He smiled revealing a row of perfectly white teeth with a few glints of gold here and there.

Shelly and I were still gasping for breath after our lively performance which helped to mask our snorts of laughter at such a hilarious introduction. I decided, at that moment, that I definitely wanted to work with Shelly, in Cairo for the summer. My ballet exam would have to wait. Eddie King was priceless and when he asked if we had valid passports, we realised the job was ours. He started packing away his gear and shuffling papers into a Louis Vuitton briefcase. The auditions were over.

~

Shelly predicted that this show was going to be a doddle and with no rehearsals planned, I started to believe her. It was to be a free-style disco show with our own DJ and by the descriptions we were given, the El Gezirah Sheraton Hotel in Cairo was a prestigious new venue. Having no Google then, we had to take Eddy's word for it.

"How jammy is that?" Shelly hooted the following day as we swooped along in a black cab to our costume fitting with Eddy King's seamstress.

I was so glad to be with Shelly, because if I had been on my own, I would never have taken a cab. I would have still been in the underground, grappling with my A to Z, arriving like a sweaty tourist. As it was, we didn't have a hair out of place and Shelly was already planning where to go for lunch afterwards, before we'd even arrived for the costume fitting. She stuffed some notes into the taxi driver's hand and yet again, I marvelled at how worldly she was.

"Are you sure this is it?" I whispered as we picked our way up a path of old red tiles that had come away from a concrete path.

The house was like something from a Dickens novel in the middle of Hampstead with a sort of scruffiness that was probably worth millions. Shelly pressed the buzzer that hung off a dodgy looking wire with her beautifully manicured finger.

"Number fifty-two darling, that's what Eddy told us. He must have quite a few shows on the go to afford this pile."

An eruption of lively barking came from within as a dishevelled figure shuffled towards the door. Through the glass, we could see Sylvia the seamstress, lifting books and magazines, looking for the key to the door to let us in. She obviously didn't go out of the house very often. Her poodles leapt about at her feet, making the task even more difficult. Eventually, she could be seen stubbing out her fag and putting the key in the lock. Her purple, crimplene, halter neck jumpsuit hung limply from her tiny frame and there were a selection of tape measures hanging around her tanned, wrinkly neck. Bits of thread, glitter and feathers were stuck to her misshapen cardigan.

"Ah 'ello girls, in you come darlin's. You're nice 'n early," she croaked with a crooked smile.

We filed behind her, pushing the poodles away politely, but firmly.

"Ouch! Little bugger!" Shelley squeaked as one of them nipped her ankles. Sylvia ignored her.

"Now are you two Cairo or Damascus?" she continued as we followed her up some steep stairs that led to her sewing room.

"Cairo!" we blurted in unison.

I could just imagine calling my parents again and telling them that I was going to have another go at working in sunny Syria. I was sure their nerves wouldn't cope after the last time, I mean, even Cairo was a bit daring. My Dad would have nightmares of me dancing in a harem, in a floaty costume wafting around a tent, feeding dates to scary looking guests in a desert camp.

"You're in for a treat then duckies," Sylvia informed us as she moved a basket of feather boas, so that we could sit down on a huge, battered, leather sofa. The over-flowing ash trays balanced on the arms bought shabby chic to a new level.

"And there are no bomb scares there, very safe, loads of tourists going to the pyramids and that, ya know? Those girls in Damascus are hauled out of that hotel day and night. I don't know how they put up wiv it."

Sylvia lifted an elderly poodle off the sofa and put him on a cushion by the coal fire.

"Nice little number the Cairo gig, five-star my dears. You look like classy birds, so you'll fit in lovely. Find yourself a nice man!!" she cackled herself into a coughing fit that came from deep within.

Winking at us, she lit another cigarette before wheeling in a rail of brightly coloured costumes. In the middle of the room was a huge industrial sized sewing machine with a spotlight over it. Pins and scraps of fabric littered the floor and everything near it. Even the poodles that had settled into the deep pile carpet in a sunny spot by the window, had sparkly bits in their fur.

"Strip orf then my lovelies, let's get you measured up and ready to roll!"

We spent the morning choosing our numerous costumes which, being the eighties, were bright and theatrical. My favourite was a red ballet tutu matched with a red, sequinned bolero jacket, finished off with high, silver leather boots. I looked like a mixture between Darcey Bussell and Danny La Rue. Shelly looked beautiful in a pink, satin ice skater dress with diamante sandals and tiara. The pièce de résistance however, had to be the red, white and blue striped shiny tailcoats for both of us, with matching top hats. We were to dance to the disco version of Putting on the Ritz. I just couldn't wait to get onto that dance floor.

Sylvia explained that our costumes were to be packed up and sent, luxuriously, ahead of us, directly to the hotel. This thought seemed to trigger off a wave of excitement as we posed for a few snap shots of ourselves in the costumes. I started to feel that, at last, it was really happening.

∽

The time at the fitting flew by and reluctantly we had to say goodbye to Sylvia and make our way back to college to await departure day. She casually waved us off and went back to her sewing, preparing for the next group of dancers.

"Be good," she rasped. She herded the poodles back as they tried to follow us down the path.

Stopping at a bistro on the way back to college, Shelly made sure that we raised a few glasses of bubbly, in celebration of the upcoming adventure.

12

CAIRO

WE HAD TO wait a whole month before we were flown out to our new life in Cairo. Shelly and I made use of the time by getting into practice, frequenting night clubs every weekend. Gradually, we'd perfected our style so that we danced in perfect unison. By the time our departure day finally came, we were disco specialists.

On arriving at the airport, I was proud of my parents for agreeing that they didn't need to come to departures and wave me off. I wanted to look cool. I was relieved with this arrangement when I spotted Shelly in a passionate embrace with her boyfriend, Mike, at the meeting point. I waited awkwardly for what seemed like an age until they'd disengaged themselves. When she turned around and saw me, her boyfriend walked reluctantly away, and I was relieved to see her face light up. She looked like she was about to set off on a rollercoaster ride and proceeded to steer me into a champagne bar where we promptly got into Cairo mode.

We'd been asked to look out for Eddy King. It wasn't long before we spotted him pacing up and down looking at his huge gold watch, anxiously by the check-in desk, waiting to see us off.

"Yoo! Hoo! Eddy!" we called as we teetered over. We peered over the top of our luggage trolley, laden with Shelly's impressive collection of designer suitcases and my Dad's old case from the loft. Eddy was not alone. Sitting nearby, behind a copy of Vogue magazine was the other half of our act, Pippa, the DJ. There followed much hand shaking and gleaming white teeth from Eddy. He was clearly pleased to see us. Eventually he managed to drag Pippa away from her magazine for an introduction. She cast a brief glance in our direction and stood up to shake hands.

"Hello girls," she muttered, looking pre-occupied.

She certainly didn't ooze DJ and I wondered what would happen on opening night at the hotel. Hopefully she had a dual personality and would transform into a compère queen, all smiles and shoulder pads.

A few hours into the flight, Pippa loosened up and started to name drop. She treated us to endless stories about her glamorous career as DJ to the stars in the clubs of London. I found it all fascinating and ooh-ed and aah-ed in all the right places. Shelly just gazed at her with a slanted sneer, before falling asleep with her mouth open.

Arriving in Cairo six hours later was extraordinary. The first thing that hit me was the heat. When we stepped off the plane and made our way down the steps onto the tarmac, I naively thought the searing heat was coming from the plane's huge engines. I quickly realised though, that it was just the temperature on a normal Egyptian evening in May. I had never experienced such a high temperature and immediately began sweating profusely. I wondered how on earth we would survive the heat as we strutted our stuff during the show. Once outside the customs hall, it took a few minutes to adjust to the unusual smells and noises in Arrivals. Weaving our way through the crowds, there didn't seem to be order anywhere and people were rushing about shouting to each other, pushing and shoving as we all fought our way through the throng of activity. Seeing as there was no-one there to meet us, we started to make our way out to the street. We were greeted by beautiful, grubby children with anxious faces, pushing at our legs and asking for money, their little grubby hands cupped in anticipation, as they stared up at us hopefully. I only had chewing gum and a few English coins to give them, but they seemed thrilled. There was a strong smell of decay from the dirty gutter, mixed with coffee, incense and tobacco. Exotic Egyptian music played from the taxis and shops, all mingling into one chaotic sound of the Middle East. The crowds of people wore brightly coloured swathes of fabric and their filthy feet with blackened toenails, poked out of old leather sandals. Big bright eyes shone out dramatically from velvety brown faces and we stood out like sore thumbs in our European outfits in the glare of the sun, with our lily-white complexions. We gazed around us, looking for the driver. We had been told he would be waiting to take us to our hotel. Shelly's shock of blonde curls had started to cause mayhem, so it was a relief when Pippa called over to us to follow her, pleased with herself for having spotted our driver first. On the opposite side of the street, we saw a huge white car with a suited driver holding up a sign saying: Eddy King.

Sinking into the cool comfort of the air-conditioned back seat, we watched the driver load our luggage into the boot. We were driven along a busy road full of beeping hooters from bicycles and vehicles of all descriptions, carrying crates of chickens and even whole sheep. The people on the streets peered in at us as we gazed out at this new environment.

"Polo anyone?" Shelly was rummaging in her bag as usual.

This small gesture of a mint from Shelly's handbag bought me back down to earth. I beamed at her adoringly. If I'd been on my own, I would have felt rather uneasy to say the least, heading off into the unknown in this extraordinary place. She then proceeded to offer little wet wipes for us all to clean our hands, experienced traveller that she was. Pippa was buried in her magazine again, making a concerted effort to ignore us, which infuriated me. How could she not want to take in the views of this exciting city as well as make friends with her new colleagues?

"Welcome to Cairo ladies," called the smiling driver proudly, as he negotiated the crazy traffic effortlessly.

Eventually we hit the highway and were able to enjoy the view of a flaming sunset in the distance. As we approached the city centre, I was so excited that I felt sick, but I didn't let on. My face must have said it all though. It took all my strength not to gasp at each new sight along the way. Little fishing barges bobbed about on the River Nile as it glowed pink, lights flickering as evening descended. Approaching the centre of the city, elegant hotels and buildings gleamed and reflected on the water. Gliding onto the magnificent forecourt of the brand new El Gezirah Sheraton Hotel in our beautiful car, was such a special moment. As we climbed out, the heat hit us again and the elegance of the steps and entrance area took my breath away. Instead of the dirty airport smell, we inhaled the heady scent of jasmine flowers that tumbled out of huge pots that lined the peachy, marble steps leading up to the hotel reception. I was speechless as I followed Pippa and Shelly up the steps, noticing that our luggage was already being loaded onto a gold trolley for us in reception. On the shiny marble tiles by the lifts, I could see a little man in a peaked cap, grappling with Sylvia's trunks of costumes.

"Well, this will do I suppose," announced Shelly, giving me a crafty wink and a grin.

"Oh, my God!" I grabbed Shelly's arm and tried to stop the ear-to-ear smile on my face as I clocked a huge poster of us, in a large frame in front of the reception desk. All the staff at the desk were nodding and smiling at us as we took in the surroundings, proud to be employed at the newest hotel in Cairo. They had obviously been looking forward to our arrival because there, for all to see, was a hilarious photograph of Shelly and I in some of Sylvia's groovy costumes. It had been taken on fitting day. We looked like a right couple of characters, which I suppose, is exactly what we were.

13

LUXURY LIFE

'GO-GO GIRLS STRAIGHT from London here at Trumps Disco every night,' screamed the poster, and I've since wondered if, being the early 80's, the club was owned by Donald Trump. I'd never heard of him at that time.

"They obviously don't know that the word Trump means fart in our house," I chortled over to Shelly.

We collapsed into giggles until we were summoned over to Pippa who was already at the desk signing for our rooms and finding out the schedule. As she gave us a set of keys each, she was obviously irritated that we were laughing and enjoying ourselves.

"We'll get our things unpacked and meet back here to see the club in an hour," she announced.

Pippa signalled to the lift man to take us to our rooms in her haughty manner. It dawned on me that she was probably cross that there wasn't a picture of *her* in reception. Shelly and

I were, clearly, the main event. Anyway, she would have had to manage a smile for a photo to be taken. I didn't know if that was possible after the day we'd just spent with her. Maybe we could take a photograph of her looking all gangster in headphones and slip it into the corner of our poster with a sign saying, Featuring Poker Faced Pippa.

We piled into the lift and stood in awkward silence trying not to catch each other's eye in the floor to ceiling mirror. Pippa had gone all bossy, creating an awkward ambiance.

Another gasping session ensued as we walked into our palatial room. To our relief, Shelly and I were sharing a twin room and Pippa was next door. I didn't fancy having to pass Pippa's sour face on my way to the loo in the night. Shelly was clearly used to these places and threw herself onto one of the beds before lighting a cigarette and reaching for the phone.

"Room service please."

She swiftly ordered two gin and tonics and a club sandwich.

"Did you fancy anything in particular darling?" she called over to me.

"Well, um ..." I stammered, trying to remember how much money I had in my student account after all our night-club trips.

"You do realise it's all free, don't you?"

Another feeling of euphoria swept over me,

"Well, I wasn't sure but yeah, great, I'll just have a sandwich like you."

I walked out onto the balcony while Shelly called her boyfriend, Mike, back in England from the telephone in the room. We had no mobiles or internet in those days, so writing letters was my only option as I had always been taught that phone calls were expensive, especially overseas. However, I decided to broach the subject of phone bills later with Shelly, because, as I walked onto the balcony, I had the breath sucked out of me, yet again, met with the most spectacular view of Cairo. The people below looked more like ants as they scurried around on the forecourt while I gazed down from the twentieth floor. Standing on our balcony felt like flying. Many of the other large hotels overlooked the river and I noticed beautifully dressed couples in designer clothes, stepping into limousines as they made their way out for the evening. The Nile gleamed at me and the fishing boats twinkled as fishermen lit their lamps ready to settle out on the water for the night. The sound of Egyptian violins and tambourines wafted up against the traffic noise while the belly-dancers entertained the diners. The whole city was preparing to sit down to eat, in the beautiful hotel restaurants along the water's edge. It was now gorgeously warm outside, and I could feel Egypt working its magic on me already.

Our room service feast arrived. Shelly and I raised our large glasses of gin and tonic with a toast to a successful summer. Leaving our unpacking until later, we tucked into our tasty club sandwiches stuffed with salad that was later to give us the squits, enjoying the atmosphere of Cairo at dusk. We sat on our balcony, marvelling at the view from this great height, that was to be our home for the next four months. We soon learnt that you avoided salad and certain fruits as they were grown in contaminated water and gave you tummy ache. We wondered if that was why the club was called Trumps.

At the end of one of Mum's letters later that week, there was a P.S. from Granny, barely visible through a faded ring from her coffee cup, saying,

> Hi darling. Don't eat anything off the streets. Marge ate kebab thingies on their holiday and they all had sore bums.
>
> Love Granny X.

Our little celebration on the balcony was soon interrupted by a sharp rap at our door and there was Pippa with her headphones and case of records waiting to go down to see the club. She still looked like Princess Anne as we set off back to the lift in search of the club. It made me all the more curious to see her in action and, after a couple of gin and tonics, I was finding it all rather amusing.

Once outside in the balmy evening air, we were greeted with a sight I will never forget, of a dance floor graced with a large swimming pool, lined with lights and a backdrop of the river Nile. Above the dance floor, there stood a perfect glowing pedestal for dear Pippa to stand behind, right above us by her decks, where she prepared to spin the sounds, like our music master. I hoped, but doubted, that Sylvia had sewn her a large gold cape or something, because she was going to love being master of ceremonies up there while Shelly and I cavorted humbly about below. The restaurant was situated to one side, in perfect view of the dance floor. The chefs had started to cook meat and fish on the enormous open-air grill, and it smelt divine. The guests were sat at tables eating dinner and we slowly realised that when it was our time to dance, we were going to have to dodge waiters, passing with trays of food and drink, while making our way to the dance floor. This could be tricky when frantically shaking our booty, but I didn't worry myself about that challenge at this stage, feeling so enthralled with the surroundings. My favourite detail was definitely a golden bridge over the pool. I immediately imagined performing my famous walk-over trick on it with glee.

I was pleased to hear that we didn't have to be Go-Go Girls that night because I was really exhausted from the journey.

However, we were summoned to another suite later during the evening, where all our costumes were hung in rows. A very beautiful woman walked up and down, scrutinising Sylvia, the seamstress's work. I felt very protective of Sylvia as this woman flicked back her mane of glossy black hair, picking her way through the rails with long manicured nails.

"Mmm … come in girls. These are going to look fabulous under the lights."

She introduced herself as Rashida, wife of the Entertainments Manager. After a brief chat, she insisted that we gave her a costume parade which I found really tiring after the journey. She was getting on my nerves after only a few minutes. It annoyed me to think that she had probably spent the day by the pool sipping cocktails while we had been lugging ourselves to Cairo. I looked rather dishevelled in the mirror but was past caring by this time. Fortunately, Rashida approved of all of Sylvia's costumes, going into raptures over some leopard print, lycra jumpsuits.

"These are sooo Trumps," she swooned.

Shelly snorted with laughter as Rashida held one of the stretchy jumpsuits up against herself.

"But not sexy enough, and very unflattering on the leg," Rashida continued.

Shelly grinned at me, impishly, not caring a hoot about the costumes. Rashida had obviously been enjoying the local cuisine on a regular basis.

Rashida turned back, enjoying the authority that, we assumed, her husband had given her. He probably didn't give a shit about the costumes and I could imagine her begging him to let her hold this ridiculous meeting with us, as they'd lunched earlier in the day. Of course, I realise now, that despite her efforts to inspect our costumes, she was probably quite nervous that her husband was working with two tall, glamorous girls every night, feeling it would be wise to be involved. I should have reassured her and felt sorry for her, but at eighteen years old it just didn't occur to me.

"Can't we adjust them somehow?" she mewed, screwing up her eyes and holding the garments up against us.

I imagined Eddy King having a fit if we took scissors to his extortionate, lycra jumpsuits, but Rashida was determined. Before we could suggest calling Sylvia for advice, she was snip, snipping away at them, reducing them to tiny leotards in seconds. The lycra leopard print legs lay crumpled on the floor as though they had been shot. The body sections bounced back merrily on their hangers.

"There! You both have such beautiful legs, we must show them off," she chuckled, quite pleased with her work. "And we can make gloves out of the leg pieces," she exclaimed.

"See you tomorrow ladies and don't be late. We're all looking forward to your show."

She flounced out, leaving the leg fabric on the floor.

"I don't know who she thinks will make these into gloves," mumbled Shelly, picking them up and hanging them up with the leotards.

We were glad to finish Rashida's meeting and return to our rooms, collapsing into our beautiful beds for a glorious sleep.

∾

When I awoke the next morning, I couldn't remember where I was for a few seconds. Then a smile crept over my face as I felt the fresh Egyptian, cotton sheets and squinted at the surroundings. Shelly was still in a deep sleep, so I tip-toed out to the enormous bathroom before hopping back into bed and propping myself up against the huge white pillows. My stomach let out a hungry gurgle. We had been so tired after our journey, costume parade and tour of the club area the night before, that we had missed dinner and crashed out.

I reached for the phone.

"Room service please," I whispered, grinning to myself like a Cheshire cat in the huge gold mirror that faced my bed. Everything was gold.

"If they could see me now," I thought, picturing the girls at college lining up for class.

"Oh yes, hello, err, I am one of the Go-Go Girls. Could I order some breakfast please?" I continued in my best, famous, disco dancer voice. I tried to remember how Shelly had ordered our drinks and sarnies the night before.

"I'll have some pancakes with maple syrup please and ...," I paused, reading the menu from a large leather folder. I wondered what would sound cool to Shelly.

"And two cold beers ...," I laughed at myself in the mirror as I spoke.

"Yes Madam, American pancakes and beer, how many please Madam?" asked the receptionist.

I decided to over order on the pancakes in case they were little titchy ones.

"Ooh, six please,"

I replaced the receiver and giggled to myself as I snuggled down again to await my feast.

"This is the life," I thought as I pictured my flat mates at college, arguing over whose turn it was to buy the cereal. I'd moved out of my digs with Mrs Ashfield when her worrying nature had reached a record high.

After what seemed like quite a long time, I heard a trundling and clinking sound coming up the corridor outside. There was a gentle knock at the door. On opening our door, I was nearly mowed down by a huge trolley.

"Good morning Madam," said a little man in a blue stripy suit and matching hat.

"Oh, sorry, I think you have the wrong room!" I whispered.

The trolley appeared to be set for a large family. Each place setting had a silver dome covering its plate. It looked like something from Buckingham Palace, with tall glasses and glistening bottles of beer standing to attention by each plate.

"No Madam, this is your order thank you, good day," insisted the little man as I gave him a dollar from the pile by the door. Shelly had organised this, after explaining about tipping.

I wheeled the trolley through with much huffing, puffing and clanking into the main part of the room just as Shelly heaved herself up reaching for her cigarettes on the bedside cabinet.

"What the fuck's going on?" she growled.

As we gazed at the banquet, we realised that instead of ordering six pancakes, I had ordered pancakes for six, with beers to match!

"You are a scream!" Shelly was in fits.

"Oh, my God I'm such an idiot," I wailed.

Well, pass me a beer then!" she cried, wiping tears of laughter from her mascara caked eyes.

We sat with the trolley on the balcony, looking out at the view and speaking in posh voices as we worked our way through half of the food and most of the beers. Lighting up cigarettes we gazed out over Cairo, discussing our imminent debut night at Trumps. Rashida had insisted that we wore her leopard creations for our opening number. It was slightly nerve racking to know that she was going to be watching our performance with all the management that evening.

Later that day, after we'd slept off the beers, we decided to try out the facilities and sauntered down to the pool. We wore the big white robes, courtesy of the hotel, to cover our bikinis. The pool looked very different during the day and the first thing that hit me hard was the glare of the sun. I just wasn't accustomed to such bright, searing heat and went back to the room to find my sunglasses. By the time I returned, Shelly had found two sun-loungers and was merrily ordering cocktails from the waiter. The other guests sitting around the pool area were predominantly mothers and daughters. As they sat in the shade, on large loungers, in their hijabs, they watched their young sons wallowing in the water. Jumping in and out of the pool, their beautiful children were like happy, plump little seals, in Speedo trunks that disappeared into the folds of their glossy flesh. The waiters were kept busy fetching and carrying large dishes of delicious looking ice-creams and cakes to their tables.

We were clearly the only Europeans at the hotel on that afternoon, so I was worried about swimming in our tiny bikinis at first. The mothers and daughters were very friendly as they waved across with big smiles though, seeming quite thrilled to see us, so Shelly and I relaxed and enjoyed the refreshing water.

As we chatted over cocktails at the bar, I suggested that we phone Pippa's room before dinner. Despite her snootiness, we thought it would be grown up to rise above it and invite her for a pre-show chat. We were going to be working together for several months and I firmly believed that any tension in a show was always sensed by the audience. We needed to take action and get her on our side, because we agreed that we wanted Trumps to be a big, jolly, rip-roaring success.

"Hi, Pippa, it's us next door, do you fancy having dinner with us before the show?" Shelly sung into the phone that she clamped under her chin as she sat painting her toenails on the white carpet. The bottle of red nail varnish was so close to tipping over.

An hour later we were sitting in the restaurant being waited on by friendly Egyptian staff. I was embarrassed at how rude Pippa was as she bossed them about and sent food back. You'd think we'd arranged a meeting with a politician as we sat around the dining table. We presented her with our play list for our performances during her DJ set and she perused it with distaste.

"Well, I wouldn't normally play any of this rubbish, but I suppose I have no choice, do I?"

We didn't linger in the restaurant, mainly because we had a few first night nerves. Pippa was not loosening up or putting us at ease by any means.

"I think Pippa was telling porky pies about her DJ career on the flight. She seems really nervous," Shelly confided, reading my mind. "I bet she's only actually ever worked at children's parties and old people's homes," she chortled.

I had to agree, "I know! Maybe somehow, she managed to win this contract by having a casting couch moment with Eddy King!" As we applied our heavy stage make-up that evening, we became quite giggly, our imaginations running riot with visions of Pippa straddling Eddy King on the back of a chaise longue. Before we could dwell any longer, we were in our tiny dressing room down by the poolside disco. We peeped through the door and took in the atmosphere of our new place of employment, Farts, as we had renamed it.

The Egyptian evenings always brought an exotic feel to the city. The lights twinkled and the jasmine plants infused the balmy evening air as it worked it's magic on us under the stars. Being an open-air restaurant, you could also hear the distant sounds of entertainment from other hotels along the river. Egyptian bands and belly dancers serenaded their audiences, with a bright pink backdrop of the beautiful sunset. It was absolutely enchanting.

"Oh, Christ. Rashida has sat the entire management team at the front table," Shelly moaned after a quick peep from the dressing room door.

Anxiously, we waited for the sound of our cue, cursing Rashida for the discomfort of our newly designed, leopard print leotards. Our debut performance was to *Two Tribes Go To War*, by Frankie Goes To Hollywood, and we couldn't resist spying on Pippa, hoping that she had become personality of the year behind the speakers but, there she was, pouting at her record collection. As she lined up our song, in a taffeta evening dress, she looked like an advert for Laura Ashley.

"At least we only have to dance once a night Shelly. It must be the easiest job we'll ever have in our entire career," I reassured her, as I tried to ease the tension and get into the mood of a wild, crazy leopard dancer.

Pippa was taking longer than expected so I did a handstand against the wall and opened my legs out into a star shape to pass the time. This warmup exercise made me very uncomfortable about Rashida's modifications of the costume. There was no time to think about it though.

"Ladies and gentlemen. I take great pleasure to introduce to you, here at Trumps Disco Show, on the banks of the Nile, all the way from London in the United Kingdom, Trumps very own Go-Go Girls!"

Pippa introduced us with a tone of voice better suited to reading the News at Ten, reminding me that, so far, we had failed miserably in our attempts to win her friendship. Added to this, the imminent performance, we would soon discover, was not going to help the situation by any means. Before we had had time to discuss leotards, our music belted out and we burst onto the stage, high fiving on the bridge over the pool and leaping onto the dance floor in true Go! Go! Girl, Trumpy fashion.

There were cheers and applause from the audience and everyone looked pleased to see a bit of glamour and excitement to kick start the dancing. As we arrived on the scene, Rashida proudly beamed across at us from next to her husband and his colleagues. Gradually though, I noticed her smile fade, as she took in the view. The guests had fortunately finished their meal and our job now, was to perk them up, in readiness to strut their own stuff until the early hours. Unfortunately, having been rather scissor happy and not a fully trained seamstress, Rashida hadn't taken into account that, as we strutted our stuff in her customised leopard costumes, as soon as we kicked our legs, our newly, un-hemmed, legless leotards went straight up our bums, back and front! Of course, some of the audience, especially her own table of male guests, were thrilled with the view. Pippa and several of the ladies in the audience were not so impressed. I saw Shelly incorporating a new dance move to yank hers back out again every now and then. I tried the same thing a few times but decided it looked worse to keep fiddling with it. I was very glad I'd given myself a thorough waxing before I came to Cairo.

The music seemed to last an absolute age. We danced, mainly with our backs to the audience, looking bashfully over our shoulders, to the crowd, or up at Pippa from in front of the speakers, where she glared down at us like an angry devil. Pippa quickly brought the lights down very low, so low in fact that the waiters had put down their trays and were clapping along, squinting for a better view. As soon as we felt we had been performing our bum dance long enough, we made a swift exit, leaping over the bridge and off stage. We ran straight to the mirrors to see just how shocking it looked and gave ourselves a ten out of ten. By the time Pippa marched through, we had recovered from the humiliation and were crying with laughter.

"Sorry Pippa, talk to Rashida, this look was not our idea!" Shelly cried as she put on her pashmina and lit a cigarette. Pippa looked furious.

"*So* un-professional! That's what I get when I am forced to work with *students!*" she snapped, glaring at us before storming out, disappointed to discover it was Rashida's fault.

"So that's her problem!" Shelly remarked indignantly as she watched Pippa marching back to her disco, narrowly avoiding a couple doing the cha-cha to *I just called to say I love you.*

"She wants her disco dancers to be graduates!"

We tried to laugh but we were exhausted and a little subdued. We changed for the next number and put it all behind us!

Later on, having finished our performance for the evening, and what a performance it had been, we went back to our rooms.

Rashida was nowhere to be seen.

The leopard skin leotards weren't mentioned or worn ever again, and the rest of the summer passed without a hitch, as it were. Our dramatic introduction had certainly broken the ice amongst the staff from the hotel bar and restaurant, who were eager to show us their home territory with great pride. Having grown up in Cairo, these charming young locals gave us the privilege of being able to see the real Cairo, instead of the tourists view. We were treated to the real Egyptian experience, which was so different to the tourist trail. Shelly and I took ourselves to the Pyramids by coach on our first day off, which was fascinating but, when we returned to work the next evening, Tarek the waiter was horrified that we had been on a tourist excursion. He insisted that we went with his sister and their friends in future, and so began, some of the most memorable moments of my life. We were taken on camel rides around the pyramids and up to the hills, away from the crowds, with this lively bunch of young people. Watching unforgettable views of the sunset, we galloped across the desert on horse-back, stopping to buy hot sweet mint tea from local ladies wearing long galabeyas. One of the waiters took me to visit his father, a tailor, who fashioned a beautiful waistcoat for me with the fabric of my choice. We then visited his relative's home, where we ate spicy kofta and mouth-watering rice dishes while his brother played the violin, and his sisters sang traditional songs for us. On our nights off, Shelly and I went on trips to the coast near Alexandria, where the sand was white, and the sea was aquamarine. We feasted on succulent, freshly caught fish, slapped straight onto the grill from the fishing boats at the beach.

Shelly, Pippa and I were invited to a small party with the management after the show one evening. I was about to make my excuses and retire for the night when I found myself drawn to the kind face of a man standing, quietly observing the party from the back of the club. He introduced himself as Babu and turned out to be extremely good natured.

"For goodness sake get out there and have some fun. It'll do you good," Shelly insisted after I pointed him out to her. I decided she was right. It *would* do me good to spend some time with someone who was nothing to do with the hotel for a change, so accepted a drink and stayed on for the evening. I had been working so hard at putting on a good performance at the disco, coping with Pippa's moods and being generally sociable that I didn't realise how much I was going to benefit from a bit of time out with someone new. Shelly was spending most of her free time calling Mike in England and sleeping by the pool, so I didn't feel guilty.

Babu was keen to spoil me, wasting no time in taking me out to beautiful places each night. It turned out that he was from Cairo but managed a large hotel in Dubai and was over to visit his younger brother. After a few weeks, he extended his stay so we could have just a bit more fun before he flew home, and boy did we make the most of it.

He took me to little restaurants on roof terraces of tall hotel buildings, with views of the distant pyramids as they peeped through the pink haze over Giza. He hired a fishing boat and skipper on my nineteenth birthday, taking me out on the Nile for the day so we could see Cairo from the water. Then one morning he picked me up from the hotel reception in a little car, insisting that I learn to drive. This seemed such a dangerously exciting plan that I couldn't refuse, and we set off, out into the centre of Cairo. In the rather clapped-out old car, I raced fearlessly around the back streets of Cairo, feeling like a Bond girl, stopping now and then, to gulp down large cups of fresh sugar cane drinks at street-side stalls. This drink, Babu explained, always reminded him of his childhood when he would run barefoot around the same streets. Later that day, he took me for a rustic Egyptian lunch cooked by his brother's chef, Sherin, who lived in a tiny apartment on the far side of town. He had cooked for Babu's family for many years and, as we climbed the winding staircase, the smell of garlic and herbs was mouth-watering. Sherin led us out onto a little balcony that over-looked the busy street below, bringing us dish after dish of delicious food, including stuffed pigeon straight from the roof top. It was so tasty after our hectic morning and I loved listening to Babu chatting in very fast Arabic to his friendly chef, as we tucked in. Sherin's wife and children peeped out at us with big smiles and giggles between each course. I felt completely contented, never wanting the day to end. After so many weeks of the glamorous city hotels, clubs and bars, this was a welcome treat of home cooking and real Egyptian life.

"When my brother and I travel on business we always take Sherin with us," Babu beamed proudly as the chef and his wife nodded enthusiastically, pouring out strong little cups of coffee from a tin jug.

On closer inspection, I noticed a little Granny, smiling her toothless grin at us from the dark sitting room. Suddenly, she decided to turn the wireless up loud. Her favourite song was playing, and they all started singing along with her, clapping and dancing to the traditional Arabic melody. I didn't want these wonderful days with Babu to end, but I knew that the summer was drawing to a close. Babu would be returning to Dubai, reminding me that I would soon be back in London, just as a beautiful love affair was beginning.

14

FAREWELLS AND PHONEBILLS

ON HIS LAST day in Cairo, Babu promised that he would keep in touch.

"We will be able to meet again in London my princess," he promised, as I failed to hide my tears on our last evening together.

"I come to London often," he smiled, stroking my hair before our final kiss.

I couldn't imagine Babu coming to England. Anyway, I didn't want to just see him when he came to England on business. I wanted to be with him all the time.

"Look at you honey!" Shelly exclaimed, hugging me as I wailed on the night he left. "When I sent you off with him for some fun I didn't say fall in love. He's probably married anyway."

Being young and naive, this hadn't occurred to me at all. Having just turned nineteen, I was horrified at the thought.

Why would he want to be with me if he had a wife? It reminded me of Dylan and the love bite.

When he was gone, I moped about for a few days until, right on cue, I felt my optimistic spirit rising out of the depths of my confusion. Rather than dwell on my loneliness, as a distraction, I decided to create a coping strategy and take full advantage of the remaining time in Cairo while I could. With this in mind, every afternoon, I would snap out of my reverie, keen to see more of the real Cairo while I still had a chance. I donned my long silk dress, covering up my arms and legs with scarves and silk leggings before slipping out on foot into the stifling city. My hair is dark, so I found that I didn't stand out much if I kept my head down and didn't take beautiful, blond Shelly with me. She was not interested in local activity in the slightest. She thought I was slightly mad, instead choosing to lay by the pool topping up her tan. I thought she was becoming rather orange and should perhaps have had a bit of time away from the sun lounger, but I left her to it.

The most exciting days were spent catching buses to backwaters where I found markets and communities to explore, a chance to see more of real Egyptian life. If ever I felt worried or overwhelmed on my walks in the heat of the chaotic streets, I would just hop on a bus or into a taxi, travelling back to the city centre to step into the safety of the grand forecourts of the five-star hotels that line the Nile. Ordering myself a cold beer on the beautiful terraces amongst the tourists, I was invigorated instantly. The Egyptians served enormous bottles of Stella beer, always accompanied in hotels with salty peanuts and snacks in golden dishes. It was most welcome after the stifling heat of my wanderings and I felt grateful to be experiencing such adventures.

The time flew, taking my mind away from thoughts of Babu and reminding me that I did have a life away from him. I knew I was going to feel reluctant to leave my luxury life in this exotic city though. Returning to my freezing, cold, student flat filled me with dread, especially as I would be even more behind in my training after such a long time away. Being an exotic disco diva for five minutes every evening didn't really prepare you very well for advanced ballet exams. Rainy London and the discipline of student life seemed another world away and I had mixed feelings about whether, or not, I could bear to return to college. I thought of Samantha in Madrid, and rather envied her brave decision to stay with Fernando. I knew that if Babu had lived in Cairo I would have been very tempted to stay.

One evening, close to our leaving date, Shelly came into our room looking rather concerned, which was unusual for her.

"Shit!" she exclaimed, throwing herself onto the bed. "Our phone bill is massive."

I hadn't used the phone at all, being religious about writing a weekly news bulletin to my parents on an airmail letter. I used to buy the wafer thin, blue airmail paper, that folded over and stuck down, once you'd written on it. It used to amaze me that something so flimsy could ever reach my parents letterbox from so far away, but it always did, throughout all my years of travelling the world.

The 'our phone bill' comment, rather annoyed me. I knew my letters had been getting through nicely and I had only used the phone for room service. I had noticed that Mike in England was being informed quite regularly of our Egyptian adventures by phone, assuming that Shelly was paying for her calls as she went along.

"It's hundreds of dollars," she moaned.

My heart sank. I couldn't think how we could deal with the problem without a disagreement.

"Shelly, you know that's not *my* phone bill," I cautioned with a smirk, praying this dilemma wouldn't spoil such a wonderful summer together. She sighed bravely, as she opened a beer from the mini bar.

"Oh, I know darling, leave it with me, I can sort it."

That evening, of course, she dealt with her problem in true Shelly style. I'd noticed her mood lift as she chatted away, later that evening before the show, so I decided to bring the subject up again.

"So, come on, what are we going to do about your phone bill Shelly?" I ventured, as we sat in our gold dresses and boots, waiting to dance our hearts out to Bronski Beat.

"Oh that! Don't worry! I have a plan," she beamed as she bouffed up her hair and started spraying it furiously with lacquer.

"We're going out tonight after work and you don't have to worry about a thing."

So, of course, I instantly started worrying.

This whole trip had all been too good to be true. I feared it was going to end badly, forcing us to sell our bodies on the streets to pay for Shelly's calls to England.

She saw my expression.

"No honey! Don't be daft, nothing awful! Trust me I know what I'm doing."

Later that evening, after the show, we changed out of our costumes into posh frocks and Shelly called a cab. She wouldn't tell me where we were going so, with the thrill of danger hanging intriguingly in the air, I went along, asking no questions and loving the anticipation of finding out her mysterious plan.

We pulled up outside a prestigious hotel, similar to ours, on the other side of town and before long, we were drinking huge cocktails in the bar area of a massive casino.

"Shelly! You, my friend, are going to get deeper into debt in a place like this. Are you going to try and win your phone money on the roulette?"

I was starting to sound like a boring person and Shelly just smiled and drained her glass.

"After this drink, we're going on a little stroll and you're not to talk to anyone, just stay close to me," she chuckled as she surveyed the casino lounge.

There were so many tables, all busy with players engrossed in their game. There were plenty of Arabs in their full traditional robes, Americans knocking back whisky and a variety of Europeans, all creating something like a scene from a Bond movie. I was speechless, feeling completely out of my comfort zone, but rather glad we had come after all. I didn't want to leave Shelly here on her own, so did as instructed and hovered quietly at her side, making sure not to catch anyone's eye. Shelly wandered around the tables and every now and then, one of the guests would spot her and pass a handful of gambling chips over so that she could join in the game with them.

She seemed to know all the rules at each table, calmly throwing in the odd chip here and there at the right time. I watched in awe. This went on for an hour or two until after stifling a yawn, she suggested we made our way home. I started to wonder why we had come, because she hadn't made any winnings that I was aware of.

Little did I know that the crafty mare had been hoarding most of the chips that she was being given by the guests, in her handbag. At the casino reception desk, she tipped them all out.

Hundreds of dollars-worth of chips cascaded onto the counter and the cashier returned a wad of cash

"Shall we, darling?" Shelly smiled, taking my arm and leading me down the grand casino steps before leaping into a taxi.

Outrageous behaviour it certainly was, but I'd enjoyed every minute of it. As we leapt into the cab and were whisked through the night, back to the familiar forecourt of our hotel, I marvelled at what a gripping end to our trip it had been.

The heady scent of jasmine hit me as I climbed out of the smoky cab, my heart in my mouth, decidedly shaky from such a nerve-wracking excursion. I couldn't help a swift glance over my shoulder as we entered our hotel, to check to see if anyone had followed us. I knew she hadn't actually committed a crime, but I felt devilishly daring all the same. When we slammed our hotel room door behind us, Shelly threw the dollars in the air and we danced a merry phone bill dance on the beds as the notes fluttered around us.

Eddy King was very cross that his leopard jumpsuits had been chopped up, but Shelly assured me that they would be very popular in some of his less prestigious clubs and wouldn't go to waste.

A perfect end to a perfect summer.

15

MAGIC CIRCLE

THE CONTRAST BETWEEN the lifestyle at college compared to Cairo was alarming to say the least. When I returned from the luxurious disco dancing world of Trumps, I found it very difficult to buckle down to student life again. The wet and windy British weather had kicked in once more and, as I battled to the railway station each morning, I would dream of sauntering down to the poolside bar, for a coffee and a swim in the Egyptian sunshine. Catching my train to college, or worse still cycling through the rain, just in time for gruelling hours of ballet class, just didn't appeal anymore. Added to this, having left the comfort of my accommodation with Mrs Ashfield and her family, moving instead into a shared flat with a dodgy heating system, although I didn't have to be a polite house guest anymore, I was always cold and hungry with a heavy heart, constantly looking out for the postman with the hope of news from Babu.

Having become rather accustomed to the good life at the five-star Egyptian Hotel, I was finding that the student grant didn't stretch very far. It was rather unnerving when my savings began to dwindle. By Christmas time, with no contracts to take me away to exotic places again, I found myself back at my flat worrying about affording Christmas presents for the family over the holidays and, more importantly, needing money for my next perm.

The eighties perm was a serious fashion statement that we all nurtured with mousse and bright shades of hair colour to match our garish eighties make up. If the curls started to grow out and you found that your student loan didn't stretch to pay for another perm at the salon, then you were in trouble. An interesting hair shape would start to develop when straight hair grew out flat at the top of the head, before puffing out into the old perms curly-ness, just above the ears. This gave you a fetching look of wearing fluffy headphones and meant that unless you could afford a new perm, the Big Hair look was going to be impossible to achieve. I was deeply concerned.

I spent the first few days of the long winter holidays worrying myself silly about surviving, with headphone hair and no food in my flat.

"At least I'll be thin," I mused as I passed the full-length mirror in the hall with my frugal bowl of noodle soup one morning. My jeans were hanging off me, my tummy was concave, and I could see my hip bones again.

Maggie, a resting actress with whom I shared the flat, along with some interesting dancers and musicians, was sprawled elegantly up the staircase in her Japanese kimono. She was weeping dramatically as usual, as I negotiated my way over her long limbs with great care to avoid scolding her with my soup. I realised it was only polite to join her on the stairs for a few minutes to hear the latest drama, so I sat down and gave her my most sympathetic smile. She sat up, pleased for someone to talk to as she peered, frowning through a curtain of red curls.

"I've had a letter from the dole office saying I have to go for an interview at the job centre. I am SO angry."

She paused for a reaction from me.

"Oh no! How terrible!" I managed, thinking that it was surely a good thing, even wondering if they could get me a job too.

"They have no idea about the theatre world. If I take one of their miserable jobs I won't be free to audition. If some TV or theatre work comes up with my agent, it's absolutely impossible to attend if I'm working elsewhere."

She looked terrified and her chin was starting to wobble as, shakily, she handed me a formal looking letter.

I'd always wanted to be able to cry easily like Maggie could, knowing it would be so useful in certain situations. I was tempted to ask if she could give me some crying lessons but decided this wasn't the time to ask, instead deciding I should try to console her. I had a very different work ethic to her, so it wasn't easy. Since leaving drama college a year previously, Maggie had been waiting in her room, for an agent to call her and offer her a job as an actress. Once a week she trotted out to sign on the dole, before returning to the flat to practice her audition pieces while she waited for The Call.

During the early eighties, it was very easy to hide up in your room and live off unemployment benefit from the government. You were sort of left to it really, with no horrible interviews at job centres where staff probed and investigated why you hadn't set foot out of your room all week. They just popped rent money into your account for you each month with a nice bit extra for food. However, by the look of Maggie's letter, the laws were changing which, I thought, was probably a blessing in disguise. These long winter days spent lurking in her room had made Maggie become paranoid about her health and future. I actually felt it would do her good to get out to the job centre and meet a few people but, at this precise moment, I didn't think that she would be too glad of such advice.

By the time I had managed to cheer her up and retreat to the safety of my room, I had made a firm decision to get myself out and find some work for the holidays, whatever it took. Anything would be better than sitting about being precious. Maggie had given me the wake-up call that I needed and that afternoon I took off with my C.V. into the centre of London. Unfortunately, it seemed that all the Christmas jobs had been snapped up and as soon as I mentioned that I had to return to college after the holidays, I was turned down. After an exhausting day of traipsing around the West End, begging for work as a perfume squirter in department stores, or kitchen slave in restaurants, it became clear that it was going to be harder than I'd anticipated to find a job. There was nothing in The Stage newspaper to get excited about that would fit in with term time either, but although disappointed, I was feeling rather virtuous for at least trying to solve my financial dilemma.

Returning to the flat in the rain from the grimy underground station, I negotiated our rickety gate. I could hear the phone ringing in the hallway inside. Not having mobile phones in those days, we had to manage with cranky old payphones in the entrance hall, provided by the landlord. I find this unbelievable now when I watch everyone constantly glued to their mobiles. Frantically foraging for my door key in the depths of my bag I saw, through the frosted glass of the front door, the sloping silhouette of one of my flat-mates, Natalia the pianist, shuffling out of her room and down the hallway. Still in her nightie and slippers, she was reluctantly on her way to answer the phone.

Apparently, Natalia was a genius musician studying at The Royal College of Music, but being rather a hermit, we didn't cross paths very often. You would know she'd been out of her room when there was a strong aroma of garlic in the kitchen. She avoided our kitchen parties and kept to her room with her beautiful piano that had been especially shipped over from Poland by her grandmother. Dancers can be rather raucous in the evenings and I think she liked to keep out of the way ever since one of the girls had drunkenly asked her if she'd like a makeover. This gesture towards Natalia, was meant kindly, but had probably come across as rather rude. We were fascinated how she constantly practiced the piano in her room all day, and late into the evening, repeating the same few notes over and over again, reminding us all of a record getting stuck.

Grateful that Natalia had answered the phone, I collapsed onto the hall floor with a groan and started pulling my soggy high heels off. As I rolled about on the floor yanking at my dripping tights, I felt her jabbing my arm, leaning over to pass me the phone. Her face was pale, and her greasy hair was scraped back so tightly into a long dry plait, that I swore she was going to develop a receding hairline if she wasn't careful. I longed to snip off the plait and fluff her hair all out just to see what would happen. She whispered in a very loud voice sending spittle flying in every direction, including my lip.

"This man! He 'as been calling you all the day and it 'ees hard for me to rehearse when I 'ave to be your receptioneest!"

She shoved the phone into my hand and marched back into her room, slamming the door in a huff.

Being in a tired, grumpy mood already, I responded rather unkindly, yelling back at her closed door.

"Pah! Sorry! Anyway, we love listening to *your* lovely, musical ditties all day, every day," I hesitated before adding, "And put some lippy on woman!"

"Hello?"

I plonked myself down on the bottom step of the filthy, manky stairs (God I missed the Sheraton hotel in Cairo). I felt guilty for my little outburst at poor Natalia and made a mental note to make her a cup of tea and do a spot of hoovering after speaking to whoever this was. Flat sharing could be such a challenge sometimes.

"Well, hello there, Jane, you are a busy lady!" declared an odd voice that I didn't recognise.

"I wish I *was*, who is this please?" I sat up straight, straining to hear better, as it was a bad line.

There was an important cough.

"I, am the one and only Desmundo of Magic Momentos of Italy, and you 'ave been recommended very highly to me to play the role of assistant for my magnificent show!"

There was the sound of coins being shoved into the phone box and a few expletives were emitted, that let slip that Desmundo of Italy, was probably really called Des from Hackney. That crafty O on the end was not fooling me. Sensing a vague hint of a job offer though, I persevered.

"Oh! have they, well how can I help you Des...mund...o?"

After the long-winded introduction, it turned out that an old school-friend, Dawn, from Ipswich, had recommended me to Des, when his glamorous side kick, Sonia, had done a runner, just before the start of his fully booked Christmas shows, leaving him in a real predicament. His show was missing a glamorous assistant to exclaim and gasp in amazement, as he sawed her in half and produced things out of his hat. Time was running out as his Christmas gigs rapidly approached. While he explained his troubles, my imagination ran riot with the real reason that he needed me to replace the lovely Sonia. Visions of her strapped to a huge, spinning wheel sprung to mind, with a dagger through her heart spurting blood at a screaming audience while Des apologised profusely for his badly aimed throw.

"So, you see Jane, my dear, Sonia 'as really dropped me innit, so to speak. She's gone off abroad wiv 'er sister. They've got this new act they conjured up, cheeky mares, nicked all my ideas an' all."

He was really reverting back to the full Cock-ann-ey Geezer by this point. I couldn't bear it anymore.

"Alright Des, just tell me, how much do you pay and when do you need me?"

There was a pause as he realised that although I had sussed him out, I hadn't put the phone down.

"Well, love, I really need 'elp pretty soon, I mean tonight would be good ...," another pause, with no mention of money. "I mean ideally, I'd pick you up in a couple of hours from Cheshunt station love, if you could get there swee' art."

"What? Are you serious?"

I realised he was, as he continued to describe how he had a gig booked that evening with a top-notch client. He couldn't mess it up. It paid so well.

I started to wonder, ridiculous though it was, if this might actually be my calling to The Magic Circle. Maybe this was all meant to be and besides, it was an opportunity to wear the divine, long, black gloves and hideously high, black, patent heels that I'd bought in a sale and never had the chance to wear. They were kicking around at the back of my wardrobe somewhere, I was sure of it, and I certainly didn't fancy a freezing evening in my scuzzy room listening to Natalia and her recitals downstairs. Everyone else in the flat seemed to have gone home early to their families for Christmas, which painted a rather depressing picture of the weeks ahead for me.

"Des, I don't mean to be fussy, but I don't know any of the tricks." I started looking in the long hall mirror and pulling magician assistant faces at myself, realising that I didn't care if I didn't know his magical secrets. It felt right and I was sure that my glamorous showgirl skills would outshine any mistakes, with any luck. I smiled at myself with the thought of being dropped off at the flat later that evening, with a big wad of magical cash in my slinky handbag, all ready to go shopping with. I wouldn't know any of the audience so there would be no embarrassment on my part when the rabbit refused to come out of the hat. I didn't let myself dwell on the 'sawing me in half trick,' deciding that I would insist early on, that any power tools were out of the question. My 'show must go on' approach was winning me round, and Des could already tell that I was a pushover when it came to adventures, especially when he hinted that we would be fed. This really swung the deal, although later proved rather disappointing at a Fish 'n Chip shop on Cheshunt High Street on the way home.

"These are really good clients, and I don't want to lose 'em. I can teach you all the tricks on the journey."

"Journey? Where is this gig?"

"Well, it's just a quick belt up the A10 and I'll drop you back home afterwards wiv a nice lump o' dosh. If it works out alright, I've got a full run over Christmas, so you'll be quids in darlin'."

I had to sympathise with Des, appreciating that he had been well and truly dropped in it by Sneaky Sonia. I was starting to feel rather puffed up at being able to save the day. Loving attention in any shape or form, I agreed to be at the station at five, ready for a crazy night of magical mystery. My original image of Il Desmundo perched, cross legged on a magic box, twiddling his pointy moustache, had turned into a more likely, Del Boy in a phone box outside The Old Bull and Bush on the London Road, and I felt quite sorry for him.

"OK Des! You're on me old mate! See you at five o'clock. Is it black dress and heels or a Merlin the wizard costume?" I asked, glancing at my watch.

"Oh, darlin', all of the above. You star!" and he was gone.

I stood in the silence for a few seconds before realising that I had very little time to get my arse to bloody Cheshunt dressed as a magical temptress.

"Crypes!!" I dashed up the stairs three at a time.

It felt great to be needed again after a whole day of rejections in town. Desmundo, with his box of tricks, had perked me right up and besides, it was better than nothing. I reminded myself, that I had chosen to work in the entertainment world, so this was what I had to do at this time. It didn't have to be forever, and I would prove to myself, when my training was over, that I would never need to sign on the dole and sit in my flat, pretending to be a 'resting' actress. This was a perfect example of really treading the boards and being a trouper. I suppose it did take a slightly mad person to set off into the unknown with a stranger called Desmundo, which, I suspected, was obviously why so many dancers gave up.

"Expect disaster and you may be pleasantly surprised," I told myself after a quick natter with Dawn from Ipswich, who reassured me that Des was a nice person, and not a psychopath.

"Oh, nah, Des is a good egg. Not much of a magician, but his hearts in the right place. Friend of me Dad's at The George and Dragon. His 'elper, Sonia, got a big break on P&O Ferries and left 'im in the lurch, so there's 'ope for you yet darlin'!"

Dawn erupted into a laughing, coughing fit.

"Thanks Dawn. I need a job and work is work, so thanks. I owe you a drink."

I spent a little time rifling through my chest of drawers, slinging anything black and slinky into a large holdall, adding a bag of make-up and the high heels.

I was at my front door, about to race off to the tube when horror struck.

"ARMPITS!!"

Back up the stairs, thinking of my strapless dress, I dived into the shower with a razor, then I was off again. I needed to make sure that Des would not fancy me and complicate matters, so I wore my scruffy tracksuit and old trainers to travel in. My black magical ensemble could be a big surprise when I burst onto the stage, before reverting back to the real me in my tracksuit for the journey home.

I was just jogging down the stairs in the semi- darkness, when Natalia's pasty face peered out of her doorway and made me jump out of my skin.

"Jeeeesus! Don't do that!" I shrieked.

When I stopped, I had to stifle a hoot of laughter. Natalia had pasted a thick layer of bright red lipstick over her grey mouth. She was looking at me with a wicked twinkle in her eye as she turned her plait over and over between her genius, pianist fingers. I couldn't decide whether to be delighted or terrified, as she actually looked like something from a horror movie with her off white nightie and pale face, in the dim light of the hallway. I glimpsed behind her to check that she wasn't hiding an axe.

"Hello Jane," she smiled a creepy, bashful smile and stepped out into the hall, "I need you to take a message to Desmundo, from me, pleeeez."

I really had not been expecting this and couldn't quite take it in.

"Of course! What is that Natalia my dear?" I side stepped nervously passed her towards the front door.

"Tell heeem I will conseeeder his offer ..."

The situation soon became clear when I realised that Des had tried to talk Natalia into performing in his show during all the phone calls throughout the day. She clearly didn't realise how quickly you had to act, in order to grab these jobs when they came along. I mean, we would have nearly finished the run by the time she'd made her mind up. I wasn't going to let this opportunity pass.

"I will tell him! That's wonderful."

I suddenly became quite protective of *My Des* and didn't want to share him with anyone, even though I'd never met the man.

"I'll see what I can do, we'll talk more tomorrow Natalia!"

As I nodded a crafty, knowing nod at the red lips and reached for the door handle, I had a brain wave.

"Actually, could I ask a favour of you darling?"

The red mouth pouted.

"Well, 'eet depends ..."

Please may I borrow your turquoise Kaftan if I bring it back tomorrow?"

It had occurred to me that her horrible kaftan, that we often sniggered about in our unkind, teenage way, would actually make an amazing Merlin costume, being covered in golden moons and stars. If I felt that the show was more Merlin the Wizard, than Paul Daniels, I would whip it on and Hey Presto!

It would also serve as an emergency cover up if Des turned out to be a lecherous little devil. I would be able to transform myself with the wave of a wand into a mixture of Natalia, a six-foot showgirl and a slightly un-hinged, unemployed wizard.

Natalia blinked at me, completely baffled as none of the girls ever asked to borrow any of her weird clothes.

"Well, why not?" she ventured, turning to go to her room and then stopping to add, "Only if you take great care of eet."

She entered her room and was gone a while, so I peered in. It was squalid with just a path between piles of books and music that led to her piano stool from the door.

"I cannot find eet."

Natalia stood staring at the muddle until she seemed to have a light bulb moment.

"Aha!! I remember!" She smiled manically to herself, humming as she went over to her laundry basket where she delved deeper and deeper into its smelly depths. Eventually the kaftan immerged, steaming, crumpled and damp.

"There you are!" the red lips announced triumphantly.

I tried not to retch and smiled as I shoved it into a Sainsbury's bag that was floating around in the hallway. I didn't want to stink out the car on the journey.

"Thanks, hun! See you tomorrow."

And with that I set off to the tube station with my bag of different personas. If I'd had more time and money, I giggled at the thought of setting Natalia onto a new career of treading the boards with Des, transforming her into a hot babe. What would her family back home have thought, when she wrote to tell them that there'd been a slight change in her performing plans? The girls in the flat would have been flabbergasted and I chuckled to myself as I was flung about on the seat, as the train rattled along to Cheshunt.

16

HEY PRESTO!

THE TRAIN PULLED into Cheshunt station and I peered out onto the platform apprehensively. It struck me as rather funny when I compared this moment to looking for Eddy King's chauffeur in Cairo.

"Bit of a come down," I quipped, handing my ticket to the guard, scanning the parking area for a bright jolly van with magical artwork on the side of it. There was nothing of that nature anywhere. I narrowed my eyes into the driving rain until I saw a filthy old Vauxhall with a trailer attached. Just as I thought. My heart sank as the window wound down and a pale face peered out.

"Jane?"

"Oh, woe is me, there is Des," I thought, smiling bravely, making my way across the tarmac wishing I'd ignored my mother's insistence that I would never need to type.

"Des! Hi!"

I opened the car door with the very tips of my fingers so as not to get black grime on my hands and bundled my bag into the back. Lowering myself cautiously into the passenger's seat next to him, I managed a bright smile. The car was obviously his office as well as his transport. There were phone numbers and messages scribbled on little bits of paper flying about, amongst less desirable items, such as empty old plastic coffee cups and crisp packets. I even spotted a snapped magic wand in the foot-well which didn't bode well. The back of the car was packed up to the gunnels with mysterious trunks and boxes and I began to dread what delights were in store for me later on. With a jaunty smile, Des lit a cigarette before putting his foot down and taking off into the darkness. He held his screwed up face close to the windscreen because the wipers weren't coping too well with the heavy rain.

"Right, so, opening number," he began in his scratchy voice. I realised that this journey was to be my rehearsal.

It turned out that Des was, in fact, a competent magician. He just needed me to jazz up his act, with lots of elegant gliding and twirling around the stage with facial expressions to match. I was relieved really, as I didn't fancy being sawn in half without a rehearsal. That particular trick, thankfully, wasn't mentioned. Halfway through the journey I had the fright of my life when there was a huge farting sound from the back seat of the car.

"Ah, yes, this is Rick, the stage-hand," explained Des.

Rick rose up from the depths of the back seat, rubbing his eyes and looking out to see where we were. On seeing me, he looked rather embarrassed and nodded politely. "Oh, I do apologise. Didn't know we 'ad a lady present."

As I wound the window down to let some fresh air in, I felt horrified and pleased at the same time to meet Rick. Despite the shock, I was glad to know that I wasn't going to have to help unload the large trunks and boxes out of the van and into the venue. Before long we had parked up at a large hotel. I was pleased to note that we were to perform at a civilised corporate event, not a sleazy social club. No wonder Des had been in a panic because he clearly wouldn't want to lose this client.

Later that evening, crouching in The Magic Treasure Chest, inhaling the eye-watering aroma of Des' cheesy socks, I was ready to wow the crowd. Having just craftily swapped places with Des, I was preparing to be unlocked and set free. The Treasure Chest was the most captivating of all the tricks. I would stand on it, pulling a large sparkly covered frame up to just under my chin, looking cunningly out at my audience. Bear in mind that I'd previously locked Des into said chest, with great ceremony, much exaggerated closing of padlocks and dastardly of expressions. While I distracted everyone with my mystical moves, he would open a secret door in the lid of the chest and crawl out ready to magically swap places with me behind the sparkly frame. Shouting "Abracadabra!" I would hold the attention of my audience, for a few moments, where it was obvious what we were doing, until Des would be revealed with a dramatic "Hey presto!" as I dropped down into the darkness of the trap door and he popped up! Once in the chest, Des expertly closed the secret door again with his foot, holding the audience's interest with some magical words, before leaping onto the stage with another "Hey Presto!" and a flick of his wand.

It was then, that I would wait for my astoundingly glamorous reveal. This was probably the trickiest of moments during the show because Des had extremely smelly feet so, as I hid in the darkness, like a tarantula waiting to pounce, the air was a trifle wiffy to say the least. After inhaling smelly feet in the chest for two whole minutes, I knew I probably looked like I needed resuscitating when I immerged. It didn't even bear thinking about that the doors and padlocks could get jammed and I've had nightmares about that trunk ever since.

"How did it come to this?" I asked myself, peeping apprehensively at the audience through the keyhole.

To Des' delight, the evening went pretty well.

The audience seemed to like me, which helped my confidence, and considering how scatty I am, I actually found it quite enjoyable to prance around the stage at my leisure. With very little choreography to remember, this was a piece of cake compared to complicated dance routines. I didn't even work up a sweat. My main challenge was to keep a straight face while executing the crafty manoeuvres. Taking one bow after another, I wondered if this might actually be a better career path for me anyway. Occasionally I fear, I managed to spoil some of the big moments in the show with my harassed expression. There was one incident that saw Des accidentally nip the skin on my neck when he closed the wooden stocks, in the *Lock the Lady in the Stocks* trick. I immediately screamed rather dramatically in shock and pain while Des shouted FUCK rather loudly, which was obviously not part of the act. We braved it to the end, and I gained a purple love bite for the rest of the Christmas season.

Most in need of rehearsal, was the fire trick, when I was supposed to light a large golden dish of fire before wafting around the stage with it to Egyptian music, while Des did a daring feat of some sort at the front. Sadly, my dish would never light to much more than a tiny flicker, so I just looked as though I was handing round canapés.

The Chamber was when Des would lock me into a tall cupboard before poking pointy swords through it. It was easy to step over them or duck under them as they came through, although I did have to have my wits about me of course. Unfortunately, the swords always managed to catch on my tights, and make big holes and ladders in them, which spoiled my glamorous 'Ta Daaa!' moment at the end.

Generally, though, Des, Rick and I made a great team and we earned lots of money that Christmas. I reminded myself, it was better than sitting in an empty flat wishing I was famous and wondering how and where Mark from The Purple Shop was, or what Babu was up to. I knew I had been right to go for The Magic Circle option and I actually felt quite sad when Des and I took our last curtain call together. Rick, the big softy, wiped a tear away as he waved goodbye and they took off down the road in their old Vauxhall. We'd certainly had a laugh.

Feeling hugely proud of myself for surviving the early Christmas period, I returned to the family bearing gifts with a marvellous feeling of self-sufficiency. Unfortunately, my mother took all the money off me when I made the mistake of flashing my cash at my brother one morning.

"That'll pay for your singing lessons," she smiled, pocketing the money on her way out to work.

It will always bring a smile to my face when I remember Des hanging out of his car window as he accelerated out of the car park at the train station on our last night.

"I'll keep your number darlin'. Loads a work at Easter," he rasped.

"Thanks! Hope so!" I replied politely, praying that I didn't have to ever get in his Treasure Chest again.

And I didn't.

17

CONCERT

STRUGGLING THROUGH THE unforgiving weeks of February, following my magical Christmas, I trogged to dance lessons through the driving rain and sleet in true British style. It was rather thrilling therefore, one evening in the doom and gloom of the flat, to find four golden envelopes looking rather out of place on the dirty kitchen table, all individually addressed to all the girls at the flat. They turned out to be invitations. After all our cheeky comments about her, Natalia the musician was about to have the last laugh.

Stephanie put down her spoon and jar of chocolate spread, to open her envelope.

"How intriguing!" she exclaimed, displaying chocolatey brown teeth. Her voice sounded hilarious as she had thick chocolate stuck to the roof of her mouth as she announced, "Ooh lithen to thith. The Royal College of Muthic, Requeths the pleasure of your company, on Thurthday 26th February at 8pm, for a rethital featuring - Natalia Perovicth!"

Maggie grabbed the invitation from Stephanie.

"That's tomorrow. The old dark horse. Fancy inviting us!! I didn't think she had time for us lot!"

It was then that it occurred to us that Natalia had been gone for days. The flat was eerily quiet without the sound of her piano tinkling in the background, and we all agreed that we missed it.

"The flat's even more depressing when it's silent as well as scuzzy," observed Maggie, knowledgably as she prodded a turkey burger.

We all agreed that we ought to rally the troops to support Natalia. It was the least we could do.

"Bless her," we all chimed together as we sat in the gloom gazing at the shining invitations.

So, Thursday evening found us all standing awkwardly in the foyer of one of the most famous music schools in the world.

"My God! I wish I'd known it was going to be posh. We should have dressed up!" hissed Stephanie.

We were clutching our golden envelopes with burning curiosity as we hadn't expected the venue to be quite so grand. People in beautiful evening dress and men in tuxedos had started filing into the auditorium and we followed, sitting ourselves down in silence, feeling rather scruffy in our dance gear, having come straight from college. As we watched an impressively full orchestra tuning up, we realised that we really should have put on a frock, but I'd assumed that Natalia would still be wearing her nightie and it would be a more casual affair. Taking in the grandeur and ambiance of a century of musical achievement, excellence hung in the air, and we could see, looking around, that there were guests from all over the world. There was even a photographer crawling about at the front. As we took our seats, a hush fell across the room as the lights dimmed, until there was just one spotlight and there she stood, and she definitely wasn't wearing her nightie. It was Our Nat, dressed in red taffeta, ruched around her bare shoulders before tumbling down to the floor, while her greasy plait had burst out into a mass of golden ringlets that fell down her back and the pièce de résistance was, of course, a bright red mouth. Gliding over to her grand piano, after a subtle nod to the audience, she took her seat. We were agog. I managed to cast a glance down our row to see that we all had our mouths open in awe, especially Michelle, who'd offered to give Natalia a makeover.

Natalia threw her head back as her manicured hands hovered momentarily in the air, pausing for a few seconds as she swivelled her eyeballs to her conductor to give him the go ahead. What followed was, basically all the twiddly bits we'd been listening to over the last year, joined together into one big piano Tchaikovsky concerto number something or other. It was completely exhilarating with a roar from the crowd at the end. I was moved to tears. Not just because it sounded so breathtakingly beautiful, but because she was so discreet and unassuming at home, and none of us had known that this little mouse was, in fact, a lioness.

So, people, never judge a book by its cover.

18

HARRODS

I HAD STARTED to feel rather worldly after my unusual stint with Desmundo, and proud of myself for surviving financially over the Christmas holidays. With Madrid and then the Eddie King show in Cairo under my belt, I was beginning to feel like a real trouper. At the end of the summer term, when I caught my train home from college for the last time, I felt full of anticipation and pleased to have finished the long course at last.

There seemed to have been three categories of student at college:

a) Smart businesswomen, planning to open dance schools of their own, never having been star struck like the rest of us, having the sense to accept that they wanted to be teachers, not performers. These girls were usually wholesome women, immaculately turned out with sturdy bodies and focused minds. They never missed a single ballet class and discipline was their middle name, as they tore through their exams as though they were shelling peas. Returning to their home territory they would take on the town, qualified to the hilt, entering students for festivals and exams, producing extravagant shows and earning a fortune from pushy mothers and daughters on quests for stardom.

b) People like me who'd been secretly imagining that they would be a star one day, since the age of ten, then realising it was rather unlikely, but deciding to go along for the ride anyway to see what happened.

c) People who had the right skill and commitment to train hard and never miss a class, in order to focus every moment on their performing career. These students were rare, standing out in the crowd, sailing through their training to be snapped up by agents or directors as soon as they left college.

At the end of my last term at college, I decided to have one last shot at finding a job in the West End. Most of my girlfriends had caught the first train to the security of Guy Stranger's showgirl studios in Paris, nervous of the discomfort of unemployment. He was offering highly paid shows at corporate Gala events in Stuttgart and Frankfurt that, understandably, proved irresistible to them.

Having declined the Gala work, naively hoping to walk into a West End role for Phantom of The Opera, I had extended my tenancy at the flat for a few months. Accepting a temporary job at Harrods, I'd started squirting perfume at people as they entered the store, in the beauty department on the ground floor. This covered my rent payments while I waited to be discovered, with the advantage of being available if an audition came up in The Stage.

Harrods is quite a visual experience exuding decadence and grandeur, a must for tourists, but during the eighties, it was still very much a store. There was no internet shopping available then, so browsing was an essential pleasure for the daily requirements of the ladies of Knightsbridge. The food hall took your breath away and drew quite a crowd with its waterfalls displaying fresh shellfish. The vast florist shop with arrays of colourful blooms, greeted you with their delightful fragrance as you entered the marble walled halls. The chocolate department was a world of its own with every kind of truffle imaginable and the aroma sending you to heaven and back as you perused the shelves of brightly coloured confectionary. I would wander around these beautiful rooms when it was quiet in the perfume department, just taking in the alluring ambiance that is Harrods. There was a great feeling of pride amongst the staff then, as we looked after our individual areas and I met some delightful people, including Princess Diana. I didn't exactly strike up a natter with her but, on one of her private visits, she wandered through my department with her bodyguard, pausing to return my gormless grin with one of her captivating smiles.

People from the entertainment world make good salespeople, so they often work as 'temps' on a daily fee when acting roles are scarce. I was lucky enough to work in Harrods with an actress called Jan, who can be seen in the Bond films from the sixties. She told wonderful tales from these exciting days and we spent many lunchbreaks in the bars of Knightsbridge hooting over anecdotes from our lives and experiences, including the day she was cast to massage Sean Connery on a sun lounger at the start of one of his Bond films.

After a few weeks, I'd really settled into Harrods, wondering whether I was actually destined for the world of retail rather than the stage. I stalked around in my court shoes and pencil skirt, smiling at shoppers as I offered them a little puff of my latest fragrance. I'm probably most famously remembered though, for my attempt at a piano recital, with no rehearsal, one afternoon during a competition.

It had been announced at the early morning meeting, that each room was to choose a theme and the best dressed room would be awarded with the Presentation Cup at the end of the month, to keep until the autumn, when the competition would resume. This was the management's crafty way of keeping everyone on their toes, ensuring the rooms looked immaculate at all times. With tough competition amongst the floor managers as they fought for recognition, ours, a lady called Kim, was going all out to make sure we won. Kim was pushing hard for promotion, so we were all walking on eggshells as she prepared a musical theme for our room, promptly arranging to have a large, white, grand piano brought down from the music department. We arranged statues of Schubert and Mozart around the room with bowls piled high with fruit that glistened under the spotlights. It looked truly magnificent by the time the big day of the competition arrived and we all dressed in our best frocks ready to impress Mr Al-Fayed, our boss.

Judges were parading around the departments making notes with clip boards as we all stood in a line, on our best behaviour, waiting for our turn to be inspected. With minutes to spare, Kim suddenly realised it would look so much better if someone was actually playing our grand piano as it stood majestically on the marble floor.

"Oh Gosh I never thought! Does anyone happen to play the piano girls? Wouldn't it be just the icing on the cake when they come in?" she exclaimed, throwing up her hands in a panic. "I'm so stupid, I should have organised a musician," she stared into space, trying frantically to think of a solution.

Everyone looked around at each other, waiting for one of the old dears amongst us to step forward and launch into Chopin's Nocturne in *B* flat Minor, but there was a worrying silence. Kim looked as though she might cry, and I couldn't bear it.

"I know *Love Story!*" I offered with a titter.

It was the only tune I could play, having mastered it by ear as an emotional teenager when the film was a massive hit in the seventies. It had seen me through many a moment when I'd needed to convince people that I had musical talents. I'd even learnt to look over briefly at my audience and wink, it was so damned impressive.

"Well, *Love Story* isn't a classical piece," snorted Cynthia, obviously jealous of my imminent Brownie points.

"Who said it had to be classical anyway?" retorted Margaret, head of Chanel. There was a buzz of discussion as the consensus came out that *Love Story* was probably better than silence.

"People won't be bothered if *Love Story* is classical music or not, you should all realise Jane works in thear-tarrr and is a *professional*," announced Margaret, very keen for me to play.

I couldn't help agreeing with her.

"S'pose so," agreed Kevin the doorman, who had wandered over from the lifts in his top hat and tails to join in the fun. "And it's been ages since the film was a blockbuster, they won't even know. Or ... tell you what, you could put a classical CD on, and Jane could pretend to play."

Everyone laughed until they realised that Kevin was serious. Cynthia was furious, "I don't think you are at liberty to comment young man, get back to your station," she ordered sternly.

Before I lost my nerve, I stepped out of the little group and took my place at the velvet stool, shuffling about a bit, testing the pedals and flexing my arms as though I were a real pro. I hesitated, remembering another tune I knew.

"Kim, I can also play *We are the Diddy Men, we come from Knotty Ash*, if you'd prefer. What do you think?" I was becoming quite cocky now and enjoying my newfound fame.

"Just get on with it, *Love Story* is fine." she snapped, nervous now as the clip clop of high heels and low murmurs of the judges approached.

"OK if you're happy with that." I declared as I took one more look around at the eager faces of my colleagues before lifting my hands high above the keys. I must say, it did sound beautiful as I launched into my favourite old piece. I found it hard not to sing, "Where do I beginnnnn ... to tell the story, of how great a love has binnnnnn ..."

God, I was good at this. As I tinkled away on the ivories, I realised that all those childhood lessons had been worth it after all.

"If my teacher, Miss Parker, could see me now!" I thought, feeling an inkling of what it must be like to be Natalia from the flat. Maybe fame finds you when you stop looking, I wondered to myself as my heart took a little leap at the sound of the judge's footsteps approaching.

There was one little teensy thing bothering me and slightly spoiling things at this point. Unfortunately, although it was all sounding lovely, I was aware that I didn't know *Love Story* all the way through. I reassured myself that by the time I got to the 'He fills my heart with wild imaginings' part, the tricky bit, the judges would have walked by and moved on to the next room. I really needed this to happen, because if it didn't, I knew I was in trouble, but as is my way, I didn't think too deeply into it.

Moving my shoulders gracefully to my music I attempted a Bobby Crush smile at the passers-by, only to see that the judges, to be polite, had stopped and were waiting for me to finish my tune. Shit.

There is a sketch by Dudley Moore that sprang to mind as I tinkled away, and it rather saved the day on this occasion. I copied what is called a false crescendo, when the audience thinks the music is coming to an end, but then, after a few little tinkles, continues. When I eventually arrived at the tricky bit, I tinkled a few high notes as I looked over endearingly to the row of judges. I could also see my colleagues, a glaring Cynthia, a weeping Margaret and a few of my closer acquaintances shaking, with tears of laughter running down their faces.

I was able to stop at this point, mid tune, faking surprise.

"Oh gosh! How lovely to see you, I didn't realise you were there!" I gushed.

It had struck me as rather funny that the words to the song were 'Where do I begin?' because I clearly knew *that*, but really needed to know 'Where did I *finish?*'

There was an awkward pause and then, with great relief, a ripple of applause. We won the competition but unfortunately, I wasn't discovered and offered a job as pianist for the beauty floor with my half of a tune. Life settled down again after the excitement of winning, until I was brought down to earth with a bump one day.

Returning from my coffee break, I was greeted by an excited Jan and Margaret.

"You had a visitor darling, he's coming back in half an hour," the words spilled out of Margaret like water from a fountain. Jan pushed past her to announce,

"Fabbo was here!"

She stood back beaming at me, awaiting my reaction.

"No darling, *Babu!*" Margaret corrected her, causing my heart to leap.

Before I could respond, there he was, Babu from Cairo. Fortunately, or unfortunately, I wasn't yet sure, Granny had picked up the phone when Babu had called my home. She had happily given him my exact location with great pride. I wondered what other details she had updated him with as we hugged and agreed to meet later that day for lunch.

"Take an extra, long break darling, I'll cover for you," said Jan with a conspiratorial wink.

Sitting huddled, in a little Knightsbridge bistro, it was wonderful to be together again and I still found Babu hugely entertaining. He seemed keen to take me on an extravagant spree around London while he was in town, but Shelly's words from Cairo echoed in my head. A gentle enquiry confirmed that he would be returning to Dubai after a week and I knew Shelly had been right. Walking in Hyde Park after lunch, we were so familiar with each other that I didn't hold back my honest feelings.

"Babu it's so sweet of you, but I can't just see you once in a while. I need someone all the time."

The light in his eyes faded as I made it politely clear that I wasn't into part-time relationships. When he didn't suggest that I return to Dubai to spend some time with him there, I knew Shelly had very likely been right, so there followed a subdued but amicable goodbye.

Jan, the Bond Girl, was horrified, when I described my relationship with Babu to her, over a bottle of Le Piat D'Or, after his visit. She'd demanded a long break together for compassionate reasons and our floor manager, remarkably, had allowed it. Jan was a very respected member of staff.

"How dare he? Stay away from that one my darling," she'd warned. "You need a real man that loves you, and only you," she reached across the table and patted me on the arm. "He sounds married to me I'm afraid love."

I continued to work for Harrods until a certain phone call, a few weeks later.

19

SAN REMO

SUSANNAH, ONE OF my friends from college, came on the line first. She was in Paris, rehearsing with Guy Stranger.

"Darling, we'll have to be quick because we only have a few francs but listen, we've saved you a place in the Can-Can line and Guy remembers you from Madrid. He says hurry up, or he will replace you. You have to catch the ferry and get here soon, so get packing!"

Having almost finished the Galas in Frankfurt, the girls in Paris were determined that I should be going with them on a new contract to Italy. Imagining them all squashed inside the phone box outside Guy's farmhouse, did make me smile. I was very touched that they were thinking of me but braced myself to explain my ambitious plans to stay in London.

"Darling. It's now or never so HURRY," Stephanie's voice echoed in the background. "It won't be the same without you."

"And bring sweets," added Susannah.

They gave me the number of their phone box and I rang them back to hear the full details of the plan. I had to admit that it did sound tempting, especially as it had been hammering down with rain in London for several days. There hadn't been anything suitable for me to consider in The Stage, so leaping on a train and getting away, began to look more appealing as the girls described the new show that was due to open on a rooftop casino in San Remo, Italy.

After a reassuring discussion with Mum about 'grabbing life by the balls,' I swiftly found someone to replace me at the flat, handed in my notice at Harrods and took off to Paris, with an enormous feeling of relief. Suddenly, I was off to join all my best friends, before heading for the Mediterranean.

As Guy came to greet me with his ear-to-ear grin at Montereau station, I was sure, as I climbed down the train steps, that I had made the right decision.

"Bienvenue ma Cherie!" he exclaimed.

It was quite a milestone really because college life was over, and there would be no more term-time ever again. This was the beginning of the rest of my life and it stretched deliciously in front of me with all its promise.

There was great excitement when Guy's old, dented van delivered me onto the driveway at the old farmhouse that evening. Arriving at his studio was like coming home and it was great to see everyone again, knowing that I had an income and a glorious plan for the summer. Reunited with the gang, we chatted over wine and crisps as we sat on our dusty old beds, with Guy's smelly dogs nestling in with us for the evening.

The girls updated me with the plans, explaining that in a week's time we would travel with Nigel the dance captain, by train, to a casino in San Remo, on the coast of Italy, close to Nice, in France. We were to perform the Can-Can every night under the stars, on the Casino roof terrace for six weeks before taking the show on the road with Guy Stranger and his tour bus. Booked all over Southern Italy for the summer season, we felt terrific. Many of the dancers had worked at this casino the previous year, so were looking forward to getting back to the beach and finding old flames that they had been writing to ever since. The air was full of hope and excitement as we went through our paces during rehearsals, memorising endless dance steps to a wide variety of themes.

The casino in San Remo is, like many theatres in Europe, an elegant, historical building of immense character. Built in 1902, it had survived the First and Second world wars. It's spectacular architecture, grand stairways, high ceilings and elegant dressing rooms were, at that time, still in beautiful, original condition. Having been frequented by many European stars over the decades and no doubt occupied by the Nazis during the war, I was sure that the walls of our dressing rooms could have told many stories, good and bad. We were just a small part of the constant stream of people from all over the world that passed through year after year from the cabaret circuit. It was a privilege to be performing there and to our delight, local nightclubs welcomed us with open arms. We were given celebrity status with VIP tables, rubbing shoulders with top class circus performers, ice skaters and singers. These lively, talented people are always a big part of cabaret life on the continent and we've only really seen them in Britain, since Cirque du Soleil arrived on the scene. This whole new world was truly thrilling, and we were all loving every minute of our engagement at the casino that was to be the first stop of quite an adventure at many picturesque Italian locations, over the summer months ahead. Guy had booked us to perform our show, with stunning costumes created by his wife Regine, at five-star hotels in a variety of breath-taking locations.

We were quite a spectacle under the spotlights in our diamante studded bikinis with towering, feathered head dresses. We kicked our legs high, whirling around the stage in perfect unison to the pre-recorded orchestral music played through the speakers from Guy's vast collection of 'reel to reel' recordings that our dance captain, Nigel, guarded with his life. We danced in a vast selection of different costumes ranging from red and black frilly Flamenco dresses, white top hat and tail suits, to elaborate, velvet ball gowns and French Can-Can petticoats. There were traditional numbers too, including an Argentinian dance in heavy white fringed capes, long black, plaited wigs and heavy leather drums. While the girls twirled traditional, Argentinian, white pompoms around and beat their drums in the background, our delectable, Argentinian dancer, Julio, would perform death defying feats with flames and knives. While this was going on, I prepared in the wings for my big moment of the night, a solo called Fashion Show. This was an opportunity for all the girls to change out of their Argentinian ensembles into the next costume of peach chiffon gowns and scarves for a dream sequence. As they rushed to the dressing room to change, I would glide around the stage in a flesh-coloured leotard dotted with bright sparkles, like a circus trapeze artiste. I whipped up different outfits out of pieces of brightly coloured silk, like a harem dancer, expertly tying the different swathes of fabric around myself to create a ball gown, a salsa frock, a Spanish skirt until the dramatic ending when I became a bashful bride in a veil, to rapturous applause. I always got the urge to pick up all the discarded fabrics at the end of the performance, and stuff them up my brides dress so that I looked pregnant, but I thought better of it, in case Italians did not find that very funny.

I loved my solo, having spent many hours mastering the act during our rehearsal week in Paris. Apparently, it looked very impressive and the audience were always enthusiastic, so it really was my big moment of the night.

To end the show, the energy of our Can-Can finale lit up the balmy evening as we burst onto the stage in heavy black velvet dresses with layer upon layer of different brightly coloured satin petticoats, bright velvet corsets and traditional ostrich feathers in our hair. The Mediterranean Sea sparkled under the moonlight at us, from just over the road. The audience sipped their cocktails at little tables around the terrace, mesmerised as we leapt into our dance, creating magical memories for them to take home.

After the show, we would remove our false eyelashes and hang up our costumes before heading off to the night-clubs of the Riviera in all our finery. The fashion, during the eighties, consisted of large bright jackets with huge shoulder pads, the standard white court shoes, mini-skirts or carefully tailored trousers, called Pegs. The most thrilling nights were when the biker boys revved their engines outside the stage door and we leapt onto the back of their huge motorbikes, no helmets on, wrapping our tanned arms and bare legs around them before taking off up to the hills, with our sun-kissed hair whipping furiously behind us. There, we would sit at cafés in the old hillside towns drinking wine and singing until the sun came up.

Knowing that we had employment for the next three months was a great feeling and we were all very excited and relieved at the prospect of an entire summer in this beautiful climate. The show only took up about three hours of our day, if you included the preparations backstage, so the rest of the time was spent on the beach, sunning ourselves and listening to music, sleeping and enjoying the brasseries along the waterfront. The summer schedule reassured us all, that we wouldn't have to return to rainy England, because we were glamorous dancers, seeing the world and living the dream. As part of our payment in San Remo, we were cared for by an Italian lady called Maria who treated us as though we were her own daughters, staying at her large town house where she prepared us hot steaming bowls of pasta in the evening before the show. In the mornings, we were woken by the heavenly aroma of fresh bread and coffee wafting up the stairs as the sun glinted through our windows beckoning us down to the beach.

One morning at breakfast, towards the end of our stay in San Remo, a message arrived from Guy Stranger, explaining that he was planning to meet us with his tour bus in Pisa, at the end of the casino contract. We were to catch the train from San Remo to meet him there, after our last show. The costumes were to be transported separately. Some of the girls seemed apprehensive at the thought of Guy and his renowned driving skills taking us to the next venue, cooped up in the smelly van. However, I was fearless, having experienced endless summers in the VW van with my family on our holidays during my childhood.

Leaving San Remo was, to say the least, emotional, but we felt driven by the curiosity of the next location that Guy had up his sleeve. We all hung out of the windows of the old train as it pulled out of San Remo station, taking us to the city of Pisa, where our trusty, dusty van was waiting for us with, unfortunately, Guy at the wheel. We had spent endless days on the beach with our handsome group of local boys, so it was quite a dramatic farewell that morning. Some of the girls were naively planning to return, to marry their sweethearts after the tour, but I didn't get my hopes up for them. I'd spotted the boys checking out the new girls arriving at the casino for the next show. This made the departure all the more depressing as the boys waved us off.

The only exception to this deluded idea of marital, Italian bliss was my friend Susannah, who had managed to meet a Norwegian holidaymaker. She was planning to go to Oslo for Christmas. As we watched his white, blonde head become a speck in the distance amongst all the glossy dark hair of the Italians, her face said it all. She was convinced that this was *it*. They knew that they were meant for each other. My Italian stallion, Salvino, hadn't turned up to wave to me at the station and I was having to be brave. Susannah sweetly reassured me that he was probably at work, while I couldn't help feeling disappointed, knowing exactly why he wasn't there. Over the last week of the stay in San Remo, I'd been devastated to notice his little drug habit with his friend Marco. As they smoked joints and rubbed cocaine into their gums, their garish grins had revealed an ugly side that had, at first, been hidden behind their Italian charm. Marco was having a fling with Jenny, my friend from the show, so the four of us had been spending many afternoons, lazing on the scorching rocks at the beach. Unfortunately, the drugs had changed their warm personalities towards the end of the summer, and they exhibited more fractious behaviour. Added to the language barrier this made communication even more of a challenge.

"Why can't we go out with successful business millionaires with yachts instead of local yobs," Jenny grumbled as we laid on our beach towels, watching Salvino and Marco smoking a joint by the water's edge.

"Because, my dear, those men are always married or unfaithful," I suggested.

By the time the boys came swaggering back up the beach, we had decided that we'd had enough of their disgusting behaviour.

"How disrespectful," I declared angrily as I gathered my things to walk back into town, feeling we certainly didn't want a lift on their motorbikes if they were high as kites. It was so upsetting to feel so disillusioned after all the romantic summer moments together. I watched Jenny as she regarded them with distaste. Reaching for her hairbrush she sat up, like a mermaid, perched on her rock, "I mean, can you seriously believe that we would, either of us, really consider coming back here to marry those two buffoons?"

Jenny's remark suddenly struck me as hugely funny as she brushed her long curls furiously. As Salvino approached, I rolled over on my towel to make room for him. Unfortunately, I was laughing so hard that I farted. It was a bright happy fart of amusement that completely took me by surprise. Italian girls don't fart, especially in front of men. A lot of English girls do though, and I could see from the disbelief on Salvino's face, that he was never going to be able to trust me in public, ever again. I didn't care anymore though. I knew snorting cocaine was much worse behaviour and threw my head back and laughed.

So, as our train left San Remo with no sign of Salvino on the horizon, I turned to my music, plugging in my Sony Walkman as I sobbed to Barry Manilow's *Could it Be Magic?* rather enjoying the drama of it all. I had to accept that Salvino wasn't the answer to my prayers, by any means. The girls filtered back to their seats on the train, but I was struggling to find closure, feeling disappointed. I was surprised at how emotional I felt but put it down to the fact that we had all partied right through the previous night on the beach, drinking Amaretto and Orange juice and Tia Maria's, dancing our last dance under the stars of San Remo. I was still slightly drunk and in need of sleep as I gazed up at the pine forest hills out of the clunky old train window. The soft Italian breeze dried my tears, but even the heavenly scent of the passing pine trees couldn't cheer me up. A little voice in my head mused, "No, Barry Manilow, it couldn't be magic darling, move on."

I knew that I wasn't going to be Salvino's wife, living by the sea with all my little, dark haired babies. Salvino was probably sipping his morning coffee at the bar by the beach already, chatting to his friends, with me a distant memory, far from his mind. Fortunately, I had girlfriends with me though, and my little bubble of misery burst when I looked through the window of the next carriage where Susannah and Jenny were setting out a very impressive looking buffet of crisps and olives. As Susannah opened a bottle of sparkling wine, she rolled her eyes at me and signalled to me to join them, pointing excitedly at her divine picnic.

"Come on misery guts! He's not worth it!" she mouthed.

I switched Barry off and made my way down the aisle to join her. I knew she was right. Salvino was going to be another photo in my album, to go with the one of Babu dancing by the Nile, Mark, that I'd taken, secretly, in assembly once and Dylan on the park. The girls were soon rolling around laughing at little anecdotes from the last few months, especially Jenny's description of our final afternoon on the beach.

The train took us to Pisa where we all spent the night in, what was in hindsight, probably some kind of brothel. Guy and Regine were planning to drive us all to our next assignment in the tour bus, and we had travelled to Pisa to meet them in the centre of town. Not being one to splash out on accommodation in between bookings, Guy was always trying to save a few Lire or Francs wherever possible, and this night was no exception. Over time, we girls learnt to accept these dodgy arrangements, knowing that he would come up with the goods eventually, with another gem of a job in a luxury location but, working for Guy was really not for the faint hearted. We knew that we could always get to the airport at any time to make a quick getaway if we really wanted to, as we never parted with our passports and kept emergency money hidden in our suitcases.

I had become suspicious that evening when, on settling us into our dark, uncomfortable rooms, Guy had made us promise to keep our doors locked at all times, and not to open them on any account. The room was like a dusty dormitory from St. Trinian's, with rows of bunk beds beneath framed pictures of Mary and Jesus. Years before, I would have been very excited about this last detail, but the novelty of Mary had worn off over the years as events had taken over, and the real world had become clearer to me. The bedside lamps had very worn-out wiring, so we all agreed not to use them, just to be on the safe side.

"This room is disgraceful," complained Alison, one of the newer girls. She bustled about trying to open windows unsuccessfully and peering suspiciously under the bed sheets. "Ugh! I can't sleep on that," she exclaimed as she stalked into the little bathroom and started testing the plumbing which was a piddly dribble of cold water from a grimy shower. Susannah and I had planned ahead and opened more wine and goodies on one of the top bunks, knowing that if we put up with this one night of roughing it, we would be in much better conditions very soon.

"Don't worry Alison, Guy has never let us down. At least the toilet works! Come and have a drink Darling," I suggested, merrily plugging in my little tape recorder and searching for my Barbara Streisand cassette. "Who's for a sing song?"

There were moans from the others as they realised that Susannah and I were going for the full album, having developed a little routine over the months. When things got tough, we always found that a few bottles of red wine and some ballads cheered us up no end. We were like tarty versions of Julie Andrews in the thunderstorm, and sometimes after a few bevvies we would plan to re-invent ourselves as a singing duo and leave Guy and his Can-Can behind.

There was much activity outside the room during the night in the corridor, so we didn't sleep very well. Guy had disappeared elsewhere for the night with Regine, returning very early in the morning with frothy, hot coffees and bags of croissants for all, probably as a peace offering. Nigel, our leading man of the show, had been to catch up with some friends, returning with a huge smile on his face in the early hours. Nigel was our dance captain and loved us all dearly, and we him. All he wanted on tour, was a quiet life, but between us, there was always a drama to deal with, however, he generally coped tremendously well. In the stifling heat of the next morning, everyone was tired and moody as we boarded Guy's old, unfaithful minibus. As we laid out magazines, crisps and sweets for the very long journey across Italy to our next engagement, the Mediterranean became history as we headed for the Adriatic. Being hopeless at geography at school, but just fancying the teacher, I had never heard of this coastline, so was thrilled to be told that it was another beach. As we trundled along the motorway, the sun pierced through the windows and we dozed, chatted, or put on our Sony Walkmans. The memories of San Remo life and the recent brothel experience faded, and we looked forward to new territory. Day turned to evening and after a stop for dinner in a roadside bar, Guy broke the news that we would have to drive through the night if we were to arrive on time for our next booking along the coast at Bari in the south. This sort of announcement always reminded us that we weren't on holiday, but working for a retired, exotic cabaret artiste. Everyone moaned and climbed back into the sweaty van. Not having google maps, sat-navs or mobile phones in those days, it started to feel like we were driving to Egypt as the miles stretched out before us in the stifling bus, the atmosphere becoming a little tense.

During the night, while I was dozing, I was woken by Susannah. She wasn't sure what it was, but she knew something was wrong. Feeling odd, she peered out into the dark night until she eventually spotted that we were driving the wrong way up the motorway. Being four in the morning, we fortunately hadn't met another vehicle yet and making her way swiftly up the aisle to the front, she politely pointed out Guy's driving error to him, in as calm a voice as possible. There was a screech of brakes and expletives while Susannah and I woke the others. We all went into the crash position.

"Girls! Out quickly, *out!*" hollered Guy as we all leapt out of the van onto the dark grassy verge. I had noticed a bit of a whiff of stale wine in the van earlier and remembered that Guy had rather tucked into the vino at dinner time. There had also been several complaints and requests from everyone, when we got back on the road, asking that he might be so kind as to stop singing *Non, Je ne regrette rien*! at top volume. After a final whack from Regine with an Argentinian cloak that she'd been adjusting, he'd quietened down, but then become unsettlingly quiet as the night progressed. I think he was trying hard not to nod off at the wheel as we ploughed through the darkness. The radio had blared loudly as Regine sat next to him, sewing sequins on thongs through the night, totally unaware of the situation, until Susannah intervened.

We waited, crouching on the dark, dusty roadside while Guy studied the map and turned the van around, ducking his head occasionally as Regine continued to whip him with her sewing,

"IDIOT! Mon Dieux tu es un imbecile!"

I was glad she hadn't been holding a pair of scissors as I was quite fond of Guy, despite the fact that he was bonkers. We decided not to ask how long we had been driving this way, instead, settling back in our seats not wanting to cause further outbursts from Regine. As we set off again, I suddenly noticed that Nigel had obviously taken one of his sleeping pills and was laid peacefully on the floor of the van underneath the seats. I could just see his perfectly manicured nails at the end of an elegant arm that poked out along the dusty floor. He had clearly missed the whole event. I decided that this was probably a good thing as Nigel could become anxious when things didn't run smoothly. He was better off asleep, and we all agreed to keep the episode to ourselves, much to Guy's huge relief. Over the years of working with Nigel, I came to admire how he was an expert at popping his eye mask on at every opportunity and going to sleep wherever we happened to find ourselves. He was always fresh and ready to resume his role of dance captain after his nap.

"I do like to get my eight hours darling," he would explain as he tucked himself into his cashmere blanket and neck pillow in luggage racks and costume baskets all over the world. Nigel craved peace, quiet and good camaraderie amongst the company and if everyone was happy, he was a joy to work with. I knew he would have had a nervous breakdown if he'd been told what had just happened, so we all agreed that it was a blessing that he hadn't been disturbed. We knew Guy had a short fuse, exacerbated by wine, so we often tiptoed around situations, avoiding outbursts wherever possible.

I once witnessed a fist fight between Guy and Miguel, one of his male dancers, during the interval of a show after too many vinos at dinner. Miguel had been swigging out of a little bottle in his back pocket throughout rehearsals that afternoon, and Guy had enjoyed a few too many red wines with him at dinner, so when Guy decided Miguel had drunk too much to go on for his Pas de Deux that night, all hell broke loose. Guy had quite rightly insisted that Miguel wouldn't manage the lifts, without dropping his rather valuable, leading lady of the moment, Nancy, a breath-taking enchantress from Yorkshire. Miguel was furious and as voices were raised, the first punch flew in the wings, during the juggling act that led up to their big number. We had all seen trouble brewing, taking cover under a rail of Charleston dresses with Nigel, dodging flying props as they were hurled across the dressing room amid verbal abuse in French that, from the French girl's expressions, were quite naughty words.

Moments later we all froze as the jugglers ran off stage and the Pas de Deux music came on. Guy and Miguel stopped, mid punch, like cartoon characters from The Beano as the audience sat gazing at an empty stage. There was no chance that Miguel could go on stage by then, because his lip was bleeding profusely and he was crying, but all was not lost. One of the French girls grabbed Nancy by the hand, and leapt onto the stage with her, to perform a wonderful dance together, with rather a lesbian feel to it we noticed. Totally improvised like true professionals, I had never seen a better example of The

Show Must Go On, as Guy and Miguel stood gaping at them from the wings, dabbing their wounds.

There was rapturous applause from the auditorium.

"Bravo mes filles!!!! Vous etes magnifique!!" Guy cried, blood all over his nose, slapping Miguel on the back, clearly thrilled, the fight a distant memory.

Guy decided to keep their girlie act in the show for the rest of that season.

20

ITALIAN TOUR

AS WE SET off again after our emergency stop on the
motorway, Nigel woke up, looking around suspiciously as
Regine wound down all the windows in an attempt to keep
her husband focused at the wheel. I quietly thanked Susannah
for saving my life and reassured an inquisitive Nigel that there
was nothing untoward going on. We'd lost quite a bit of time
during this drama and it was very unsettling to think that we
still had a long journey ahead of us. We settled down though,
having no choice but to assume Guy had everything under
control, and let him drive us to Italy in the clapped-out van,
as he sobered up.

As morning dawned, he drove the minibus down a hillside
towards a stunning bay where our next home was waiting.
Woken by the change in engine noise as we put-putted round
the hair-pin bends to the sea, we all sat up, stretching, yawning
and squinting at the bright, morning sunlight that beamed

through the windows. Taking in a most beautiful view of the Adriatic coast, the treacherous journey quickly became a distant memory. Down a steep hill, nestled in the pines, overlooking the glistening turquoise sea, was our big white hotel that was to be our home for the coming days. It seemed very proud of itself, gleaming up at us with its little tree lined path, that led down to the beach. Yachts bobbed merrily on the water and you could see the guests making their way down steps to the beach from their rooms, ready for breakfast on the vast terraces that overlooked the sea.

"How long are we staying here again?" quizzed one of the girls.

"One week, ma Cherie," announced Guy proudly as he grappled with the bus on the rocky road with what was probably a hang-over from hell. Sounding very pleased with himself, no doubt hoping that we would all forgive and forget his performance on the road during the night, Guy turned to smile at us all, taking his eyes off the road for far too long, as he batted his eyelids innocently. Regine was gently weeping in the passenger seat, as fatigue got the better of her, muttering in French to herself about how much she loved us all.

"Yey!!! Bravo Guy!!!" everyone cheered as Regine broke into a sob.

We were not looking our best as the minibus rattled onto the palatial forecourt of the hotel. There was a dodgy burning smell from the bonnet and the exhaust backfired loudly as we came to a halt amongst the vast planters that were heaving with Bougainvillea. Our Italian agent was waiting with the entertainment staff to greet us and, as we were supposed to have arrived hours earlier, he could only have been thrilled to see us, despite our shocking mode of transport. Their eager expressions showed how much they were looking forward to meeting the new Balletto. Waiters and bar staff were peeping out from the restaurant to catch a glimpse of the latest totty. I loved being called Il Balletto because it made me feel as though I were part of a ballet company, which I was pretty sure by this time was never going to happen. There was very little ballet in our show, rather more leg kicking and doing the splits through the air. But the Italians seemed to use Il Balletto to describe us, and I felt rather good about that, knowing it was certainly the closest I would ever be, to becoming a ballerina. The smiling, eager expressions of the managers and staff, turned to concern and slight disappointment as Guy opened the sliding door of the bus and they were hit full in the faces by a waft of hairspray, stale wine and Jaffa cakes. Toni, a six-foot beauty, rolled out sleepily onto the amber marble tiles of the entrance, with her Walkman wires entangled around her crotch in an interesting fashion.

"Thank fuck for that," she bellowed, staggering to her feet after kissing the ground. Nodding briefly at the management, she set off up the glossy steps in search of the bar. After a brief meeting, Guy announced nonchalantly that we would be performing that night. After cries of disdain, everyone started to bustle around the luggage looking for vanity cases and essentials in preparation for a transformation job. We really had no choice and it's amazing what a bit of Max Factor can do to a young face. Our tools included long glossy wigs, tiaras and false eyelashes, so you would never have guessed that beneath this exquisite exterior were exhausted, slightly traumatised teenagers. Our costumes had thankfully arrived before us, safely in another van, probably reassuring the manager that we were on our way. In no time at all, Regine had hung them all up, ready for the show. The beautiful pink plumes always stunk of Regine's sewing room, a sort of a pub, booze and fags whiff. On stage though, they always looked stunning, as long as she hadn't adjusted anyone's costume after a few vinos. Once one of the girls had found that her bra cup had been sewn on sideways and the leg of her cowboy trousers had been taken up twice on the same leg, so we had all had to roll our trousers up for the show, so we matched. The poor girl had a very sore tit that night as we squashed and taped it down sideways, so it didn't peep out. On this particular evening at our new venue, there was simply no time for a technical rehearsal because of the travel delay the previous night. The sound and light technicians had gone home at lunch time and weren't due to arrive until just before the show. Technical rehearsals were very important, and we were always anxious if we had to just go out there and hope for the best. We had no choice in the matter on this occasion as we scurried around backstage, having run out of time. The fact remained that no show meant no pay and by the evening we knew our audience would be dressed up and looking forward to seeing us perform. Having finished their dinner, they would make their way to the cabaret stage in great anticipation of the spectacular show promoted in the main foyer of the hotel. That evening found us waiting in the wings, ready to strut our stuff, our transformation from weary travellers to breath-taking showgirls having been achieved with great skill and speed. After dancing for six weeks, every night at the casino in San Remo, we had become masters of our craft.

It was a known fact amongst the girls that the quicker you could get ready for the show, the later you needed to set off to the dressing room, giving you longer recreational time with the boys on the beach. This was essential if you were on a boat trip out at sea and you were due on stage in an hour. The worst case of this was when one of the girls was swept off a rock into the sea and we had to cover her grazes up with make-up, so she didn't put the diners off their meal as she danced in her sparkling bikini. She insisted on doing the show, trying her best not to limp, because she knew she wouldn't get paid otherwise. There was no clause in her contract, on close inspection that excluded damaged goods.

Another day, Salvino had been speeding us along the coast on his friend's fabulous speedboat, while we leaned glamorously against the maple wood cabin of the boat, sporting our white Bond Girl bikinis, our faces turned to the sun. Unfortunately, Susannah changed the mood suddenly by announcing she was going to be sick. I signalled to Salvino to stop the boat so we could have a little swim and she managed to puke up discreetly into the water, avoiding a classic Kodak moment on the deck. Salvino got a bit bored while we plopped about in the waves, and on spotting his friend a few hundred metres away on a pedalo, he coasted over for an in-depth chat about the football results. He'd been gone for just enough time for us to feel that perhaps we should start swimming along a bit until he caught us up, aware of the time slipping away before curtain up at the casino. Waving over to us at this point, he seemed to assume that we were Olympic standard swimmers enjoying ourselves, promptly zooming off, leaving us to make our own way back to shore. It took us a long time to get to the beach and then walk to the harbour to get our bags from the boat where Salvino was happily making coffee in the quay.

"Bravi Regazzi!" he called as we staggered up the slope, sea urchin spines sticking out of our feet, pretending we had enjoyed a little pre-show swim. We certainly didn't resemble Ursula Andress and the drama made us rather late for work.

So, after our night-time journey from hell in the minibus with Guy, we stood poised, relieved and glad to be alive, waiting excitedly for the cue for our opening number at our new five-star venue. Of course, we were quick to spot a dashing waiter, smartly dressed in a tuxedo, standing by the freshly set dining tables. His section for the evening was not busy yet, and he was obviously looking forward to discreetly watching the new show as he poured the wine and offered olives and bread rolls with his fancy tongs, to the guests as they arrived. Susannah went into raptures straight away about how he was her perfect man, while I thought how lovely it would be, to eat some of the olives and fresh bread dipped in olive oil and balsamic vinegar from the table.

"What about Olav in Norway?" Toni reminded Susannah in disgust. Olav, was the Norwegian who was waiting for Susannah to visit him in Oslo, having sworn un-dying love in the rock pools of San Remo.

Before Susannah had time to answer, the familiar sound of our opening number boomed out of the speakers. The spotlights glared down on us, illuminating our diamonds and lip-gloss, transforming us all instantly, into beauty queens, especially Nigel.

However, many times that you perform a show, you always feel a bolt of nerves and excitement when your music starts. There is a mixture of pride in the magic of the show, tinged with the fear that, at any moment, you may go blank and forget what to do. This last theory didn't apply to the other girls, but it certainly was the case for me anyway. Susannah had not been looking forward to the show after the tiring, stressful journey, but the sight of the mystery waiter had cheered her up no end. She beamed across at me from the wings on the other side of the stage, looking breathtakingly beautiful and there was no doubt that our latest heartthrob was about to be bowled over. From past experience, being glamorous showgirls meant that there was little effort required to woo a man. It was more a case of, 'Ooh, let me see, I think I'll have *that* one,' so I could see that a new romance was imminent.

"She'll have to be quick," I thought, as I leapt across the stage, "we're only here for a week."

However, as we glided around the stage that night, it all unfortunately, went horribly wrong, as is occasionally the case on tours. Having had no technical rehearsal that day, the sound and light crew had forgotten to mention the rather important detail that there was to be a firework display during our opening number. Added to that, there would be a large water fountain that would start up amongst the foliage at the back and at various points on the stage. I often wondered afterwards if the stagehands always made a point of, conveniently, not mentioning this warning to the new dancers, as a form of amusement. Of course, when the first firework went off, we all screamed with surprise, managing to turn our screams into theatrical whoops when we realised what was going on, almost sounding convincing. Susannah, however, was not so brave, and I knew that she was absolutely petrified of any loud noises. We had experienced trouble in the past when, one evening in San Remo, there had been a thunderstorm. She had spent the whole show backstage, underneath the faithful rail of Argentinian cloaks while Guy and Regine had begged her to come out for the finale. On this occasion, it was no different and she could not contain herself. Careering across the stage, dramatically dodging the unexpected water fountains, she ran for cover. We girls had a very 'show must go on' approach to our work and carried on with the routine while Susannah dived into the wings. The lovely waiter looked puzzled, and then concerned, unsure if this was part of the act, or a real emergency. The rest of us danced on with our cheerful performance as though nothing was wrong, and the music blocked out the noise of the abuse being hurled across the stage from Nigel.

"What the bloody hell is she thinking of?" he hissed through gritted, porcelain, pearly pegs. His teeth were smiling at his audience, but we could tell from the way that his eyebrows were darting about his tanned forehead, that he was furious. At the black-out, we left the stage and followed the trail of fountain water to the dressing room. There, we were greeted by the sight of Regine, head-to-head with Susannah. She was trying to remove her precious, pink feathered head dress because it had to be dried out with a hairdryer before the finale.

"*Mon Dieu! Mes plumes!*" she twittered, fag hanging out of her mouth, gold bangles flashing, as she shook out the pink rats' tails.

"Get me a 'airdryer! My poor fevvers!" she whimpered.

"They could probably all do with a wash," tittered one of the girls.

Later that night, I felt it was a good moment to tell Nigel about the motorway drama, and if it hadn't been for Susannah, we wouldn't even have arrived at the hotel.

~

The tour continued and the time flew, bringing the usual air of camaraderie amongst us all by the time the filthy tour bus rattled into the courtyard of Guy's farmhouse in Paris several months later. The smelly dogs ran out to greet us, bringing us all back down to earth.

"OK girls, meet in the studio in ten minutes I 'av a leetle surprise to tell you all." Guy lit a cigarette and staggered up the stairs into his office, clutching his back.

We collapsed into the shabby old studio to wait for him, thinking how nice it was, to be in the friendly surroundings again. Some of the girls had new dance contracts signed, back in England, and were keen to get home. We sat around chatting and planning which ferry to catch until, after a few minutes, Guy appeared in the doorway with a folder of contracts under his arm.

"Who wants to come around ze world on a sheeeeeep?"

"I hope he means ship and not sheep," piped up Susannah and we were so exhausted from the journey that we fell about into hysterical giggles.

It turned out that we were being offered four months at sea, on a luxury cruise liner.

"I don't think we're going home for Christmas," I thought as I put my hand up for a contract.

21

WORLD CRUISE

Hello Darling,

I showed Elsie and Dot the photo you sent us from Italy in all your sparklies, and we all think you would make a marvellous Bluebell Girl, but yes, don't turn down a trip around the world poppet. Cruise ships! Whatever next?

There was one hijacked last week in the news but I'm sure yours will be fine ...

Gran x

A bundle of post from home had been delivered to the rehearsal studios at Guy's when we arrived back from Italy. We fell upon it like scavengers. Unsurprisingly, there were no declarations of undying love from the Italian Stallions in San Remo. Guy seemed to have a knack of keeping our spirits up though as, time and time again, he tempted us with his offers of exciting shows around the world, discouraging us from auditioning elsewhere and putting any of our ambitious career plans on hold. The exotic locations were usually in places that I hadn't even heard of, and besides, during the eighties, travelling further than Spain and France was only for the elite.

We felt like the luckiest girls in the world.

On the way back from the tour in Italy, as the bus trundled its way through the night, back to Paris, I decided that it was time to return to England to resume my original plans. I'd always imagined living near Pineapple Dance Studios in London, attending ballet classes every day until I was in tip-top condition before walking into a job in a theatre show. As usual, all my good intentions had had to wait, yet again when, arriving back at the rehearsal studios, Guy had offered us the unbelievable opportunity of a lifetime. A world cruise was unheard of in those days. Only millionaires went on world cruises, so we were all ecstatic. I knew that I couldn't turn it down, even if Andrew Lloyd Webber offered me the part of Christine in Phantom of the Opera. A world cruise was the stuff that dreams were made of and I grabbed it with both hands, literally signing there and then. After a brief flit home to our families, we found ourselves back in rehearsals with Guy and the gang at the old farm where, after the initial excitement of the up-and-coming adventure, the challenges that lay ahead of us became alarmingly clear. We were expected to learn twenty-four dance numbers, fitted with twenty-four costumes, in preparation for a four-month voyage, providing an array of entertainment for eight hundred guests. The cruise company were a new client for Briac, and Guy was proud to have won the most prestigious contract he could ever have hoped for. The pressure was on us all to shine.

We were to be flown from Paris to Djibouti, on the Gulf of Aden, where our beautiful ship would be waiting in the harbour to take us across the Arabian Sea to Colombo in Sri Lanka. This first part of the journey was to take six days and the wealthy passengers would expect to be entertained at every moment of the day, having paid eye-watering amounts of money to be on their trip of a lifetime. They would enjoy banquets, gala nights, midnight buffets, formal dinners, tea parties and cocktails with the captain. Celebrities and world class cabaret artists would be flown over to the different ports of call, to visit the ship and perform their acts. And then there was us lot, the resident cabaret dancers who would fill in the gaps, assigned with the daunting but exciting task of keeping these passengers entertained as we floated about at sea on this grand boat.

Our first week on board was going to be the longest journey, with no stop-offs until we arrived in Sri Lanka. After Sri Lanka, we were to sail for almost four months, around Malaysia, various ports of Indonesia, Sumatra, Bali, all the large ports of Australia, New Guinea, New Caledonia, Fiji, Tonga, Samoa, Bora Bora, Tahiti, Pape'ete, Hawaii, Honolulu, San Francisco, San José, L.A., San Diego, Acapulco, down the Panama Canal, Cartagena, Jamaica and finally Miami, where we would then be flown back to Paris. Looking like the stops on the London Underground, this extraordinary list made it impossible for me to comprehend the enormity of such a trip, especially at the tender age of twenty.

We were to be billed as the Olivier Briac Dancers, the mysterious man that I'd never met, the founder of our company, managed by Guy Stranger since Briac had retired to Tahiti. With the exciting voyage fast approaching, the responsibility felt huge, so we buckled down to tackling the endless list of dance numbers. The pressure was on and there was constant tension in the air as Guy kept a close eye on our rehearsals from his mezzanine office that overlooked the studio. Barking unhelpful comments at us when things got tough, he would stamp down the steps to demonstrate exactly how he wanted us to move. He knew all the choreography inside out and it was hilarious when he walked us through parts of the routines in his scruffy old jeans and jumper, wild grey hair flying about with several pairs of glasses stuck in it.

"*Non! Non! Non! Ca n'est pas comme ca*! Watch me girls!" He would parade across the studio counting as he went, demonstrating kicks and turns until he saw us trying not to smile.

"Fetch me Regine!" he would roar.

His wife, Regine, would be sent for, anxious that we performed at our best for this prestigious company, bringing him notoriety in the entertainment world, and of course further bookings. The reality of the challenge ahead became clear when the list of dance numbers was pinned to the wall in the rehearsal studio one morning. The list was, basically, all of the choreography that had ever been performed by Guy's dancers. The Hippies, The Pirates, The Gypsies, The Air Hostesses, Spanish Dance, Gala Finale, Top Hats, Mermaids, Viennese Waltz, Argentinian, and the Can-Can, to name but a few.

"I'll never learn all that!!" I wailed as Nigel stood back to admire his new noticeboard, put up especially for the cruise preparations one morning.

"You will darling, we know half of these already!" he patted me reassuringly on the back as he lit his tenth fag of the morning. He was clearly a little anxious himself, especially as he knew my tendency to glaze over on stage and forget which dance I was doing. This job was clearly a big deal and a great opportunity for Guy, so we all knew we couldn't let him down. Nigel had been given the nerve-wracking responsibility of training us up, ready for the biggest gig in Guy's career. Joining us on board as dance captain, Nigel would be leading all the performances in shiny suits and top hats. With his dapper moustache and spritely figure, he was quite a showman, especially in the Can-Can where he proudly led the kick lines with practised ease.

Regine had gone into melt down in the sewing room, surrounded by the rails of pretty much all the costumes that the company owned. We were to take all of them on the ship with us, so she had employed an assistant from the village to help her with the preparations. There had been no response to her advert for a sewing assistant after she'd stuck a sign in the window of the village boulangerie. However, a lady called Margaux appeared one morning and although she hadn't a clue how to even sew on a button, she was proving very useful. This gargantuan woman could shift an entire rail of costumes with one hand and Regine was also grateful for someone to bring her a glass of burgundy or go out to get cigarettes when required, which was most of the time. This new recruit was a quiet lady and to Regine's delight we were all a little bit afraid of her. We started to behave better when called into the sewing room for fittings, because Margaux had a rather creepy presence that kept us quiet as she hovered, passing pins and scissors to Regine, with an amused smirk. There was none of the previous hysterics and larking around that must have made Regine's job a nightmare, because Margaux would be glaring at us from the corner, like Lurch from The Adams Family. We dreaded going into the claustrophobic fug of the smoky costume department to be prodded, measured and poked. This was usually the place that weight gain was noticed which was a constant battle for me, but these visits were essential if you wanted your costume to stay on during the show. We would patiently stand for ages, while bikinis, jackets, ball gowns and cowboy trousers, to name but a few of the ensembles, were adjusted to fit us perfectly and then labelled ready to go. If you moved, you knew you would be stabbed by a pin as Regine hurried through her work, especially if she had been on the vino.

"Pfuf, 'old this Margaux!" she would instruct, grappling with huge headdresses that towered over her tiny frame. We would stand stock still while she sewed a chin strap in place, with Margaux rather too close for comfort, grinning next to us like Regine's very own bouncer. As she breathed her garlicky, lunch aroma into our faces we would inspect her extraordinary facial hair while Regine managed to sew and smoke at the same time, our eyes streaming as we stood patiently waiting. Girls had been known to faint in the sewing room.

One afternoon, I had the responsibility of reminding Susannah why we were making all this effort, when, she suddenly decided that she missed her Norwegian beau from San Remo. We'd had a particularly trying day when, with all the stress of rehearsals, she lost her focus and reason for being there. Throwing down her wooden, pirate sword, she'd stomped out of the studio. I'd followed her like a lamb to find her on her bed, buried in a quilt with two of the dogs.

"I'm fed up with all this rehearsing shit," she sobbed into her pillow. "I just want to be with Olav in his cabin by the lake."

She looked up for a second, pausing, with a blotchy tear-soaked face, "I think … I even want to have his babies."

More crying into the pillow. I had sat myself on her bed and opened a packet of Jaffa cakes from my emergency supplies from England. I kept them zipped in my case for times like these, to calm the nerves. The dogs, keeping one eye on the rustling packet, tilted their heads with concern. For a few minutes, she continued to cry tears of exhaustion, which I was sure was all it was. She didn't love Olav, she was just knackered from learning dozens of dances with names like Panthers and Disco Girls. My worries were far more serious. I seemed to have put on a bit of weight during the three weeks of rehearsals. We'd been enjoying a few too many cheese and wine nights, and I wasn't sure how I would look in my sequinned bikini at the imminent dress rehearsal.

I crammed another Jaffa cake into my mouth for comfort and looked out of the window, chewing slowly as I contemplated the situation and waited for Susannah to recover from her little outburst.

"God, I could do with a cup of Tetley," I murmured.

One of the dogs lazily swung his head around to look at me, and I swear he rolled his eyes in agreement and it made me chuckle. The dogs turned to look at Susannah as she sat up, sniffing loudly. She didn't want me to eat all the Jaffa cakes. I agreed that Norway did sound rather tempting and horny, even wondering if Olav had a nice neighbour for me, but I couldn't let Susannah give up on the cruise. I knew she would regret it for the rest of her life. We were so close to setting off and I knew it was going to be amazing. I had visions of scenes from the Titanic, well, obviously not *all* the scenes, just the nice dining ones, and conversations with the Captain on the deck earlier on in the trip. Ball gowns and cream cakes also sprang to mind. Maybe, I thought, to cheer Susannah up, we could make up a Norwegian themed dance for the show, with lots of beating of herbal twigs, nakedness and water features. We were so close to departing for the cruise and I really didn't want her to miss out, so I decided to take drastic action. Susannah would never forgive herself in years to come, if she sacrificed a free trip around the world, just because she fancied a Norwegian. And for me, I knew it wouldn't be the same without her. Anyway, the novelty of a Norwegian log cabin would probably wear off really quickly and, I mean, all those herrings you have to eat, whilst plunging into icy water after your sauna. I reminded Susannah of these important points and she smiled a bit. I chose not to mention that, even I, in a moment of weakness and insecurity, had popped out to the phone box, attempting to call Salvino, my wayward lover from San Remo. A woman had answered which had rather thrown me, and from the torrent of expletives - at least I think they were expletives from the tone of her voice, although you can never tell with Italians - she hadn't sounded too pleased to hear from me and cut me off. It was obviously, either his mother, wife or girlfriend and it dawned on me that he was probably going out with a new girl by now. Fair enough. I handed the Jaffa cakes to Susannah and she shoved two in whole. One of the dogs had noticed a change of heart from the smile on her face and he dived on top of her.

"Poooh! Get off!" she shrieked, heaving herself up. We made our way back into the studio to finish learning The Pirate Dance with our wooden swords. The rest of the girls had taken full advantage of Susannah's wobble, and were smoking on the terrace. I gave them the thumbs up. Nigel stubbed out his ciggie and adjusted his tights.

"Guy wants to watch us dance the Finale, in full costume. Let's run it through darlings."

My heart sank as I attempted to hide my dread. My biggest battle as a dancer was keeping a sylph like figure because I just loved food so much. It would be such a shame to get thrown out of the show for over-eating and such a wasted opportunity, all because of my greed. With this in mind I put all my effort into my performance that afternoon. Unfortunately, just as I anticipated, before dinner, I was called into the office to be told to go on a strict diet for the remaining week of rehearsals.

"What 'appen ma Cherie? 'ow you get so biggerrr?" asked Guy anxiously, through a forced expression of kind concern. I knew he wanted to throttle me. I tried not to smile as Guy explained that I wasn't allowed near the buffets on board the ship for the entire cruise. Then he announced an unexpected, warning of the first degree.

"Also, you 'ave a visite from Olivier Briac when you go to Pape'ete, in Tahiti," he paused, enjoying my surprise,

"and 'e will not be 'appy if you are fat dancerrr!"

I could tell it was going to be a grand occasion when Monsieur Briac, our mystery boss, joined us on the ship for cocktails with the captain and no doubt to watch the show.

"Of course, Guy. Trust me I won't let you down," I promised as I bowed and scraped, walking backwards out of his office, my heart pumping. When I got back to the terrace where the girls were chatting and smoking their heads off, everyone cheered with relief that I was to be given a chance to redeem myself. They were probably mainly pleased that they wouldn't have to rehearse a replacement dancer. Like me though, when I broke the news of Briac's proposed visit on board the ship, they were flabbergasted.

"Right my darling we have work to do," Nigel muttered. He grabbed my arm before I attempted to sit down with the others. Nigel knew that I was quite a gymnast, as we had performed the Can-Can together on many occasions. I was proud of my cartwheels and walk-overs that I'd perfected as a child and these tricks were now bringing me fame and fortune in the cabaret world.

"Guy wants to see the Can-Can tomorrow and I need you to wow him. We don't want to lose you sweetie so you can take the solo. Get in that studio this evening and work out an amazing couple of minutes to impress the old man with everything you've got," he explained.

I hugged Nigel as he whispered in my ear, "I promised Guy we would have you back on track by the time we get on the ship. I want you to sing for him too. Here are some backing tracks and you can really show him what you're made of darling."

He gave me a kiss on the cheek and started to walk away but stopped when he realised we were alone, the other girls having wandered off.

He whispered loudly across the studio, "And stop *eating* so much, I mean, whatever have you been *eating*? You should smoke like me, it's much better for you."

I gazed adoringly at him as he marched off to the garden, before I went to find somewhere to rehearse. That evening I worked so hard into the small hours and all the Jaffa cake evidence started to disappear. Susannah kept bringing me bottles of water and I worked out an impressive mix of cartwheels, hand stands and walk-overs, landing into the splits. My body was wracked with pain the next morning but when we got to the afternoon run through, everyone was very complimentary about my Can-Can solo and singing rendition of Goldfinger that seemed to gain approval from a grinning Guy, as I belted it out at him with gusto. Before long, the days had passed and we were packed up, and heading to the airport.

All was forgiven, and the struggling tour bus was clearly more of a worry to Guy than my wobbly bits. The bus really was on its last legs, and we worried it wouldn't even get us to the airport, having gained a trailer full of costumes. It puffed and wheezed its way around La Peripherique while Guy lectured us on how to behave on board the ship.

"I want you to be the teepical Eeengleeesh ladies and no drinking or getting fat," he paused here, to look at me in the rear-view mirror.

"You are there to work and I 'av my spies." He winked and swigged his bottle of beer as he overtook a lorry. The van collapsed in the airport car park, with a puff of black smoke, and we were grateful that this painful departure was soon to be over. Guy was so highly strung by this time, that it was bringing out the wild side of his nature. We pretended not to be with him at the departures desk, as he bellowed at the check-in lady, handing her our pile of passports, as he clutched his chest. Nigel advised us to keep a low profile while he assisted Guy with organising the trunks and checking us all in. It had been a tough few weeks obtaining our long list of visas, with several trips into Paris, before loading us all up with our vast collection of costumes. It was a good thing that we were soon to be out of his way. I could imagine him falling in a heap once we were through security and out of sight.

Landing in Djibouti in the early hours of the morning, there followed quite a culture shock. We were driven from the airport to the harbour by coach, through dusty villages, where families were going about their daily chores. Women carried water pots on their heads with babies on their backs, their children running in the dust, kicking punctured old footballs, waving up at us as we passed. Huge smiles spread across their faces as they chased the coach, until they couldn't keep up anymore. I'd never seen such happy children as I gazed out of the window at them, but it was also a stark reminder of the privileged life we were leading. Eventually, we spotted the ship waiting for us in all its glory and we left the locals behind. Everyone exclaimed with joy as, walking up the steps of our beautiful ship, the warmth of the morning sunshine rejuvenated our aching limbs.

We set sail pretty much immediately and it was wonderful to be on board at last. Susannah and I were given a delightful cabin to share and set to work arranging our photos, tapes and make-up with great joy. Strolling around the ship, nodding and smiling at the passengers on deck, created great interest when guests realised that we were the cabaret artists from Paris. Cruise ships these days are enormous, with the capacity to house four thousand or more guests, not to mention the staff. Our ship, Le Mermoz, was part of a French cruise company called Paquet. Much smaller than cruise ships of today, with approximately eight hundred guests and three hundred crew, she had immense character and charm with a delightful colonial feel about her. I've learnt recently that in later years, Mermoz was bought by Costa, the Italian cruise company, and then after a short spell sailing around the islands of Cyprus and Greece, with Louis Cruises, she was put to rest and sadly, scrapped in 2008. As with a car, you can become very attached to a ship, so this news made me sad. Had she still been sailing, I would have booked myself a cruise on Mermoz, for old-time's sake, during my retirement.

During the first evening, we were summoned to a meeting with the entertainments team and the plans for our cruise life became clearer. Any ideas of grandeur that we had developed from passenger compliments, faded quickly when a busy schedule of duties was described. These included teaching aerobics, calling the bingo numbers, making fancy dress costumes, organising board games in the piano bar, welcoming guests on board, and of course, performing our cabaret shows several times a week.

One afternoon, a nervous Nigel called us all over to the lounge bar when the guests had gone to tea. He was smoking furiously, a vision in velour, glaring at a list that he had obviously been up all night composing, as he prepared to inform us of the details of the proposed schedule. After groans of horror from everyone we waited to hear our fate.

"Right, Jane, you can teach aerobics every morning darling, so I don't have to worry about ... well ... you know ..."

I knew he was referring to my passion for eating. I could only thank him really, as I was still grateful for being forgiven for my greedy spell in Paris, which had almost resulted in losing my job before it had even begun. Little did he know that I had been taking full advantage of all the various eating opportunities on board already. There were French pastries being served every day in the tea rooms and it was heaven. The girls had been keeping it a secret from me for a few days, but I sniffed it out one afternoon on my way to rehearsals in the theatre.

"Oh, my God everyone, there are free cakes every flipping afternoon in really posh tea rooms. You sit there just like in Titanic!" I'd announced with great joy throwing myself down on the floor to warm up.

"We know!" came a chorus from the whole group.

I coped well with the realisation that I was being watched and decided to make a sterling effort to avoid the temptation of High Tea with The Captain each day, by going on a power walk on the deck instead. Sampling chocolate eclairs, and the vast array of exquisite French gateaux I'd seen in the elegant dining area that afternoon, was hard to resist, but essential, if I was to hold onto my privileged position of Beautiful Showgirl of Paris.

Nigel went back to his list.

"Sue, can you do puzzles in the piano bar after lunch please?" One of his eyebrows arched high on his forehead as he waited for her response.

"Yippee," she murmured, staring into space.

"I'll take that as a yes then ..." he scribbled furiously.

Susannah, an excellent seamstress in her spare time, was put on fancy-dress costumes, which we all knew she would be good at, but actually proved problematic over the four months. The guests turned out to be quite spoilt. Used to having what they wanted, if they didn't win first prize during the parade, there were often terrible tantrums to deal with. Some of the elderly passengers were reverting back to childlike behaviour with the constant treats and excitement, and we were learning to keep a sense of humour and be patient. We'd all been given our jobs but there was one left that Nigel had clearly been dreading.

"There is one more thing actually," he took a huge drag of his cigarette and slowly blew the smoke out towards the ceiling as we waited, transfixed.

"Albert, one of the compères, requires one of us to don a sparkly frock each afternoon, and call the Bingo numbers out to the audience," he paused, surveying our row of gloomy faces, "and I don't have a sparkly frock."

I let out a little snort of laughter, finding this hugely funny and when no-one put their hand up, I couldn't resist.

"I'll do it!" I was feeling sorry for Nigel now, who was already on jig-saw duty himself every morning. I knew jig- saws would kill me. I've never seen the point of them. Fortunately, one of our dancers, the lovely Nadia, was French, and since Nigel had heard me practicing my French conversation one afternoon at a tea-party, he swiftly delegated all activities involving French conversation, to her.

"Are you happy to play scrabble Nadia?" he asked. Nadia nodded gently, calm and serene as always.

I was thrilled to be up on stage so quickly, for my debut as The Bingo Babe. I was working with a charming man named Albert. Albert, pronounced Al-bear in French, was the Bingo Master. He took it all very seriously in his shiny blue and red suit, white shirt and slicked back hair. He invited me to take a ping pong ball out of his whirly-gig, before holding it up to show the number to everyone in the audience. With my newly manicured red nails and my sparkling red dress I knew my Granny would have been thrilled.

"Bienvenue à Mademoiselle Jane," he announced with pride, beaming, as I held my ping pong ball up high with great skill. The audience applauded and I gave a little Anthea Twirl, really getting into the role, and certainly enjoying the attention. It was just like my magical work with Des, so I felt hugely experienced, until he proceeded to bring the microphone to my face and wait for me to announce the number.

"Oh! of course. Silly me ..." I muttered as I tried to keep up with Albert and his bingo routine.

"Twenty-three, Ladies and Gentlemen, our first number is twenty-three!" my voice rang gaily across the theatre. I had assumed that Bingo wouldn't be hugely challenging, but it's surprising how these things can become more complicated than you expect.

"Et en Francais s'il vous plaît ma Cherie?" Albert looked up at me quizzically.

It suddenly dawned on me that, with mainly French passengers on this cruise, to add to the fun I was expected to call the bingo numbers out in French. I spotted Nigel's face crumple as he loitered nervously at the bar. I was relieved that I had paid attention at school and knew my numbers.

French numbers are a nightmare. For example, the word for eighty is quatre-vingt, which means four twenties. I mean, who thought that was a good idea? I'd been planning to say witty bingo-isms like Legs Eleven, but didn't trust myself to cope with the translations, so I decided to keep it simple. I could have been the cause of a punch up amongst the passengers on the first day if I wasn't careful and announced the wrong number. Some of the prizes were extremely valuable and people were out to win them. I could see that beneath his showman smile, Albert was dealing with a serious business here, nervous that I would cock up his act. He started to whisper the number far too loudly in French to me each time I took a ball out of his whirly-gig. It was infuriating, but I managed to beam at him lovingly. Nerve wracking though it was, I soon got the hang of my role of Bingo caller, adding yet another string to my bow, that I would, no doubt, embellish hugely on my C.V. in the future.

Ipswich: Wishing I could play Mary (front right)

Ipswich: Waiting for the parents to come out of the pub

Ipswich: First attempt at ballet with friend Michaela (left) and Granny and I chatting about Bluebell Girls with my cousin and aunt

(Left) With my ballet teacher, Linda Shipton. (Right) With Mixed Company. Hannah (front) Lynn with toe on front tyre, and me (back row, second from the left)

College: Young and naïve

College: Stephanie was a Can-Can dancer from the beginning

Madrid: Top Hats backstage (centre)

Madrid: Spanish dance and Tania's Finale

Ipswich: My one and only role in a professional musical
(left) - Cabaret at The Wolsey Theatre

Egypt: The closest to Pan's People I would ever be.
Disco Diva at the Gezirah Sheraton

Egypt: Out on the desert with the cool kids of Cairo

Egypt: Pyramids at Giza

Egypt: On a fishing boat on the River Nile on my 19th birthday and last night in Cairo

Italy: Tour with Guy Stranger. Steph,
Mandy, Sue, me and Susannah

Mermoz: Performing the Charleston. Me, Sue, Steph,
Susannah and Nadia

Sardinia: Singing 'My Heart Belongs to Daddy'

Tokyo: Looking like Karen Carpenter in Tokyo

Lido: Too Marvellous for words

Lido: Relaxing backstage

Lido: Backstage with Diana(left) Gale(centre) and Paul (right) and Me, Paul, Diana in the wings

Lido: Waiting for the Ancient Egyptian number

223

22

SAILING THE SEAS

I HAVE LOVELY memories of sitting on the ship's deck at one of the many elegant bars of the Mermoz, sipping cocktails under the stars as we sailed majestically through the night, on seas with names like Laccadive and Java. Occasionally we would hear shouts from the crew to come up to the bow of the ship, to watch the flying fish and dolphins as they skimmed above the water, ahead of the ship. Some of the ports were in busy, exciting cities, and others were tranquil, idyllic islands bringing us breath-taking scenery and extraordinary new culture. Susannah and I quickly learnt the meaning of cabin fever though. Being on a ship for long periods can be slightly claustrophobic at times. It caused us to be easily excitable and rather raucous. Managing such young dancers, poor Nigel was constantly trying to keep tabs on our highly spirited outings at ports, as we careered ahead, planning all sorts of exciting events whenever an opportunity came our way. Occasionally, he organised long rehearsals on the ship just to keep us on board and safe. I was furious at the time, watching from the deck as the guests were whisked away to explore the sights of the city. Of course, Nigel was quite right to worry that we might unintentionally walk into a dangerous part of town and get into trouble, but I'm sure the local bandits would have swiftly given us back if we'd been captured, we were such irritating, squawky youngsters.

Assigned as the aerobics instructor in the mornings, I found that my pupils were never completely committed to the challenge. I couldn't complain because I was of a similar mind set. Appearing late for their class, often in high heels with a gin and tonic in hand, they would stop halfway through an exercise, to announce that they were going to sit on the deck for some fresh air. Thinking of what Betty Laine would say to them, I would beg them to keep going until the end of class, but they were on holiday and if they lost interest, there was nothing stopping them from drifting out onto the sunny deck for a rest. I just had to smile and carry on.

One afternoon Susannah and I spotted a visiting jazz singer from America as he relaxed by the pool. His name was Tommy Garrett and Susannah, and I wasted no time in joining him for a spot of flirting. He was delighted to meet us, so we plied him with cocktails, persuading him to include us in the opening number of his cabaret show, due to be performed in a few days. Tommy was thrilled, so we became rather full of ourselves, proud of our big break in his show. We even, naively, began to set our sights on a possible appearance on Broadway with him, when the cruise was over. It didn't occur to us to suggest to Tommy that he might like to include the other dancers from the show in his act. Nigel and the others were understandably a tad fed up with us for this and, having no gowns to wear for our performance, we didn't feel we could ask to borrow something from the costume cabin. However, Susannah wasted no time creating sexy sarongs from some black and gold fabric, purchased from a market in one of the ports we stopped at. On the night of the show, we proudly escorted Tommy across the stage, holding onto his muscular arms as he strolled around, singing the song, *Fever*, to his fans, followed by a selection of 'babbadoo wow' style jazz songs. We were on cloud nine.

The next night we were distracted from our little brush with fame, by the weather. It became remarkably choppy and, worryingly, this weather coincided with a very special French evening of wine tasting, fine French cuisine and of course, the famous Can-Can at midnight. This was to be one of our most flamboyant performances, so the guests focused on the evening ahead, perusing the programme of events to keep their minds off the increasing rocking of the ship as they attempted to sample the culinary delights in the dining rooms.

I knew things were going to be tricky when we started to hear the occasional crash from the direction of the bar, causing us all to gasp in horror at the frightening sound of breaking glass. The staff were completely used to this and remained reasonably calm as trays of glasses continuously slid the full length of the bar. Although they didn't fly off the end, having safety catches in place, they still shattered to smithereens. The situation was even more dangerous in the kitchens where pots of boiling water, sauces and soup, slopped over the sides of the ovens, soaking and sometimes, scolding the chefs as they worked. They all had burns on their forearms and had to wear wellington boots because the water level on the floor was so high. I was feeling very sorry for these committed chaps, assuming that we wouldn't have so much trouble with *our* work, until we eventually took to the stage that evening. The captain had insisted that we perform the show, to occupy the guests and hopefully keep sea sickness at bay. The sea was rocking us about as we lined up, and I've never known such a genuine case of The Show Must Go On. Putting our make-up on was hard enough and we gave up with eyelashes, but then as we ran around the edge of the stage, hollering our crazy, French whoops, we realised the challenge ahead was going to be unforgettable, as we were thrown about like ragdolls.

The audience bravely refused to give up, hanging onto their seats, as the ship battled its way over and through the whopping great waves. My biggest challenge was my walk-over trick because I had to perform it either uphill as the ship leant over, requiring the strength of an Olympic standard gymnast, having to pull myself up at an awkward angle, or downhill with such force and speed, that I nearly ended up on the laps of the front row audience. Cartwheels were the same and it was with much hilarity that we persevered until our triumphant splits at the end. This proved to be equally grim as we jumped high in the air ready to land on the floor into the splits, not knowing whether the floor would have moved up to meet us, or down, resulting in a long drop and crash landing. The applause was rapturous, even emotional, but I hoped desperately that no-one had filmed it.

We were sent to our cabins after the show and feeling rather anxious, Susannah and I put on our tape recorder, opened a bottle of wine and proceeded to sing our way until the early hours, when eventually things calmed down and we fell asleep. We woke up the next day to a bright, calm and peaceful morning. If it hadn't been for the faint aroma of vomit in the air, as I made my way to aerobics the next morning, you would never have known we had just endured a force eleven storm, until we spotted the musical director. Engrossed in animated conversation with the magician, he was huddled in the bar, nursing a large coffee. With his toupée slipped slightly to the side, he was explaining that he'd spent the night in the orchestra pit, protecting all his instruments as they had crashed about during the storm. The grand piano, being on wheels, had kept him very busy. The magician was most upset, describing how all his tricks had failed during the show.

"AAGGH!! It was impossible," he ranted, "I am finished! Last night was a disaster. I could not keep my balls on ze table!"

We were quite excited that we were going to be on the ship for Christmas and Nigel had started mentioning it on a regular basis. I could tell he was one of those people who love Christmas, and as the day drew nearer, he sweetly organised a Christmas morning event in his cabin. We were to take gifts for each other, drink tea and sing the National Anthem. He even arranged, at great expense, to go up to the top of the ship a few days before Christmas, to pay an exorbitant amount of money to phone our families in England when we were in a port. I will never forget Susannah getting through to her Dad in Surrey, at hideous expense, only to hear him explain all about his trip to the builders' merchants earlier that day.

"Bought a ton of sand for the new terrace, it's goin' down Monday ... or is it Tuesday?"

Then his doorbell rang.

"Doh! 'ang on love ... all 'appens at once Susannah dunnit, wait a minute babes," he cried.

There was a groan from everyone as we all had to listen to him let his neighbour in, at millions of dollars per minute. Things didn't really improve when it was my turn. My mother took ages telling me that my Dad and brother were down the garden, drinking cider in the shed. Apparently, they didn't want to join in with Christmas because they didn't believe in God. Mum was drinking sherry by the television with Granny.

"It's The Sound of Music followed by The Wizard of Oz, this afternoon. It won't be the same without you though darling. We'll save you all the strawberry Quality Streets," Mum announced with a heavy heart.

The whole conversation just left me feeling a bit glum really until our new friends, Gary and Peter, two charming entertainers from the piano bar appeared. These chaps had worked with Ginger Rogers during the 1970's, on television specials. They had become firm friends with her so, as we were scheduled to stop in L.A. they had made plans to visit her. To confirm the arrangements, they needed to give her a call, so we stayed excitedly behind to listen in. When she answered her phone, she went into raptures about hosting a British lunch by the pool for them and we even hoped that we might be invited along too. Unfortunately, we didn't get that lucky. However, during the call, Peter kindly passed the phone to Susannah and I.

"Hi Girls! Hope you're enjoying your cruise. You're so lucky to be travelling with Gary and Peter," Ginger's merry voice came through loud and clear and we were almost speechless for a change.

"Thank you Ginger it's wonderful to speak to you!" was all I could think of, although I seem to remember saying something daft about her beautiful dresses. I was sure she was used to it. Ginger passed away a few years later, so I hold that moment very close to my heart when I watch the old films now.

∿

There was one rather close shave, on the same day Gary and Peter went to visit Ginger. I wanted to do something exciting during our time in Los Angeles, and seeing as we had, unforgivably, not been invited to have lunch with Ginger Rogers, I called an old friend, Noel. Noel had been part of the social circle in Madrid, while he enjoyed a hiking trip around Europe. It was there, whilst performing in my first ever show, with the infamous Samantha and Fernando, that Noel had become part of our crowd from the theatre. I had often wondered if we would cross paths again. Clutching my scruffy little address book, I had managed to get through to his mother to ask for his number. He'd insisted on coming down to take us out to lunch, and it turned out that he had completed his medical degree since his travelling days and was enjoying quite a successful career. Within an hour of calling him, Susannah and I found ourselves lunching in exquisite surroundings.

"See, I know all the right people Susannah!" I joked as we raised our glasses on a sunny terrace at a place called Pastel in Beverly Hills. Noel treated us to a delicious meal amongst the stunning greenery of this sophisticated restaurant. I had assumed Noel would still be the backpacker I'd known before, so we were rather self-conscious, perched in the immaculate surroundings wearing track suits, sipping our champagne, but Noel didn't care at all and, as the sun started to go down, I decided that I would really love to stay in L.A. with him forever, and he seemed quite keen. As usual, Susannah saved the day when she mentioned something about the show that night, bringing me back to reality.

"What time does the ship leave again honey?" she asked casually, stretching her arm out to the waiter for a champagne refill.

"Isn't that Siegfried and Roy, the tiger tamers?" I whispered.

It was when I looked around for their tiger, that I was jolted back to reality, realising what she had said.

"I thought you knew when we had to leave darling. I have no idea."

We froze, before sitting bolt upright, staring at each other in alarm. Noel found this hugely entertaining, but my heart was in my mouth.

"Great! You've missed your boat! You can come live with me!" he laughed.

The journey back to the port was of the white-knuckle variety. Noel drove like a nutter. As we swung around the bay, we prayed with all our might that the ship would still be there. If it had not long departed then, in my optimistic way, I reassured myself that we would get out to it somehow. My mind raced, with visions of us in a little fishing boat, begging the captain to throw us a rope down, with Nigel wringing his hands at us from the deck. The next port was hours away, in a different county. You couldn't just hop on a train to get there, America is huge. In those days, we had no credit cards to pay for incidents such as this, so the consequences didn't bear thinking about and made me realise how ill prepared we were for any emergency. I could just imagine Nigel pacing the deck, dragging hard on his cigarettes as he looked out to sea, and it made me feel sick with shame.

We were very lucky girls because, as we careered at break-neck speed down to the port, we saw our beautiful ship majestically waiting for us in the evening sunshine. I could just see the last of the passengers returning in coaches and making their way up the steps to board. The relief was overwhelming. After shrieks of joy followed by a very emotional farewell to Noel, we managed to stroll serenely up the red carpet, nodding politely to the captain and his crew. There, at the end of the line was Nigel, eyebrows knitted together, smiling through gritted teeth.

"How could you do this to me!" he growled.

I reassured him cheekily,

"Nigel! We'd *never* let you down."

There was another time that poor Nigel nearly lost his dancers, when we held an impromptu party on the beach in the area of Salina Cruz in Mexico. Susannah and I had spent a wonderful day in a hammock being blissfully serenaded by some local chappies, on their guitars. As day turned to evening, we hit the tequila straight from the bottle, with a group of jaunty chefs from the ship. Our thick ponchos and over-sized sombreros, bought at the market earlier that day, were silhouetted against the bright orange sunset, making a beautiful Mexican scene. It eventually got dark and some of the crowd dispersed, but as is often the case, we decided to go for a swim in the balmy heat of the evening. It was particularly beautiful under the stars with no artificial light, apart from the glowing ship at the other end of the beach. Stripping off, we dived into the cool water with much merriment, frivolity and shrieks of joy. As we ducked and dived in the silky waves, we were fortunately spotted by a local man as he walked along the beach towards the harbour. Running towards us, he signalled urgently that we should get out of the sea at once. In our tequila infused state, we had forgotten about the safety notice, posted under the cabin door that morning, warning us of sharks.

"You're not in Clacton now dear," Nigel scolded us, as sheepishly we filed back to our cabins, dripping under our ponchos and swaying all over the corridor after our fiesta.

~

Eventually, the ship reached Tahiti, with its anxiously anticipated visit from Briac, the king of our company. I was nervous because I had been enjoying the French tea parties on the quiet, so felt rather self-conscious that although I was slim, I wasn't dancer thin.

Before Briac came to visit the ship, he invited us to take a little boat out from the port, to his paradise island of Moorea for the day. It is one of the most memorable days that we experienced. After quite a long ferry journey from Pape'ete, we boarded a bus that took us along winding roads lined with palm trees to his home. It was stiflingly hot but through the trees you could see the beaches and aquamarine sea. Briac lived in a large house on a hill with vast windows that over-looked the bay. He welcomed us at the tiny harbour wearing just a sarong around his slim waist and after black coffees all round, a sign that he had already decided at a glance, that we were eating too much on the ship, we were taken down to a row of speed boats and whisked out to reefs and little islands of white sand. There we lounged in the rock pools and sipped the bottles of water that Briac had kindly handed out as we climbed into the boats.

"I would kill for a Pina Colada," announced Susannah as we laid, surrounded by coconuts on the sand. By the afternoon we still hadn't eaten any food but, like a vision, Briac's girlfriend arrived on a speed boat with a large container that looked like a picnic.

"Aha! Dejeuner!" announced Briac. There was great excitement as we helped him with the basket onto the beach. To our dismay, there were just large boxes of grated carrot in vinaigrette and more water.

"Is this all we are having today?" I whispered, "I think I might faint."

By the time we returned to the ship that evening we were famished but sitting up at the dinner table with our guest, we knew we had to decline the desserts and cheese!

The show went well and, as we waved Briac off later that night, we breathed a sigh of relief as our ship set off to the next location and we dashed to the midnight buffet.

The weeks flew and we all became quite accustomed to waking up in a different port each morning. My favourite city was Sydney because to sail by ship from out at sea, into the vast sprawling harbour with its beautiful Opera House glinting at us by the water, was exhilarating. Equally thrilling was the day, in Bali, when a group of us hopped on rafts with the local fishermen and paddled over to a village to visit families in a truly magical hamlet of mud huts and paddy fields, welcomed with tiny cups of tea and dishes of starfruit.

The ship chugged along to each exotic location and we were leant on quite heavily to entertain the guests. Often devising impromptu shows, games and competitions, we managed to keep the elderly millionaires from complaining, as, encouraged by the management to befriend them, we indulged them with entertainment and company during their trip of a lifetime and last throw of the dice. These wealthy passengers proved to be quite demanding at times. One couple refused to speak to Susannah for most of the cruise, after she'd spent a whole day fashioning a three-piece suit and a crinoline dress for them, made expertly out of newspaper, for the Black and White themed fancy dress party. Furious when they failed to win first prize, so used were they to getting their own way, they ignored us for the rest of the trip.

There was a well-respected, elderly Commandant staying on the ship that we often sat with for tea on the deck. He had rather a twinkle in his eye and one evening, he requested that we walk him back to his cabin after dinner. On arrival at his cabin, he begged us with pleading eyes to admire the view from his porthole, so we followed him in. After we had ooh-ed and aah-ed at the spectacular view of the waves for a few minutes, we turned to leave just as he lurched towards me, lips puckered up for a kiss. I shrieked, causing him to reel backwards in shock, to be caught by Susannah. This response turned him on hugely, and roaring with laughter at us, as we scuttled out of the cabin, he hurried towards the door like something from an old Carry-on film. We avoided him after this, but he could always be seen amongst the guests, grinning at us with his beady eyes. He would wait for us at various points around the ship, and during the shows we would be able to spot his little face, eyes glistening hopefully from the audience. Sometimes, as I sunbathed, I wondered whether I should consider accepting his advances and become a gold digger, returning to his mansion in Paris to be his Benny Hill style wife, inheriting his millions to the horror of his children.

With just a few weeks to go towards the end of the voyage, our excitement reached new heights when we received a long-awaited bundle of post from home. As we started reading letters from loved ones, we looked forward to catching up with family again. One letter that arrived from Granny was very exciting because, she had enclosed a letter from Babu in Dubai.

Granny wrote

Hi darling Girl,

Thought you would want this letter that came from that foreign gentleman. Not so sure about him myself. I saw it was from Dubai so knew you would want it as soon as possible, so I opened it and wrote out a second copy to keep here, in case it got lost at sea. Didn't read it of course, but I know how much you like him. Don't tell your Mum, this can be our little secret. Gran x

Susannah was fascinated by this, so I asked her to read Babu's letter out to me as we laid on our sun-loungers that afternoon. Since Shelly, and then Jan, in Harrods had warned me that he might be married, I had put him out of my mind, knowing that there would be no point in pursuing any chances of a reunion.

Susannah began, "My sweat ... and lovely Jane."

She looked over at me, baffled, "charming I'm sure!"

I grabbed it off her. "NO! that means, my *sweet* and lovely Jane!"

The letter just became funnier and funnier as she tried to read it out to me, and I felt guilty as we held our aching sides with giggles. Babu spoke fluent English but obviously hadn't fully learnt to write it yet. I wasn't excited over the letter though. Since our lunch date during my weeks at Harrods, I could tell that he'd wanted me to be his girlfriend in London, along with the girlfriends in all the other cities he visited. I folded Granny's letter away, ordered another Tia Maria on ice, turning my thoughts to our imminent return to England.

I cheered everyone up by getting my headdress stuck in the overhead spot-light railings during our last show on the ship.

Cruise ships do not have particularly high ceilings, so, with high heels and a feathered headdress jutting skywards, it was easily done. Stopped in my tracks, mid kick, I knew I would rip the hugely valuable feathers to shreds if I yanked myself free. I couldn't move and the girls had to carry on without me while I stood stock still, with a surprised grin on my face like a deranged statue. Nigel glared at me across the stage as he danced on, not for the first time in the cruise I might add, wondering what I was up to.

"I'm stuck!" I hollered through a toothy showgirl smile. The performance seemed to last an eternity and I felt so silly until the curtain closed and everyone rushed over to see what the problem was. A chair was brought over for Nigel to investigate. Painstakingly he set me free and we left the stage in the nick of time as the magician burst through the curtain with his box of tricks. Nigel couldn't be angry but was not finding the whole fiasco as funny as the rest of us.

"I suppose it would have been more ridiculous if you'd pulled your head out of the head dress and left it suspended from the ceiling," he conceded pensively, causing us to all to cry with laughter as we packed our costumes away.

We were sad to say good-bye to the merry band of Mermoz staff, but as the ship sailed into Miami harbour, I felt ready to disembark and head to the airport.

Teetering from the plane after a long flight to London, sporting our large sombreros, ponchos, and cases of souvenirs, it took all of five minutes of waiting in the icy, winter winds in the taxi rank at Gatwick, to turn our thoughts to the next audition, for a new adventure in the sunshine.

23

YUGOSLAVIA

APPEARING UNEXPECTEDLY ON a winter afternoon, clad in my sombrero with a mahogany tan, caused an emotional outburst from my mother as she rushed to the front door to welcome me home from the cruise. It was the middle of February, and I was back looking for work again, in need of shelter and encouragement from the family. Understandably, they weren't hugely sympathetic, as I wandered around the house with my tan and sun-kissed hair. Britain was at its annual low, with Christmas over and a winter mood descending. There was a cold grey hue over the country that seemed to seep into the soul, making everyone exhausted and vexed. My irritating complaints about the cold were ignored, as I stamped about the house in layer upon layer of jumpers.

"Why do we live in this country? It's freezing and depressing," I would announce as I prodded the logs on the fire, willing them to burst into glowing flames. It never occurred to me that I was the luckiest girl in Suffolk, as everyone smiled with a shrug.

Seeking refuge in the sauna at the local gym, my friends sat wide-eyed with fascination as I described the people and places I'd seen on my recent trip. Recounting my adventures around the world to an eager audience had started to make me feel rather important, although I was slowly realising that it was probably the closest to fame that I would ever be. Our evening newspaper printed a wonderful article all about their local dancing girl, hitting the big time and travelling the world on a cruise ship. I was certainly loving every minute of it.

"Where are you off to next?" everyone wanted to know.

"Well, it's unpredictable really, but I know I won't be home for long," I would explain, loving all the attention and starting to feel rather fabulous as the local journalist took photos of me in the park.

After a few weeks of spending quality time with family and friends though, when the snowdrops had swiftly been followed by daffodils, I remembered how equally lovely England was, with its four seasons and familiar traditions. It was so comforting not having to learn complicated dance routines, and constantly starve myself to maintain my showgirl silhouette. I so enjoyed drinking pints of local ale at the pub with my Dad and brother. Baking cakes and bread with Mum in our glowing kitchen brought instant comfort and calm. However, staying at home by the log fire all day with no particular projects to do, and having only your next meal to think about, was dangerous territory for a dancer. I knew I had to make some decisions soon, whether it was a job in the town in Ipswich, heading back to London or having another travel adventure. The long-discussed audition with Miss Bluebell, that Granny was anticipating, beckoned but, having no internet, I knew I needed to check The Stage newspaper or just get myself over to Paris to investigate. Some mornings, when all the family had gone off to work, I would peruse the classified ads in the local paper, fantasising about finding a normal job in a shop. Some of my friends in Ipswich were planning to get married, which made me feel rather isolated and lonely at times, with my unusual lifestyle of flitting here and there. Hannah from school, had married a farmer as soon as I'd gone off to college. I had been horrified when she'd announced their engagement because we'd both been so ambitious in our teens. She had once planned to travel the world and go to drama college, when we'd sat up late at sleepovers. The news of her wedding had left me completely baffled. However, when I was introduced to the handsome man who'd won her heart, and saw the contentment shining in her eyes as she folded his laundry at the ironing board, I appreciated her new life and understood why she had accepted his proposal so readily. She was where she wanted to be and I could only feel absolute happiness for her, knowing deep down that if things had been different with Mark, Babu or Salvino, ironing my husband's shirt for work every morning would have been a priority.

Every time I returned from a trip, Hannah would invite me to dinner at her pretty cottage in the countryside where there would be an extra place setting at the table for their friend, a dairy farmer that lived in the next village. He was a lovely chap, but unfortunately, he didn't make me go weak at the knees. Hannah was playing Cupid, hoping that there was a chance that I would settle down with this fine fellow. Not one to give up easily on matchmaking projects, she planned for us all to be neighbours, and live happily ever after. She had visions of us pushing our prams together, running the local Women's Institute and comparing jam recipes. I was quite relieved when the dairy farmer found a different sweetheart to marry, realising as he watched me tuck into the wine at these dinner parties, that I was not a morning person, and would not be keen on milking his cows for him at 4am. The dinner parties stopped.

My savings were seeping away, and my tan was fading. I was urgently in need of an income of some sort, as my waistline expanded, and dancing became a distant memory. When I took to gazing at the photographs of Salvino and I on the beach in San Remo, I realised it was seriously time to take drastic action and find a new adventure.

I knew I wasn't quite ready to settle in Suffolk when, as was often the case, there was suddenly an irresistible advert in The Stage, that caused my heart to leap with joy and anticipation one Thursday morning.

"Yes!!!! At last!!" I cried as I danced around the newsagents with Jean, the shopkeeper.

Jean loved my auditions and would tell all her regulars about my latest travels as though she were my manager. A tiny little entry in the classified ads announced that Yugotours were looking for a singer to work with a resident, British band at a Yugoslavian holiday club hotel. The advert shone out at us, as I thumbed frantically through the paper at the counter of the newsagents. With the usual adrenalin pumping through my veins, Jean and I gazed with joy at the page.

The venue was on the Montenegro Riviera, which part of Yugoslavia at that time. I stared in wonder at the map on the kitchen wall, once I was home. I was thrilled to see that it was on the Adriatic coast again, opposite the Italian beaches I had been touring, only the year before. The main temptation, by this time though, was that the job was due to start immediately. What is more, it was a singing job in a warm climate, so a *win-win-win* situation. After a quick phone call to the holiday company, I was invited to meet a member of the entertainment department that same week, whilst they were in England, holding auditions. Clad in a tight black dress, killer heels and big hair, I took off on the train to Birmingham for my meeting. To my amazement, after a quick performance of my faithful *Evergreen* song, the job was miraculously mine. I was ecstatic, my emotions soaring to new heights as my adventurous streak returned on the train journey home. Freelance work is not for the faint hearted and after beginning to feel lost and out of the loop, I was suddenly back on form, with a wonderful plan. Things were hotting up again on my rollercoaster, and I couldn't wait to set off.

A few days later, with my newly purchased Shure SM 58 microphone, a carefully chosen case of pop songs, and an impressive array of fabulous outfits, I bid the family farewell and set off on the train, to Heathrow airport.

When pushed for more information, the Yugotours rep had explained that the band had lost their singing diva, Cheryl, when she had run away with a local Yugoslavian musician, leaving them pretty desperate. I chose to ignore that last detail. Instead, I smirked, with visions of my predecessor changing from raunchy pop star, to that of a Yugoslavian country girl, with hankies and baskets of flowers replacing conical pointy bras and hot pants. I wondered if the same would happen to me. It was clear she'd well and truly left them in the lurch when the lead guitarist, Dougie, explained that he was fed up with having to sing *Like a Virgin* and *Girl's Just Wanna Have Fun*, every night.

"We need you as soon as possible!" he had begged on the phone. Not quite the reason I had hoped to be going to my first singing assignment, but I didn't let it spoil my departure, settling into my seat as the train left Ipswich.

"Yes, I'm a professional singer," I explained to a lady sitting opposite me.

She'd politely spotted my music and nodded encouragingly, as I'd sat learning the words to *Agadoo doo doo, push pineapple up a tree*, as Dougie had asked me to do.

"Yeah, I'm flying out today and I won't be back until the autumn," I explained, as though I did this all the time, even allowing myself a little flick of the hair.

By the afternoon, I was in arrivals at Dubrovnik airport feeling rather fabulous, as I waited for my luggage amongst all the holidaymakers. As we all stood in line, I wondered to myself if they guessed that I was the star, due to appear at their hotel. I looked down at my white boots and stretchy red mini skirt, whilst deciding what to wear for my first performance with the band that evening. My case was jam packed full of leotards, crop tops, strapless dresses, shiny suits with enormous shoulder pads and plenty of killer heels of true eighties fashion. I was really excited, and Dougie from the band was due to meet me at the airport, so I looked eagerly for a David Bowie or Bryan Ferry look-a-like. We were to travel on the coach transfer together to the hotel along with all the new guests, as this, he'd explained over the phone, would give us time to chat about the songs planned for that evening. It reminded me of my rehearsals for the magic show on the motorway, travelling to my first gig with Des. I had assured Dougie that I could perform on the night that I arrived, at least for the Madonna songs, if we had a quick run through before the guests appeared. I'd been practicing the set list at my parent's house right up to my departure, so I could imagine my Dad now enjoying the peace and quiet that would have resumed since I'd left, as he sat at his desk with just the ticking of the clock and the snoring of the dog.

Unfortunately, although I can laugh now, things didn't run as smoothly as I'd hoped, and my first experience of Yugoslavia is not a happy memory.

After what seemed like ages, my luggage hadn't appeared through the plastic ribbons that hung above the entrance of the carousel at Arrivals. Everyone else had left the baggage claim area excitedly with their cases and were chatting as they queued with their passports at the ready. I stood alone feeling awkward in my groovy attire.

"I can't leave without my luggage," I muttered to myself as I briefly glanced at my new Swatch watch, purchased at the airport in Heathrow especially for my trip.

There was no-one around to assist me and I became more and more anxious as time passed, noticing through the large windows that people were already boarding the coaches to leave for the hotels. I tried not to panic and eventually spotted a guy hovering around the exit door in a brightly patterned shirt who I assumed was probably Dougie. Not quite David Bowie or Bryan Ferry I noticed, but I knew I couldn't face him without my luggage. My case was an important part of my act, containing my entire wardrobe of sexy outfits that I was to perform in, every night, for the next six months. I just couldn't show my face at the hotel without it.

In desperation, I decided that there was nothing else for it, and I was going to have to take over the situation. After being shrugged at by a member of staff when I'd asked about my luggage for the third time in my best shouty Yugoslavian, I turned and marched crossly up to the luggage carousel, just as the conveyor belt stopped with a shudder. I peered through the plastic ribbons into the dark, murky corridor beyond, where the luggage was delivered from the plane.

"Hello?" I called, "Anyone there?"

To my amazement, there, in a dark corner, I could see my case standing with a couple of other bags. I could just make out the stickers from my previous trips and the red ribbon with my name label on it. I always tied this to the handle on my travels, so that I could recognize it quickly amongst all the other cases. A final, quick glance around, confirmed that no-one was going to help me to retrieve my case, and there didn't seem to be any security staff around, whatsoever. I was on my own with this predicament and it was clear that I would have to get my case myself, because otherwise I may as well go home.

With a deep breath and a few expletives, I hitched up my skirt, which didn't take long, and clambered up on to the carousel. I was pleased that I had put good, tucked in knickers on that morning as I crawled through the ribbons into the dark mouth of the luggage bay, feeling like it was swallowing me up.

As my eyes adjusted to the darkness eventually, in the murky gloom, I saw two faces look up from a scruffy desk in the opposite corner to my case.

There was someone in there!

This really made me furious.

"Do you mind?" I yelled, "Could you not hear me calling just now? I would like my luggage please," I bellowed from my un-lady-like position on all fours.

The shocked members of airport staff in the corner stared at me in horror from their desk.

"It's *there* for fuck's sake," I growled, pointing at my case, and hoping in hindsight that they didn't understand swear words. I hadn't meant to let that slip out, but I was pumping with anger by now at the thought of losing all my carefully thought-out ensembles for my singing debut.

"Pass my case!"

I was nearly screaming now, deeply concerned that I would miss the coach and have to hitch-hike to the hotel.

One of the men looked terrified and rushed over to my case and heaved it up onto the carousel while the other one switched the conveyor belt back on. With a jolt, I was reversed back out, bum first into the arrivals area, followed by my precious suitcase, just as a concerned Dougie and a very handsome companion by the name of Dino, walked through into the arrivals area in search of me. This was not the entrance that I had anticipated for my arrival at my first singing job. Helping me down apologetically, I could see that Dino was pursing his lips, finding it hard not to roll about on the floor laughing.

I cursed the country I'd only just arrived in, demanding to know what had been going on, but no-one seemed to have any idea. As we were driven down the hill in the air-conditioned coach, my nerves calmed down a little. The breath-taking views of turquoise sea and the rich green pine forests cheered me up. I rested my head back and listened to the dulcet tones of Dino, as he spoke into the microphone, from beside the driver at the front, pointing out various views and landmarks of the stunning scenery of the Montenegro Riviera. Maybe I was going to have a lovely time after all, now that I had overcome the hideous start.

"I need to put this all behind me and start again," I told myself, gazing at Dino's handsome profile, enjoying his witty remarks that caused the ladies to titter as the coach swept around the coast.

The little harbours that we were passing, looked so quaint. I hoped I would soon be sailing into them, to enjoy delicious lunches and relaxing days on the beach. The scenery was absolutely delightful, and I knew I should be glad of that, as alongside me, Dougie chatted about the show during the journey. As soon as Dino had finished his little spiel, he made his way down the coach to join us. He had been sending little nods and engaging smiles at me throughout, and I was starting to feel rather giggly and delighted.

Eventually, Dougie remembered that the last singer, the escapee, had also lost *her* luggage on arrival at Dubrovnik airport.

"Now I fink about it, Cheryl lost 'er bags when she got 'ere di'nt she Dino? I remember she 'ad to wear shirts and jeans borrowed from us boys in the band 'til she got summink sent over from England. The shops are useless 'ere."

All became completely clear to me then, and it freaked me out that someone, had very likely planned to pick out my luggage, knowing that I was the singer. I was glad that I'd had my tantrum and I felt proud as punch that those cheeky buggers had been stymied.

It turned out, from stories told over the summer, that there was often theft of clothes from Brits, because there were no fashion outlets in Yugoslavia at that time. Any fashion merchandise generally came over from Italy and was hellishly expensive, so big business for naughty thieves. One morning during my stay, I went out onto my balcony to find that my washing had been stolen from the line overnight. Later in the summer I spotted my favourite shorts walking around the marketplace on a boy's pert buttocks, but there was nothing I could do about it, I just had to accept it. People weren't hugely shocked when things went missing or were openly stolen in broad daylight, it was just how it was.

I didn't have time to dwell on my little drama because after a swift introduction to the rest of the band and a few cups of tea, I was up on stage running through my songs. The guests were due into the night club area in an hour and sure enough, bang on time, they came trailing in from the restaurant, ready to order their drinks from the bar and bagsie a table near the front. After the day I'd had, I felt tremendously proud of myself as I pulled on my homemade, fuchsia, sequinned boob tube and black satin trousers in my room that evening. As I slipped my feet into my patent black stilettos, I was really feeling ready to wow the crowds, with my first performance of *Like a Virgin*. No-one could stop me, not even a fashion thief. They hadn't realised who they were dealing with.

24

YUGOTOURS HOLIDAY CLUB HOTEL

THE SUMMER TOOK off and, of course, the handsome Dino, who'd met me at the airport with Dougie, wasted no time in becoming my boyfriend. Speaking excellent English, he was the tourists' 'host with a heart of gold,' taking care of everything, ensuring their stay ran smoothly. He thoroughly enjoyed telling people about the first day we met.

"I knew she was the girl for me when I saw her arse coming through the luggage hold at the airport," he would recall in the bar, holding his sides in hysterics. It was his party piece and I hated it, but looking back, it probably kept my feet on the ground and stopped me from becoming a singing diva. His dark eyes and shock of black hair gave him such a dashing demeanour and whenever there were little dramas and disagreements within the band, Dino would embrace me, roaring with laughter at the trivial squabbles that I found so upsetting.

"My beautiful songbird! Leave these English boys to their little problems and come with me to the hills," he boomed, his powerful voice vibrating from his large frame as he held me to his chest. One night as we looked out at the moonlit sea from those hills, it felt right when he turned my face to his and kissed me.

The summer romance took off and I became, very much, a part of Dino's family life, away from the tourists. Dino was proud of his culture and loved to show me the traditional way of life, especially the cuisine which we both shared such a passion for. The local people went to the market every morning to choose what they would eat that day, from the heaving stalls of produce gathered from the local fields, mountains and sea. If we slept late and missed the morning market, we would go to the local supermarket, where there was a deep freeze filled to the top with frozen fish. There was no packaging. It looked like the fisherman had just walked up from the harbour and tipped it all into the deep freeze, and he probably had. You just had to pull out which fish you wanted and take it to the cash desk in your basket.

Dino's family welcomed me into their home instantly, tickled that I was the singer at the hotel. Tourism was the town's main source of income, the local people understandably proud of their beautiful coastline that brought the British people flocking to their authentic restaurants and rustic shops of the pretty towns and villages.

Dino's mum would turn the crackly radio up loud when their Yugoslavian country songs came on and encourage me to sing along with them in the evenings. His brother, Misko, was less jovial though, feeling that I was just treating my relationship with Dino as a summer fling. Protective of his brother, he was convinced that I would be leaving Yugoslavia at the end of the contract, never to return. I often feared he may have been right, although for reasons that they weren't aware of. I was beginning to find the atmosphere in this tourist area rather superficial and I had started to notice how Dino would fuss over me, adjust my hair, tell me to wear certain clothes and occasionally, heaven forbid, even dare to comment if I was eating too much. When we had a night off work to go out together, he would parade me around at the bars and restaurants as though I were his prize.

"Darling, you are *number one!*" he would say as we set off. I started to wonder if he would still like me as much if I was number two, or three, and it made me anxious. He was a vivacious man and popular with the girls at the hotel, which I found amusing. However, I knew that if I'd chatted to the male guests as ardently, he would have been furious. Dino's distrust in me was highlighted one day after I received a card from Emmanuel, one of the jolly chefs from the world cruise, forwarded from Granny, my trusty correspondent in Ipswich. Emmanuel explained that the Mermoz would be docking in Dubrovnik for one day only and, along with many of the people I remembered so fondly from the cruise, he wanted to meet up in the city. I immediately booked a seat on the coach, for the city daytrip with the hotel guests. Jacqui, one of the hotel reps agreed to join me for company and we were really excited to be getting away for a day. I told Dino all about it without a thought but when we arrived to board the coach early in the morning, the driver shook his head.

We weren't on his list and there were no seats for us, although I could see clearly that there were. As we went back to our villa, I could see Dino down in reception at the desk sorting through some paperwork and it struck me what had happened. He had obviously had a word with the driver, convinced I was catching up with an old flame.

"What a wanker!!" Jaqui fumed when I suggested this to her.

Commiserating over a coffee at the beach bar, we decided not to be beaten or make a scene, instead, taking ourselves off for the day, on a local bus from the main road outside the hotel. Finding a traditional taverna that proved to be a reasonable compromise to the bustle of Dubrovnik, we spent the afternoon sampling Kruskovac, a popular pear liqueur, returning high as kites, much to Dino's displeasure. I was glad to have seen this side of his character though, before a particular visit to his family home, weeks later, when I was given a clearer idea of their plans for us. Dino took me up to look at the top floor of the house where I assumed there was a lovely view that they wanted to show me. I became wary when his Mum patted my arm and smiled at me, her eyes twinkling as we went up the stairs. His little old grandmother was nodding and winking at us from her chair in the dark corner, clad in a grey shawl that enhanced her wisps of silver hair as she merrily plucked a chicken. As we went up the steep stairs, I wondered if there was a weird Yugoslavian tradition, especially for couples. Maybe we were expected to have rampant sex to decide if we were well suited or not, but we had been doing that already, and I think that was obvious, so I wondered if there was some other tradition awaiting me in the lovely sunny apartment at the top of the stairs. Overlooking the fig trees in the garden, there was a huge window with a delightful view of the sea. We took in the scenery for a minute until Dino turned me around and pulled me towards him.

"This is where we can live, one day, my darling," he explained proudly, holding me in his arms.

It all became clear and my heart melted from the warmth radiating from him as he held me close. I was rather alarmed though when, after a few glorious minutes, he stood back and gazed quizzically into my eyes with love and complete adoration. In his delectable, broken English, he asked,

"Will you married with me?"

Dino wanted me to be his wife and it felt beautiful. I was so flattered and strangely enough, quite up for it at first. But as I hugged him tightly, drinking in the moment, I had flashes of uncertainty from recent events and suggested that we make a trip to England for a visit to *my* home before we discussed marriage.

As the reality of his proposal set in, and I acknowledged that I would be expected to live in this apartment above his parents, I started to panic and back pedal rapidly. Aware that it was happening just far too quickly for me, I felt Dino was rushing things because he knew I was due to return to England in a month or so, at the end of my contract. He wanted reassurance. As is often the case when I am nervous, I suddenly felt the urge to collapse in hysterics, having visions of myself sitting in a corner plucking chickens and preparing meals for the men folk, with his Mum and Granny for the rest of my days. A beautiful life I was sure, but about as far from show business as you could get. Still, I couldn't resist imagining what our babies would look like, proving that I had a growing maternal instinct, which was a nice feeling.

Apart from the pressure to live with Dino's parents, combined with keeping up appearances for my proud husband to be, I was also nervous at the thought of becoming part of their family because of the heated debates that the men always seemed to start at meal times. Sometimes they would raise their voices and shout at each other so loudly that I would be forced to make my excuses and leave. I never understood their language, and Dino never wanted to translate these particular discussions for me. Of course, what I didn't realise at the time, was that they were all terrified about the political unrest that led to ten years of war a few years later.

The family were intrigued and uneasy when Dino announced that he wanted to visit England with me at the end of my stay. I suggested that perhaps I should cook them a traditional English dinner before we left as a celebration of our wonderful summer together.

"In England, we eat turkey for a celebration dinner," I explained to Dino while he translated to his parents and brother one lunch time. They all looked at me, hugely impressed, and I relished the moment. I suddenly felt very patriotic and proud of my country, feeling the urge to burst into God Save the Queen or Rule Britannia, realising that I was getting fed up with all their Yugoslavian tunes.

"No problem! We can bring a turkey this Sunday morning and we will have a feast!" Dino translated to everyone with glee as his father clapped his hands in anticipation.

The next morning Dino and I were sat on the little kitchen terrace as his mother served up strong coffee in little pots with dishes of figs from the tree. We enjoyed this daily ritual while she updated Dino with her latest gossip from the marketplace and he would translate it all to me with great interest. I was just thinking how I was certainly experiencing the real Yugoslavian life, compared to the guests at my hotel and the rest of the band, when the peaceful moment was disturbed by yet another example of how the people lived. At the end of the lane, we could just make out the alarming silhouette of his father staggering up the drive, being led, by what looked to me, like an emu.

"Aha!" cried his mother in delight, putting down her coffee pot and smoothing her apron. Dino cheered and rushed to greet his Dad. They handed me the string that was around the emu's neck and the penny dropped.

"Turkey!" the men announced proudly, standing back, arms folded. The poor turkey looked at me awkwardly, like a muppet, as I recoiled in fear. It wasn't even a joke, although, it was probably the start of many tests to see if I was good wife material. I immediately proved, very successfully, that I wasn't. Scuttling to the other side of the garden in terror and, with my hand clamped over my mouth so I didn't scream and scare the emu-turkey, I signalled to Dino to take it away.

"They're not like that in England!!" I cried.

He led it over to the fig tree and fastened the string to the tree trunk, roaring with laughter. Feeling like a huge disappointment to them, I begged them never to kill it. I believe it was kept in their garden forever more, happily living on figs under the trees, probably reminding them of the un- reliable English girl for many years.

The summer season drew to a close and, as usual, I was really starting to look forward to heading back to England. There had been so many dramas especially within the band. Musicians can be feisty characters and the Yugotours band were no exception. Being highly skilled musically, they seemed to have an inner confidence and ego, that clashed at times. Audiences across the globe always wanted British and American music played in hotels and restaurants everywhere, so musicians really could find work at the drop of a hat. It gave them an air of confidence which sometimes led to trouble. There were the occasional, drink induced, disagreements between Dougie and Phil, the guitarists, and many squabbles over who took which solo. When I looked out at the audiences during the shows that consisted of old grannies from Stockport and families with toddlers racing around the dance floor, it amused me thoroughly because it was hardly Wembley Arena. Usually, these rows between the boys in the band blew over after a day or so, but one night I really knew it was time to pack up and get home, when the guests were involved, and things turned unpleasant.

It had been a special Yugotours Holiday Club Gala Night, with a posh, black tie dinner, so the Lambrusco had been flowing. After a successful set of our opening numbers, we went upstairs for a short break, leaving a CD playing over the dance floor. Chatting about the next set-list of songs, we were alarmed suddenly, to hear the sound of the drum kit being played and some loud twanging of guitars from downstairs. Dougie and Phil leapt up from their seats and took off down to the lounge bar where they found that some of the hotel guests, after a few too many beers, had decided to have a little go with the kit on stage. Most of the other guests were outside by the pool admiring the sunset with their drinks.

"Alright mate, that's enough now," growled Phil as he picked his way through the instruments that stood on stands, precisely placed in readiness for our next performance.

"Put it down and leave the stage please."

The two guests were having far too much fun and chose to ignore Phil. This was too much for Dougie, a large man, who marched across to them, pushing chairs out of his way.

"He said, that's enough!" Dougie towered over them like Popeye, his shirt buttons straining against his enormous belly. I was watching nervously from the wings, thinking how inappropriate the jolly Grease CD sounded, as it played *You're the one that I want!* throughout the scene before me. Dino wasn't around, so I started signalling to the barman that we had a problem, but he pretended not to see me, as he carried a tray of glasses through to the kitchen out of sight.

"Well!" answered one of the guests, highly amused and clearly very drunk as he pulled himself up, face to face with Dougie. "You, my little fairy, can just fu-"

I turned back to the stage just in time to see Dougie's fat, fist fly across and punch the guest sharply on the jaw, sending him straight down, crashing into the cymbals.

There was a pause.

"You better shape up. Cos I need a man," continued Olivia Newton John, "And my heart is set on you-oo-ooo!"

Dougie, Phil and the guests then dived into a full-on-fisticuffs with great glee, as their noses and lips began to seep with blood, and guitars were swiped through the air like weapons. Fortunately, it all stopped, as the air was filled with a high-pitched scream from the front of the stage. The men froze. Dougie and Phil collapsed onto the floor and stared in amazement as their new friends, guests one and two, dropped the guitars and staggered over to heave the newcomer up onto the stage with them.

"Sorry Mum, we 'ad a bit of trouble wiv the band."

Their mother had obviously sensed there was trouble with her boys, as she'd sat drinking shots by the pool, and had made her way to their rescue.

"You!" she wove her way across the stage, crashing into the keyboard, stopping to hitch up her dress that was struggling to restrain her ample bosom. Lurching towards Dougie, she pointed accusingly at her sons,

"You two! Get back to the room I'll deal wiv you later!" she instructed, giving them a shove. They swaggered out of the lounge, guffawing as they went. Turning back to Dougie and Phil, she continued her ranting, jabbing her finger at them.

"You two hav 'ad it! I swear you'll never work again after this!" she hissed, listing sideways, grabbing a chair for support. "I'm reportin' you to the manager ... and ... the British ... British ..." she struggled for words here, "British tourisht ..."

With that she turned to leave but unfortunately spotted me lurking by the curtain.

"And as for you, what are you doin' in a place like this swee'heart? I could get you loads a work in England at my club. You're wurf more than this. Let me give you my card babes."

This was too much for Phil. He was already finding the situation quite funny and had been chuckling quietly as he pulled a handkerchief out of his back pocket to dab the blood from his nose. But this last comment tipped him over the edge at the thought of me rushing back to England to start working for this classy bird. Of course, his howls of laughter didn't help to placate her, and I made a quick exit as she collapsed onto a chair just when her husband arrived to save her.

"Babes! Whass goin' on?"

He picked up her handbag that had spilt its contents over the stage as she'd searched for her business card. But when there was silence, we realised, conveniently, that she had passed out.

A few weeks later the hotel closed for the winter and Dino agreed to come to England with me to meet my family. It was a real adventure for him as he had never left Yugoslavia before, but as I had dreaded, all he would talk about, to my parents and friends, was his own home and culture, comparing

258

everything competitively, until it was clear that he would never consider living in England.

I started to accept that if I wanted to marry Dino, we would have to live in Yugoslavia. I was adjusting to this idea with difficulty, because since arriving home, our differences had become more apparent. A few days before he was due to fly home to Yugoslavia, we went out for the day with Hannah, my school friend, and her husband. After a lovely day at the chilly beach, we were drinking tea and eating cake by the fire at Hannah's.

"You look so relaxed darling," commented Hannah warmly, as I stood up to pour the tea.

Dino smiled and patted my bottom, "She look like a woman who have some kids and eat too much!" he laughed. There was an embarrassed hush until Hannah ventured,

"Is that a bad thing Dino?"

Little did he know, but he had just tipped the balance of a wavering ship. It wasn't the first time he had made comments of this nature and I realised that when the glamorous singer that he was so proud of, became a mother, she wouldn't be able to maintain the image he loved so much. Hannah looked over lovingly, and we shrugged.

I shed huge, fat tears at the airport, as he prepared to go through the departure gates at Gatwick, knowing that, as his brother had predicted, this would possibly be our last time together. Our relationship was not quite right, and I felt confused and anxious at the thought of leaving England to become a Yugoslavian, despite my love for him and his family. There is always something about airports that makes me slightly emotional anyway but knowing that I was not at all prepared to go back with Dino, to be his wife, made me feel sad. There had been an air of melancholy between us on the train journey there and I felt lost for words as we embraced at the departure gate. He knew I was having second thoughts after our spell with my family, that had brought various differences to light. He held my face close to his as we embraced, staring deeply into my eyes as they filled up with fresh tears.

"Call me tonight my darling, everything is going to be fine. Take some time with your family and then come back to me. I'll be waiting."

I stood transfixed as he set off. He did a funny walk to try to make me laugh and I tried very hard to smile until he became a speck in the distance, turned to wave, and then, was out of sight. Slowly, I walked back across the concourse and lurched into the newsagents to buy a packet of tissues because I was sobbing steadily now. People smiled kindly and nodded knowingly at me, like they do in airports. I stood blubbering and staring blankly across the rows of sweets and crisps, while I queued to pay at the cash desk until, out of habit, my gaze dropped down to the low shelves of newspapers nearby. This shelf is usually where The Stage is found. There, through the tears, I spotted my old faithful paper. I stopped sniffling, my tears mysteriously subsiding, as I staggered over to grab a copy. I paid and found the nearest bench, holding my breath as I scanned the audition pages with practiced ease. I stared at an advert, unblinkingly as I crammed a Cadbury's cream egg into my mouth, because there, in all its glory, complete with the vital criteria of 'minimum height 5ft 8in', was my next job.

25

SARDINIA

AS I STARED at the newspaper, my heart racing, I decided to grab this job if I could, and escape from all the complicated, emotional distractions I'd managed to get myself into. I knew it would give me the time I needed to think about my plans. I was completely perplexed, feeling rushed and unsure whether, or not, I was really ready, at the tender age of twenty-one, to embrace domestic bliss in the sunshine with a lovable rogue. Stopping at a phone box on my way out of the airport, I rang the number on the advert. The contract was offered by an agency in London, working on behalf of a dance troupe in Barcelona and I hoped they might let me audition that day, as I passed through London on my way back to my parents in Suffolk because there were no open auditions taking place for this job. An open audition is when a studio is booked for a certain day and dancers can just turn up and take part in a class where a routine is taught, and the company make their choice of dancers for their show on that day. Agencies on the other hand, tend to invite you into the office for an interview, and look at your CV, sometimes asking you to learn a short routine. Fortunately for me on this particular day, they picked up the phone immediately and, as I'd hoped, agreed that I could stop by at their office on my way home. Having no mobile phones or internet then, this approach was much more common. I decided to focus on an adventure and not allow my mind to wander back to the emotional turmoil of recent days. I needed to get away and luck was on my side when I told the girls at the agency that I had worked for Guy Stranger.

Their faces lit up, "Oh, that old rascal! Don't tell us he's still there!"

We laughed about the old farmhouse and they were impressed to hear that he'd won the world cruise contract. They trusted that I would be up to the challenge of the exciting show they had on offer in Sardinia so, thanks to Guy, the job was mine.

Just a few weeks after the emotional farewell to Dino, I found myself travelling out to rehearse a glamorous show in Barcelona. The show was set to open at the Truste House Forte Hotel on the coast of Sardinia, Italy and it was exciting to meet the rest of the dancers at Heathrow with the thought of sunny months ahead together. I immediately hit it off with Sammi from London, a dancer on the run from heartbreak, just like me. Before long, I was in the throes of learning new routines, but determined to see Barcelona while we were there, I made sure we went out to explore the city at night.

During the balmy evenings, we discovered that, conveniently, the MacDonald's served Rosé wine in plastic beakers. Wandering the streets, plastic cup in hand, taking in the atmosphere, we found welcome relief from the gruelling rehearsals. Unfortunately, the dance captain was a bully, managing to knock every ounce of confidence out of Sammi until, one night it all seemed too much for her and she mentioned going home until I convinced her to stay on and see where the adventure took us.

"You *could* go back to England, but then what would you do?' I quizzed, as I sipped the delicious wine in the evening sunshine. "Come to Sardinia with us and see what happens. I'm sure the situation will cheer up when we get there."

Sammi agreed and before long we were setting off with our glamorous show. Choreographed by two Spaniards, Gino and Paco, there were plenty of sparkles and feathers and their style reminded me of the show in Madrid. Having spent the entire summer strolling around the stage singing ditties with the band in Yugoslavia, I found the rehearsals for the Gin-Pac show extremely tough. Gino gave me some great solos to sing when he heard about my previous job, so I was on cloud nine, despite finding it hard to straighten up each morning as I attempted to find my dancer strength again. Sporting my rhinestone bikini and feathered headdress, I wafted about the stage belting out *My Heart Belongs to Daddy* and, bizarrely, *Spinning Wheel* by Blood Sweat and Tears. At the end of my songs, I would join the rest of the dancers for a spectacular show of high kicks and turns around the stage. It was as exhilarating as I remembered.

The show was performed several times a week on an open-air stage, set on the main square of a five-star, luxury complex on the beautiful coastline near Cagliari. During the day, the guests sat at bistro tables sipping cappuccinos and at night the candles flickered, turning the square into a romantic vista from where each table had a perfect view of the stage. The dancers shared a villa, up in the hills overlooking the hotel, and we were also allowed to use the peaceful hotel beach during the day, with its white sand and crystal-clear water. Our meals were served in a canteen for hotel staff, set under shady pine trees where we could sit around chatting and tucking into steaming bowls of pasta with the Italian bar staff and chefs. To my delight, Sammi turned out to be excellent company as the Mediterranean sunshine healed her broken heart. Life was good again as she found comfort in the arms of a delightful boy from the hotel reception who adored her, making the pain of her abandoned relationship in London, a distant memory.

Michael Jackson's *Bad* album had just hit the charts and was driving the world crazy. It could be heard in bars and cafés everywhere and was played constantly on our Sony Walkmans at the beach, as we lazed on the sand.

After the show, during the balmy late evenings, we drank wine and devoured delectable, oversized pizza in the little tavernas up in the hills, amongst the fragrant pine forests. Of course, this was when I met a new beau, Giovanni the chef, a true Sardinian boy. Our eyes had met across the crowded staff bar one evening, and very soon we were tearing around the island in his bashed up old Fiat. Wearing cut off denim shorts, bronzed to perfection in bikini top, plaits and espadrilles, feeling high on espresso coffee and Marlboro lights, I was rapidly becoming an Italian girl, and I loved it. After work, under the bright moon, Giovanni and I would drive out to a deserted beach, away from the tourist trail. Constructing a frame with bull rushes from the nearby marshes I would drape my brightly coloured sarongs across it while Giovanni lit a fire on the large rocks. Drinking wine, we would sit looking out to sea, enjoying the view until the soft lapping of the waves lulled us to sleep. At sunrise, we would stroll out into the searing early heat and swim naked in the calm blue water, the whole beach to ourselves with no-one for miles. Packing up the car, we would then lazily make our way back to the hotel.

Having learnt to speak French, during my childhood trips to France, I picked up Italian very quickly. Being a Latin language, I found it very easy to make the shift and there was no greater incentive than a beautiful Italian boy holding me in his arms, asking me questions all day long, as we basked in the sunshine. When I described my plans to return to London at the end of the summer, Giovanni announced that he was very keen on moving to London, sure that he would find work easily in the Italian restaurants of Covent Garden where he had many friends. He was confident that they would welcome him into the fold. It all seemed like a perfect plan as we lay, discussing our futures, late into the night, stretched out on our quiet, moonlit beach, looking up at the stars.

One evening the situation took a startling turn, as Giovanni explained that if we were to go to England together, he had something important to tell me before we left. It turned out that he had a baby daughter in Cagliari but had separated from the baby's mother. This unexpected news was a shock that left me reeling in disbelief. After the summer we had just enjoyed together, I tried desperately hard to see the bright side of this baby I'd never met. It wasn't that I was disconcerted that Giovanni had a baby, I just couldn't help feeling disappointed that he hadn't mentioned it before and was prepared to leave her, to go gallivanting off to England with me. A different mood shrouded our plans for a while after this revelation, added to which, Giovanni's mother made it quite clear that she didn't approve.

Giovanni was one of seven sons of a lady called Maria. Within the Catholic faith, large families weren't unusual in the little towns of Sardinia. Maria's boys all looked identical and their mother, or Mama, as they called her, was a strong woman with a very protective nature. I could never believe that she honestly knew which of her sons was which, unless they all stood in a row and were measured. With a set of twins amongst them you really could not tell them all apart. Maria worked all day long in her small kitchen and little yard, preparing evening meals of monumental proportions for all of her handsome boys when they came home at night. Most of these lads were chefs at the hotels and restaurants along the coast, so there were always plenty of chef's whites to be laundered each day. She was not an idle woman. If you've ever tried getting Italian tomato sauce out of white cotton, you'll know what a challenge she had on her hands. It's hard enough with Ariel ultra and a turbo charged washing machine set at ninety degrees, but this little woman washed all their clothes for them in a tub in the back yard with a mangle, lots of scrubbing brushes, a bar of old, strange soap and a funny, bumpy board thing. Astounding.

From my last experience with Dino's family, I decided that I should make it quite clear from the start that I was not a domestic angel, quite unreliable in fact. This didn't go down at all well and much as I admired Maria hugely, she didn't seem to warm towards me at all, understandably perhaps, in the circumstances. I suspected that she was worried that I was planning to take her handsome boy away from his responsibilities. She was right to be concerned because that was exactly what I was doing. At first, I'd assumed that she would be glad to have one less mouth to feed and one less uniform to scrub, until of course I learnt about the baby.

Maria constantly did her best to deter me from my amorous advances towards her Giovanni. Speaking very quickly to me in Italian, while serving up goat casserole was the first tactic. Showing me photographs of Giovanni's ex-girlfriend as she wrung her hands, and wept into her apron, was another. The latter made me depressed and uncomfortable but did nothing to dampen my affections for him, of course. All I had to do was glance across the table at his smouldering, slanted smile, with cigarette propped sexily on bottom lip, and my knees would turn to jelly. All his, almost identical brothers would also be smiling, slantily at me across the table, with their cigarettes on their bottom lips. This had the same effect on me, but I usually managed to pick Giovanni out successfully, just in time to return the smile after a few seconds concentration, without offending anyone.

In October, as autumn crept in, the show finished and despite Giovanni's baby news, we threw caution to the wind and made the trip to London. It was a strange start to the visit because Britain had just had the extraordinary hurricane of 1987. Britain was in turmoil with electrical lines down, no train service and crashed cars and trees blocking all of the roads. Entire forests had disappeared overnight, and I hoped that this wasn't an omen. We eventually managed to find a coach back to Suffolk to stay with my parents for a week, before attempting to set up our new life in London.

I learnt over the years of my dalliances with handsome locals at all the exotic places of work that I visited, that bringing a boyfriend to stay with my family in Britain was a good test of character for all of us. First of all, the boyfriend had to get used to my Dad calling them by the name of my previous lover, without feeling offended. Then there was the language barrier, so they had to get used to being shouted at by everyone, as though they were hard of hearing. We Brits are inclined to do this to foreign visitors, and it always accentuates the fact that no-one in England ever bothers to learn a second language at school. Then, my family had to nod and smile while my visitor would explain how much better the food, climate, pace of life, colour of the sea water and coastline was, in their own country. Our bleak, freezing weather was the next hurdle and as soon as we came out of the airport at Heathrow on that first morning, we were hit with an icy blast from the north as the sliding doors opened.

"*FREDO*!!!" Giovanni yelled in horror as we staggered against the wind with our cases, to the coach station. Our eyes and noses were instantly streaming in the wintry blast as I prayed to God that my parents had put the central heating on in readiness for our arrival. I had a feeling that they would still be saving on bills, by wearing six jumpers instead. This was our usual rule. Just going about simple daily chores is such an effort in the British winter as we wince and grimace, trying to get to work or just nip to the shops. Giovanni's relaxed, slanty grin became a pinched, angry scowl, as he attempted to light his ciggie in a force-ten gale. In my opinion, you can only really seek comfort in the British winter if you sit next to a roaring log fire drinking brandy. This, of course, involves lighting the darn thing every morning, which is exhausting and requires great skill, and an un-ending supply of logs that you have to chop. Shopping seems tiresome as you scuttle from shop to shop to get out of the rain, dodging puddles and being splatted by passing vehicles as you notice the start of a cold coming at the back of your nose. Then follows sniffling and sneezing for days on end before waiting for the snotty phase to pass. What intrigues me to this day though is that, with all the chances I had in my life to put my roots down in beautiful, warm climates, after a few months I always hankered after Britain, with its terrible weather and familiar comfort food.

Winter approached and Giovanni found himself battling to adjust to our British ways. I became very concerned for our future. He was not impressed with the weather, obviously, and every evening I would make him a bowl of plain spaghetti to cheer him up. That was as far as my cooking skills went at that time but before long, Giovanni had started making pizza for everyone. He was a chef after all, so this was a great way of introducing him to my friends. There seemed to be an underlying melancholy about him though, that was probably due to the fact that, coming away from Italy, only accentuated the fact that he had a huge responsibility back home. Moving to England hadn't take it away.

We went to London as planned, and he immediately started working for a bistro which, to my joy, turned out to be a great success. However, once we'd had a look at Big Ben and he had come to the end of his clean pants, I could tell that he was definitely starting to miss his home and realise that he had to face the fact that he was a father. To add to his battle, he was struggling to take part in the raucous discussions in the kitchen at the flat we were sharing with my friends. The language barrier was becoming arduous, despite the girls making a huge fuss of him. I knew he craved his beautiful warm beaches and pine forests, but we both knew I wasn't keen to go back with him and be an Italian stepmother just yet.

"Give 'im a chance honey," Phillip, one of my flat-mates reassured me as we waved a pale Giovanni off to work one morning. "He'll learn to love London, just you wait and see darling. Give it a chance."

Phillip returned to his sock sorting at the kitchen table, where we spent many afternoons gossiping and drinking copious amounts of tea, before he went off to work in a casino as a croupier. He loved my Cairo, phone bill story and often asked me to tell it when we had his friends over from work. My work opportunities hadn't been progressing at all well so, as the British weather continued to turn colder and I battled my way through the sleet and drizzle, I began to feel rather miserable. I couldn't face tracking down Des and Rick for a second stint of magic tricks, so eventually, when my savings ran out and I could barely manage to pay my share of the rent, I found myself a job at a little hotel in Holland Park. I hadn't managed to get myself to class in Pineapple Dance Studio and after a few rejections at auditions for chorus work in musicals, I had started to lust after the glamorous adverts in The Stage newspaper again as was often the way. There did seem to be an awful lot of juicy offers going, for shows in far-flung places, with generous wages and luxurious accommodation advertised. These companies looked so tempting, but I knew that I couldn't leave poor Giovanni in the lurch after up-rooting him from his home, his daughter, and his spaghetti making Mama. I would just have to roll my sleeves up and find something in London. It was only fair to work as hard as Giovanni if we were to stick to our plan, so I took the first job I could find locally, a position as hotel receptionist on night duty, with as much optimism as I could muster. It was rather an anti-climax after being the glamorous singer in Sardinia. Not one to stew though, I put my best foot forward and celebrated the fact that I had an income again, feeling a glimmer of hope that Giovanni and I were going to survive.

26

HOTEL RECEPTIONIST

HAVING NO FORMAL training for my new job at the hotel, meant that I did create a few Fawlty Towers moments at first. My interview was with the manager, a man of mature years named Dick, who declared immediately that I was a fine young filly, and just what they'd been looking for, to cover the night duty. Set in a typical London square made up of elegant terraces overlooking a private little park of tranquillity, the hotel was a really, homely, little gem amongst the chaos of London.

"Think we've won the lottery here Reg, wouldn't you say?" Dick called over to the lounge, where one of his long-term residents was sat, reading The Racing Post by the log fire.

Reg peered briefly over the top of his paper amidst a plume of smoke from his pipe, that made his eyes close and his teeth clench into a strange grimace of agreement.

"What a smasher! Bloody marvellous eh?" he agreed, "Don't know where you find 'em Dicky old boy."

He went back to his racing results.

Dick gave me a brief tour of reception before introducing me to Salvatore, the young barman, who seemed to be running the place single-handedly. Apparently, Dick's wife, Joan, ran the hotel during the day but was nowhere to be seen, so guests seemed to be helping themselves to their keys at reception as they came through the large oak doors of the entrance. Despite Dick's confidence in me, I learnt quickly, that receptionist work is not just smiling and greeting people.

I settled behind my desk, early one evening, after pouring my coffee, and laying out a crafty bag of knitting ready for a long night. There was no internet in those days, and we were forced to think of things to do, instead of scrolling on Facebook for hours so I had decided to design a range of knitted bras. I had always wanted to pursue the idea, since my successful attempt in the seventies as a child and felt this was the perfect time to do it. I was just thinking what a cushy little job I had stumbled across, when a very handsome guest came through the revolving doors. His crisp, white shirt, sharply cut suit and glint of gold watch made a fine impression on me, so I gave him my most welcoming of smiles and small talk. I looked through the book for his name and room number before handing him his key. He was about to make his way to his room when he turned back to ask if we had some aspirin for his headache. I was obliged to disappoint him.

"I'm awfully sorry, Sir, but we're not permitted to administer drugs to guests. However, there is a little shop on the corner down the street, that sells everything you could possibly need," I explained in my finely tuned, well- rehearsed receptionist voice, with smile at the end.

Well, you would think that I had told him that his bed was actually out on the car park and the weather forecast was rain. Grabbing his key, he stomped up the stairs, muttering to himself that English hotels were the worst in Europe. I was inclined to agree with him completely there but thought it better if I kept my opinion to myself at this particular moment. Thinking that this was the end of our little Tête à Tête and what a tolerant receptionist I was turning out to be, I settled down in my chair, sipped my coffee and went back to my knitting, keen to rustle up the first little number for my woollen lingerie portfolio.

"How grumpy some people can be, even devilishly handsome ones," I muttered to myself as I recalled the exciting flash of anger from his dark brown eyes.

It was then that, from the top of the staircase, there came an angry cry, which, annoyingly, made me drop a stitch. I froze, my heart pounding rather furiously, as I had a very good inkling of who it was. My first reaction was to hide under the desk, but it was rather a small desk, so I scuttled into the back office and shut the door. Peeking through the blinds I watched Mr Angry marching down the stairs with a rather distorted face that sort of trembled slightly around his chiselled jaw. I couldn't help noticing that he had unbuttoned his shirt slightly, revealing some impressive pectoral muscles. On reaching the reception desk, he started bashing on the brass bell incessantly. I was really glad at this point that I hadn't hidden under the desk, but it was clear that something was bothering him, and I knew it was really my job to sort it out. After a while, I decided that I would have to go out and face him otherwise he was going to wake the other guests and seeing Salvatore in the distance at the lounge bar, I was reassured that if things turned nasty, I would be able to run through to him for protection.

I waited until Mr Angry had stopped bell bashing and was nicely slumped over the counter, before opening the office door, with faked surprise to see him again,

"Oh, hi again! Everything alright?"

"You!" he jabbed his finger at the air in front of my nose. I flinched slightly but managed to maintain my receptionist smile, which probably riled him even more.

He was so livid that he was whispering now,

"What sort of a place are you running here, you just sent me up to someone else's room you ... you blithering ... blithering ..."

It was too much for me.

"I'm sure you aren't about to call me a blithering idiot are you sir?" I asked politely but firmly, feeling a little angry myself now, as I searched his deep brown eyes for clues. I'd been called some things in my time but that was definitely a new one, although I was inclined to agree with him rather. There was a pause of a few seconds while my brain blithered about like an idiot, deciding my next move. It was such a shame he was so beastly, because it was quite clear by this time that he was hellishly attractive.

"Oh! I'm so sorry Sir! There must have been a mix up. How remiss of *us*, I do apologise." I waited for him to hand me the key back, but he just stared in astonishment, laying it slowly on the desk, our eyes locked. I fluttered my eyelashes at him which, unusually, had no effect whatsoever, so I knew I was in trouble. This tactic had never failed me before. On realising that I couldn't blame someone else for my faux pas, I rummaged about, checking the book a little more carefully this time, for an available room, before handing over a new key with a smile. I tried my best to look really concerned as my imagination ran riot with what must have just happened up in the room. Images of him throwing down his case in the dark and flinging himself onto the bed on top of a politician or an opera singer meant, I have to confess, a little titter escaped me. I hoped he would see the jolly side of the situation and get the giggles with me, but it wasn't looking likely. After nervously checking for clearance along the hallway, preparing to run to Salvatore for safety, I stopped in my tracks as he just turned and stormed back up the stairs. I sank back into my chair realising that I was rather shaky and Salvatore, sensing there was trouble, came scuttling over to hear the whole story.

"Wait till he's gone, before you come to my aid, why don't you?" I whimpered. I told him what had happened and when he'd stopped crying with laughter, Salvatore wiped his eyes and pottered over to the bar to make me a drink, letting out plenty of Mamma-Mia's as he went. My jolly outlook slowly returned, but I couldn't help feeling sure that Dick would be forced to let me go, when he received a furious complaint from Mr Angry the next day.

~

Due to this unfortunate error in reception, I became most concerned about my working life. I scanned The Stage newspaper anxiously, coming to the conclusion that I was, possibly, not cut out for normal jobs in the real world. There still seemed to be a continuous amount of opportunities advertised in exotic locations, away from all this mayhem. With Giovanni working so hard at the bistro though, I decided that I owed it to him to stick to the plan we'd made on those beautiful beaches in Sardinia only months before. Instead of running away again, I decided to look for another job locally, in readiness for my likely dismissal from the hotel. Salvatore insisted that my mistakes on reception were trivial and that much worse things happened on a regular basis.

"No! No! No! You-no-leeeave-a-this-place!" he announced, handing me a large glass of champagne, having learnt the way to my heart very quickly.

"Mr-Dicky-he-love-you-so-march-and-you-make-a-my-life-a-so-happy-with-a-so-much-a-laffing!!" he cried.

Sure enough, to my amazement, Mr Dicky seemed positively pleasant whenever I passed him in the lobby.

"Evening Jane, looking lovely again tonight my dear!"

However, back at the flat, with my strange nightshifts, Giovanni and I had become like passing ships, so I knew I needed to find a day job to bring some sort of normality to our daily schedule. One morning on my way home from my night shift at the hotel, I spotted a little advert in the window of a jewellery shop nearby. Duke and Sons were looking for a sales assistant, so I decided to pop in to enquire, later in the day.

Duke and Sons was owned by two elderly sisters, Hilda and Molly Duke. The shop had been in the family for decades but being spinsters, there were no offspring to take over the business. The location of the shop meant that there were always wealthy customers popping in for gifts, keeping profits rolling along, as they lunched and shopped them away again with their decadent lifestyle. The tiny advertisement in the window was the only step they had taken to find a new shop assistant, so they were very thrilled to have an applicant at last.

"Well! Come in! Come in! You divine creature! Look at these long legs Molly!" Hilda had bustled over to greet me, steering me into the office, actually patting my bottom.

Her sister Molly was sitting at a dusty little Victorian desk, powdering her facelift scars as I walked in. On seeing me, she snapped shut her golden compact and reached for her diamante spectacles.

"Oooh, yes! Hello there darling, isn't she lovely? Do come and sit down, we need to really get to know you first." Hilda's eyes darted over to the grandfather clock in the corner.

"Now when can you start?"

It quickly dawned on me that she meant what *time* I could start, not what *date*. It sounded like I had passed the interview already when they suggested we went for lunch to discuss my future in the jewellery trade. I was starving, so agreed that it was an excellent idea, and we took off down the street, receiving waves and nods from other shop owners as Hilda and Molly led me to their favourite little restaurant.

"We've been coming here for decades. We have our very own table in the window, don't we Hilda dear?" Molly beamed proudly while the waiter set an extra place for me at their table.

Then began a full interrogation, as they demanded to know every detail of my life and loves which, I realised for the first time, was actually starting to sound quite colourful.

"You must bring this Italian fellow to meet us darling. How thrilling!!" gushed Molly as she adjusted her pearls before lighting up yet another cigarette as we waited for our food. In those days, it was perfectly acceptable to smoke in restaurants. Hilda saw me watching with fascination and shook her head.

"Molly not only smokes between courses. She smokes between mouthfuls darling!"

All they wanted to talk about was my dance training and life on the stage, going into raptures when I mentioned my ambition to join Miss Bluebell's girls in Paris. To my joy, they made me promise not to turn down any dancing work if it came along, as they were sure they would like to fly over and watch the show. So, within a few days I had managed to acquire a second job. I have to tell you that working a sixteen-hour day is not actually humanly possible. I've tried it. I decided that, since we needed the money, I would have a go at bluffing my way through night shifts on reception and then lurching through the day at the jewellers, grabbing the odd hour of sleep here and there, until I knew which job was going to work best. It wasn't even Christmas, but the winter seemed to be stretching endlessly ahead of us as Giovanni and I dragged ourselves to work in the dim light. I started to fear that, as we were seeing less and less of each other, the inconvenience of my ridiculous work schedule and the English weather were managing to cast a grey light on our romance. My lack of sleep was giving me a rather dishevelled appearance of puffy eyes and wild hair, as my tan faded and I gained a few pounds. I actually started to hope, for Giovanni's sake, that he would see sense and consider flying back to his daughter and the country he loved so much. He never mentioned his baby and his lack of concern about her had slightly marred my opinion of him. I wondered why he wasn't sending money back to her mother or making any contact with them. I'd even started to feel that I was keeping him away from her, which I probably was. I fell into a haphazard routine of sitting in reception at the hotel for the night where I would doze, knit and eat sugary snacks. After popping home for a kip, I then set off to my jewellery counter for the day at Duke and Sons.

Despite having no skill or experience with jewellery, persuading people to part with their hard-earned cash at Duke and Sons came quite naturally to me. I seemed very convincing when assisting customers with their choices, although I've personally always found jewellery rather a nuisance. The responsibility of looking after something so miniscule, that has cost a small fortune, fills me with dread. I have had to empty many a Hoover bag in my time, in order to retrieve a lost earring or a sentimental necklace. However, as a keen saleswoman, I quickly learnt a perfect sales spiel, that worked every time.

"Oh! Now, that seems to pull the entire look together. I think pearls enhance your complexion beautifully madam, sort of ... lifts you!" I would gush.

It worked every time.

27

JEWELLER

HILDA AND MOLLY really were something else, arriving
each morning by taxi in full make up, little Chanel suits and
diamonds the size of Foxes Glacier Mints. They reminded me
of celebrities arriving at the Oscars, seeming to come from a
different era. They spent their days in the little office at the
back of the shop where they would drink tea and play Frank
Sinatra records, often asking me to dance for them before
setting off for lunch. After a sherry sharpener, they would
leave the shop in the capable hands of a girl called Viv, with
me as her assistant.

Viv was a smart girl with a shrewd business mind, disguised
under an abundance of bleached hair and some interesting
tattoos hidden under a silk blouse during working hours. She
would tap her long nails on the glass counter with frustration
if there were no customers, and Hilda and Molly made sure
that she was rewarded generously for her sales. She wore some

pretty impressive rings and bracelets and although she was cautious with me at first, Viv and I quickly hit it off. She was completely fascinated by my dance career. There were often quiet spells during the afternoon when I would tell her about my travels around the globe, as we sipped cups of tea and watched the world go by on the busy street outside. I didn't tell Molly and Hilda about my other job at the hotel, but Viv knew and when they went for lunch, she would bury me under coats in the office so I could catch up on some sleep until she heard them twittering along the pavement on their way back. Viv's favourite story of mine though, was the recent tale of the angry man in reception at the hotel. To her joy, one morning, as we were changing the window display, I dived to the floor and begged her to lock the door and put the closed sign up because there, perusing the window display, was the man himself.

"I don't believe it, Mr Angry's here! Help me Viv! He can't come in or see me! It would be awful, in fact there is a good chance that he would be abusive."

My heart was racing as I looked around desperately for an exit or somewhere to hide. Viv stared at me with a mixture of amusement and horror, not for the first time that day. Sauntering gaily over to the window she watched Mr Angry. He was frowning at a velvet pad of ancient lockets from the vintage section. I sank down to my knees, whimpering in dismay, crawling behind the glass counter trying to shrink my six-foot frame into Mrs Pepperpot size, causing all the jewellery to clink and clank as I squashed myself into the shadows amongst the brooms and dusters.

"Just please get rid of him somehow, this is really serious," I pleaded with my colleague, cowering, as I gazed up at her from the darkness, tugging at her skirt.

"What? You can't be serious, how bad can he be?"

"Bad! It's him! The guy from the hotel that hates me!" I cried.

Instead of rushing to the door and locking it, Viv strolled back over to the window and flashed a smile.

"Mr Angry! Well, well, well," she mused, folding her arms and leaning on the glass.

"Oh, my days, I see what you mean. Very attractive and looks pretty loaded to me," she acknowledged.

I realised then, that there was no way that she would lose a potential sale just because a mad woman with a dodgy past had joined her workforce. Glancing around, I frantically took in the lay-out of the shop, planning my escape route. Fortunately, Hilda and Molly were still out on their little luncheon foray, so that was one less hurdle to worry about. They would probably have been thrilled to return to this scenario, inviting him into their office for a sherry, delighted to hear about my terrible behaviour as a hotel receptionist. I imagined them nodding and looking out at me with amazement at this revelation, as I stood looking down at my thumbs, humiliated, pretending to be a jeweller. They were due back any minute, so I knew I had to act fast to deal with this situation. Unfortunately though, my nerves and lack of sleep were really slowing down my usual quick thinking, people skills. Fortunately, Mr Angry hadn't seen me through the window, mesmerised as he was by the lockets on the vintage display pad. My heart sank though, as he entered the shop, the tinkling of the doorbell reminding me of the bell in reception, the last time I had seen him. Feeling rather nauseous, I suddenly decided that the glass needed polishing on the back of the counter over on the other side of the shop floor. I made myself busy, low down and out of sight with a duster while Viv advised him which locket would be a good choice, especially if worn with a pair of vintage studs. The studs happened to be displayed in the very counter that I was dusting, and she sent him over with a smile.

"Haven't we met?" said that familiar voice, instantly filling me with terror.

Mr Angry had bent his knees and lowered himself down to browse the earring displays in my glass cabinet, while eyeing me suspiciously through the glass. I continued to rub the glass until I realised that he was staring straight at me through the display. It was just like a horror film, his face lit up under the fluorescent light bulb that gave a slightly green tinge to his olive complexion.

"Oh, sorry! You're speaking to me!" I replied in what sounded like a much higher pitched version of my voice. I stayed where I was and polished furiously but to my horror he also stayed down on his knees, watching my cleaning efforts with interest. After a while my dodgy Can-Can knee twinged painfully, and feeling a flash of anger, I decided I was not going to let this horrible man ruin my dance career.

"Oooh, I'm afraid your face doesn't ring a bell, have you visited us before?" I continued, in as calm a manner as I could muster, realising I'd just given away a huge clue with the reference to the bell.

Bracing myself, I stood up to face the music. There was a hush across the shop as, slowly, we both rose in unison until we were eyeball to eyeball. I was convinced that he knew that I knew that he knew that I knew ... and I was terrified.

Viv stood stock still by the door with the tray of lockets in her hand and a sloping, fascinated smile on her lips. I also detected a glint of complete recognition in Mr Angry's eyes and wait, was that a smirk of amusement?

Viv attempted to break the tension by marching over and placing the tray of lockets in front of him, with a flourish. I made my escape to the gift wrap area on the other side of the shop.

"You're Aquarius, right?" she asked, out of the blue, leaning seductively across the glass counter, to where he stood. I appreciated that she was frantically attempting to distract him, but his eyes had lit up and he was jabbing that finger at me again.

"You! You're from the hotel. That's it, I knew it!" he remarked walking over. Confusingly, he was smiling broadly now, showing no sign of anger whatsoever, just perfect white teeth. I'd never seen him smile before and decided he might be rather nice when he didn't have a headache or a bone to pick with an innocent jeweller, receptionist person. Viv appeared at my side again.

"Oh, no Sir! You must have mistaken Jane for her sister." Amazingly, Viv continued to come to my rescue, kicking my leg far too hard, making me cry out slightly as she continued,

"Jane has a sister, Juliet, that works at the hotel. You two are so alike, aren't you?" she explained, forcing a little laugh, as she turned to me with a slightly crazed expression.

"Pah! Taurus, both of them!" she declared to a baffled Mr Angry.

I nodded awkwardly, hugely grateful for Viv's unexpected acting skills. She was turning out to be an even better fibber than I was, as she continued with her little performance.

"Are you staying at the hotel? This always happens," she explained with a shrug.

"Oh, really?" He looked disappointed but not completely convinced, staring at us both momentarily, before returning reluctantly to the lockets. He sneaked a crafty look at me every now and then, as I stood humming to myself like a deranged person. I was so relieved when someone else entered the shop, giving me a chance to escape this awful situation and immerse myself into a conversation with someone that didn't hate me.

Viv managed a cracking sale from Mr Angry and called me over as the old cash register clanged. We always worked in unison, Viv usually making the sales and me, finishing off the performance with gift wrapping and small talk. On this occasion, the small talk seemed to escape me as I became more and more exhausted and embarrassed. He watched me closely, loving every minute as, attempting to wrap his purchase, I wrestled with the Sellotape machine, sweating profusely. It was excruciating.

"There we are," I yelped as I passed him the Duke and Sons bag. The parcel inside looked like I'd wrapped up a starfish. My traumatised state and lack of sleep were making voices sound loud and scary, like a nightmare, as my head spun with fatigue and panic.

"I'm sure your Mother will be thrilled" I blurted, as I lurched across the shop to open the door for him, hugely relieved that it was time for him to leave.

Viv stopped what she was doing and glared at me as Mr Angry stopped in his tracks on his way out.

"Whatever makes you think this is for my mother?" he asked.

"Yes Jane," sneered a little voice in my head, "whatever made you think that it was for his mother?"

"Oh! Sorry! Well … I just assumed that ... well, you know, it looked ..."

Twisting my hands awkwardly I noticed Viv's face drain of colour, as she waited for my next comment. I continued to dig myself deeper into a hole of embarrassment.

"Whoever the lucky lady is, will be thrilled I'm sure. I know I would be," I added giving him a knowing look that probably came across as psychotic. "I mean, not that I would, you know ... want ... be ... um ... well anyway, let me get the door for you," I stammered.

I was about to talk about which photos he was considering putting in the locket, feeling rather lightheaded by now, when I suddenly changed tack, lurching for the door handle.

"Thank you for visiting us here at Duke and Sons today, I hope you've enjoyed your ..." I nearly said stay but managed to awkwardly change it to "self."

Now I really had gone and blown my cover because that was my receptionist speech. I was acting like someone from the National Trust and I knew that, as I opened the door for Mr Angry, he could see that I was definitely Juliet, as well as Jane. Annoyingly, he was grinning at me though, creating rather lovely dimples. Strange man. He walked away, looking back to give me a beautiful smile,

"You're right, it *is* for my mother," he laughed.

I stood cringing from the door of the shop, my heart banging against my chest.

After the jewellery shop drama, I was becoming increasingly keen to leave the country, and very tired of working most hours of the day and night. I say working, but most of the night shift was spent with my head on the desk in reception, dribbling and snoring until I was woken by guests arriving through the, conveniently loud, revolving oak doors of the foyer or as they stamped down the big squeaky wooden staircase from their rooms. Salvatore was pretty good at warning me of guests approaching with a quick rendition of La Traviata from the bar. He'd found the whole situation highly entertaining since I had confided in him about my daytime job, and it was nice to have someone in on my little secret, to cover for me.

At home, however, Giovanni and I were drifting apart, spending less and less time together as he spent more and more time at work with colleagues. I was always asleep when he got back to the flat and as soon as I woke, I had to rush out again. I started to crave a dancing job, far away from the daily grind of London life with it's exhausting transport system and busy streets. By the time Christmas was over, I was quite prepared to take a pantomime job as the back end of a horse if there was nothing else available, just to get away. At least then, if Mr Angry took his mother to the show, they wouldn't see me. The days drifted by monotonously, until one morning I arrived at Dukes to discover a large bouquet of red roses waiting for me.

I was stunned.

"Oh no!" I gasped, realising it was Valentine's day and I'd forgotten to give Giovanni a card. "Bless him, he shouldn't have spent all that."

Opening the card there was just a kiss and when I took them home to the flat, I hugged Giovanni tightly.

"Thank you darling. You shouldn't have."

Giovanni hugged me back and we went for a drink at the pub before I had to rush to work at the hotel. Later that evening I was surprised when Phillip the croupier popped in to see me in reception.

"Darling, I have to warn you, I don't think those roses were from Giovanni, just so you know. I have no idea who they could be from, but I know he would have told me if he was doing that. Italians don't even know about Valentine's Day, anyway ... just saying ... thought you should know."

I could tell that Phillip was hugely excited and desperate to find out the identity of my mystery admirer. I was too exhausted to care by this time, and as the weeks dragged by and Giovanni and I battled through the sleet and gales each day, on our way to work, I started to feel subdued. This mood was partly from lack of sleep but also because I could see that we were both putting on a brave face with no light at the end of the tunnel. I was starting to realise that his Mum had been right, that he shouldn't be in England, but in Italy, providing for his daughter and building a career there, where he was needed.

One evening, as I was leaving Duke and Sons to stagger to the hotel, Molly and Hilda called me into their office, their sweet little faces contorted with concern.

"What's going on sweetie, you look exhausted?" Molly demanded, taking my hand and leading me over to her little satin armchair by the grandfather clock, while Hilda poured me a large sherry. Their kindness was too much, and I burst into tears.

"Haha! I knew it!" cried Hilda, sitting on the arm of the chair and tilting my chin up to meet her gaze.

"We knew you were unhappy didn't we Molly darling? Now come on, you're not going anywhere until you spill the beans my sweet girl."

As I confessed my outrageous working schedule to them, I realised how ridiculous my life had become and I started to feel totally embarrassed. The whole story of Giovanni and the baby poured out, along with my fears of not being able to pay my rent in London as I continued to be rejected from auditions for West End musicals.

"Darling why didn't you tell us?" demanded Molly as she threw back her head dramatically, blowing a thin line of smoke from her long French cigarette.

"We could have given you more money. We didn't realise how poor you were poppet," Hilda added. "Gosh! It's so hard for *les artistes* these days isn't it, Molly?"

Molly nodded furiously and welled up with tears.

"How unbearable it must be," her voice was barely a whisper.

With a whacking great inheritance in their bank account and a huge home of their own, Hilda and Molly really had no idea of the stress of day-to-day survival for normal people. This was clearly very shocking for them.

"My poor lamb," Hilda patted my knee and re-filled my glass as Molly beckoned me over to her desk.

"Look darling, this was what we wanted to show you. It looks just up your street!"

The glow of the amber liquid was making me feel restored as I went to join her. To my surprise, spread out amongst their Vogue magazines was the latest copy of The Stage newspaper, opened out on the advertisements page.

"This is for you surely. Dancers-required-minimum- height-five-feet-and-nine-inches-tall-for-show-in-Japan," she read out excitedly. Hilda scuttled over,

"Show her that cruise audition as well Molly, in the Caribbean Islands!" she pointed to another advert that was circled in red pen.

"I thought I might audition myself!" she cried before they collapsed into a fit of giggles, clearly ecstatic at the thought.

"We're concerned that you're wasting your time here, hiding those long legs, when you could be having a ball in these beautiful places darling. And now, hearing about all the turmoil you've been coping with. Oh! If only we could have enjoyed such adventures in *our* youth."

Hilda and Molly, flushed with excitement and sherry, insisted that I hand in my notice at the hotel, explaining that they were firm friends with Reggie and knew all about it. They urged me to get myself to an audition and start planning a trip at once.

"Life is too short to waste time darling. You must get back to the world of show business, where you belong."

~

The next day, it was with great relief that I handed in my notice at the hotel.

"Oh, that *is* a shame."

Dicky's face was forlorn.

"D' ya hear that Reg?"

Reg was still by the fire.

"Hmph! The good ones never stay," he murmured from behind The Sporting Life.

Salvatore couldn't speak, hugging me before rushing into the stock room. The biggest challenge, however, was going to be telling Giovanni about the audition. As it turned out though, it was the easiest. He nodded, relieved I could tell, that I was encouraging him to face the music back home, and accept that our plan wasn't working. We agreed that he should go back to Italy and make some arrangements with his family, with a view to meeting up with me again later in the year, when he was back at work in Cagliari, with a place to live.

So, I took myself to the audition for the job in Japan that Molly had pointed out, and in no time at all I was planning to leave for rehearsals in Sydney, Australia.

Molly and Hilda were beside themselves that they had relaunched my career.

"Oh, we have to visit!" they clucked on my last day at Duke and Sons as they opened a bottle of champagne at ten o' clock in the morning. Of course, I knew they would never fly to Japan in a million years, but it added such a thrill to the moment. Giovanni made his way back to Sardinia and the next adventure began.

Life was grand.

28

SYDNEY

AS GIOVANNI TURNED and smiled that slanty smile at me for the last time at Gatwick, I wondered if I would ever find a man with no complications. I stopped in my tracks with horror, as I had a brief vision of Mr Angry, turning to smile at me on his way out of the jewellers. This awful thought and the fizz of excitement it created, was rather unsettling and I put it down to emotional exhaustion.

A week later I was gladly distracted from my hectic love life, stocking up on goodies and books for the journey to Sydney, where I was to rehearse for my next engagement. An Australian cabaret company by the name of Stanley Starsmore Productions were taking a show to a mountain resort, on the coast of Shizuoka, Japan, and they wanted *me* to join them. In those days, you could take whatever items you liked on flights with you, so amongst the supplies of Anne French Deep Cleansing Milk and Aqua Net hairspray was an impressive selection of classy Jackie Collins and Jilly Cooper novels that were now stashed in a rucksack, with plenty of chocolates, ready for the long flight ahead.

I was travelling alone because the rest of the dancers, in the show, were Australian. Stanley Starsmore Productions had been over to London in search of dancers to launch their new show that was booked to perform in Japan. Excitingly, Stanley had been looking for a dancer who could also sing, so I was feeling rather full of myself, having won this rather prestigious role. My *Evergreen* song and a fierce Can-Can performance had done the trick, although I was left dreading rehearsals because the day after the audition, I'd found it rather difficult to walk. Being rather out of practice, my muscles seemed to have gone into shock, so I was very glad of the slightly later departure date and extra time to get back into practice, before rehearsals began.

Once I was settled on my flight to Sydney, it became more noticeable how exhausted I was, from coping with my various commitments and responsibilities. Within minutes of taking off, I drifted into a deep sleep, just waking for meals, my books and chocolate left untouched.

The spell in London with Giovanni, and my extraordinary work schedule, had been draining. I couldn't think about Giovanni without welling up, but I was pleased to be jetting off with an exciting, new adventure ahead of me. I gazed out at the inky sky, turning my St Christopher's pendant over and over. Molly had fastened it around my neck when I'd left the shop on my last day and I felt calmed by the encouragement of my sweet friends. I was going to miss them. Phillip, the croupier at the flat, had been inconsolable when I'd announced my departure, but I was irritated by his dramatic outburst, and suggested that he apply for work on the cruise ships, with all his knowledge of gambling.

"Really, do you think so darling?" he gazed in astonishment at me.

"Well of course you should Phillip. The Americans would absolutely love you to bits, especially if you put on a Prince Charles voice," I chuckled, shoving The Stage newspaper into his lap. I had often seen adverts for work in the casino world and thought of him. Phillip had taken the newspaper and wandered off to his room in a trance.

~

Landing in Sydney was rather exciting, the bright blue sky and searing heat most welcome after the gruelling British winter that I'd just left behind. I relaxed instantly.

At arrivals, I was greeted by a handsome, athletic fellow, with a charming smile. He introduced himself as Stanley Starsmore, my new boss. It was our first meeting because my audition had been held, on his behalf, by two of his dancers.

"Welcome to Australia Jane," he gushed, shaking my hand and helping me courteously with my case. I followed him outside to an immaculate van full of beautiful costumes, reminding me of my first meeting with Guy in the dusty old van in France. Stanley was as slick and smooth as Guy was rough and wild, but I wasn't sure which I preferred.

"I'm taking you to stay at Bondi for a few nights until the Osaka girls have left. Your rehearsals start on Monday in town," he explained.

I nodded happily and agreed, as though I knew all about the Osaka girls and, after a brief drive, we arrived at Bondi beach. I mean, twist my arm, who would complain about going to

Bondi for the weekend. I was relieved on arrival, to find an apartment full of dancers and notice Stanley leaping back into the van and speeding off.

"I'll call you tomorrow," he'd shouted.

At one point, as Stanley and I had been driving along the highway from the airport together, I'd wondered if he and I were going to Bondi, just the two of us, for the weekend. He was handsome, that was for sure, but I felt I would need to get to know him better before spending a weekend at his beach apartment. The Osaka girls were preparing to take a Stanley Starsmore Production over to Osaka in Japan, for a six-month stint at a hotel spa resort. They had all had a terrible row that evening, so I was glad to make myself scarce, strolling bare foot along the sand on Bondi. As I sipped a melon smoothie, I had to pinch myself at my situation. It was so beautiful, and I chuckled as I paddled in the clear water, looking out at the waves. The whole laid-back atmosphere was indescribable as people smiled and nodded at each other, strolling around the beach cafés in their swimming trunks, not a sign of cellulite anywhere. Melon was the staple diet from what I could see.

In the morning, the dancers at the apartment left for the airport, so after another sleepy stroll along the warm promenade, followed by coffee in the sunshine, I had the apartment to myself. I was so disappointed on Monday when Stanley phoned up, telling me to hop on a number 52 bus into town with my luggage. It turned out, that from then on, I was to stay with one of the girls from my show, for the duration of the rehearsal period. Damn, I was just getting used to Bondi life. I did have a job for the next six months though, so putting on a brave face, I set off on the sweaty bus, for the next chapter of the trip, just thrilled to have been able to stay at Bondi Beach for the weekend, with Japan to look forward to.

Things changed rapidly from that day on.

~

Stanley Starsmore turned out to be a retired footballer, cabaret singer and shrewd businessman. He managed many cabaret shows, all choreographed by his adoring entourage of dance captains. Stepping onto the stage to sing songs like, *Can't Get Used To Losing You* and *Suspicious Minds*, he made guest appearances at venues all over Australia and Japan. Popular for his charismatic performances, supported by his glamorous beauties as they graced his stage in alluring costumes, he was quite the showman. Stanley had quite a twinkle in his eye, so with his perfectly flicked, shoulder length, footballer's hair and beautifully tailored suits, he convinced most of his dancers that they were extra special, and that he just might be falling in love with them. This caused mayhem and heartache throughout the company as he wined and dined his way through his troupes. If they could not be his lover, then they at least fought to secure a principal role in his shows. This crafty approach of his, ensured that competition was tough and his dancers, vying for his attention, always looked immaculate, giving him their best performance at all times. I have to say, that I too, was quite enamoured by his good looks and charisma at the airport. However, after only a few days in Sydney, I cottoned onto his little system, finding him irritating and rather cruel. Stanley didn't bother me in the slightest though, because I was loving the weather and had a big show to learn, so life was good. My previous dramas and the grey skies of London were becoming a distant memory, and the new people I was meeting were giving me plenty to think about, especially my host, Kerry-Anne.

Kerry-Anne was an ill-tempered girl who turned out, unfortunately, to be the dance captain of the show that I was to perform in, which made me rather anxious about the future politics within the group. During the evenings at her family home where I was staying, she bullied her own mother, so I already had a few concerns as to how things were going to work out for us when we opened the show in Japan. I kept my head down as we entered the rehearsal phase, not wanting to be seen as a troublemaker as soon as I arrived. It was hard to witness the rudeness towards her family at meal times, and then her impatience during rehearsals as we all battled to learn the numerous routines. I wasn't surprised to learn from one of the other girls that Kerry-Anne was one of Stanley's previous girlfriends, recently replaced by the newly appointed Veronika, a beautiful girl I remembered seeing at the London auditions. Kerry-Ann had been forced to take a back seat since Veronika had arrived. Veronika was a vision of showgirl exquisiteness in her designer leotards with high cheek bones and silky-smooth skin, buffed to perfection. She was annoyingly nice to everyone, walking around in her white silken kimono, sipping smoothies and bringing coffee to Stanley, sitting with him at the front of the studio and generally making us all feel self-conscious as the two of them wrote mysterious notes on their clipboards, and made hushed comments to each other as they watched the routines, scrutinising our every move.

After our first day of rehearsals, it became clear that our show was more of the three-star version, in comparison to Veronika's group that were preparing to appear in a larger hotel further up the coast from ours. I could only admire them as they danced in perfect unison, looking breathtakingly beautiful, immaculately turned out and professional in every way. If Kerry-Anne hadn't been so rude and unkind to everyone,

I could almost have felt sorry for her, having the humiliation of being conveniently demoted to the less prestigious show, rather explaining her miserable behaviour.

The rehearsal weeks flew by and we worked hard in the city heat, learning numerous routines in Stanley's stifling studios until we were ready to roll. Our show was a mixture of glamorous showgirl numbers in sequined bikinis and feathered head dresses, acrobatic Can-Cans, traditional Roaring Twenties and a bit of Flash Dance, the most popular dance film of the moment. I was really enjoying singing my only solo of the show, New York! New York! as the opening number, until one of the girls let slip that previously it had been Kerry-Anne's song, until she'd been sacked from the role and replaced by me. This did not bode at all well for our future friendship, which was already struggling. On the walk from the train station to the dance studio each day, I would take in as much of the Sydney atmosphere as I could. Everyone seemed so relaxed in their shorts and flip-flops in the city centre as I hurried to the rehearsal studios in my dance kit, frantically trying to remember the routines in my head from the day before. There was simply no time to enjoy the little fruit carts dotted around the city, serving up smoothies and ice-creams and I yearned to return to Bondi beach for an evening swim. It wasn't to be though, because in no time at all, we were off to Japan.

29

THE GREAT ESCAPE

THERE WAS GREAT excitement as we left on the long flight from Sydney to Tokyo, and then a further journey by coach to our hotel on the coast. Arriving late at night in darkness, I was so thrilled to think that we were actually in Japan and I looked forward to going on a good walk in the morning to take in our surroundings. We were shown to a little apartment at the back of the large five-star hotel where we settled in quickly, two girls to a room. Kerry-Anne had been complaining that we weren't staying in hotel accommodation and although the same thought had crossed my mind, I immediately pointed out that it was lovely that, at least we wouldn't have to be on our best behaviour all the time, being out of sight of the guests.

"It's a great flat for parties!" I exclaimed, trying to lift her mood, but failing miserably, as my comment was met with a glare of disdain. After a few days of meetings with the hotel management, we held technical rehearsals before waving

Stanley and Veronika off. I was rather glad to be rid of their watchful eyes as they went to join his five-star beauties, in a different hotel, located a few hour's drive away. As I'd anticipated, Kerry-Anne immediately held a meeting in our little kitchen to explain the schedule for the show under her supervision. I could see immediately that things were going to be unpleasant when, sitting herself high up on the fridge, looking down at us all with her clipboard, she took control at last.

"Ok, so I'm going to weigh you all now, and you will keep to that weight for the entire run of this show. I want you warmed up on stage at seven tomorrow morning ready to rehearse."

She paused here, looking around at our anxious faces, before continuing,

"And if anyone is late, I will dock your wages."

There was a hush in the room, and I looked over at Nicole, one of the troupe, as she rolled her eyes and lit up a cigarette. I had sat next to Nicole on the flight from Sydney and we'd had quite a laugh together. She had warned me that Kerry-Anne was tricky, and she was concerned how things were going to turn out.

"I wouldn't have come if I'd known she was dance captain," she'd confided.

I couldn't see how we were going to cheer things up at all at this point, and it also dawned on me that we hadn't even been paid for rehearsals yet, so I decided to speak up on behalf of the group.

"Could I ask a question on the matter of wages please Kerry-Anne?"

She froze, before slowly looking up from her paperwork, then down at me from the fridge, in disgust,

"Yes, what is it Jane?" she barked, with an angry glare, drumming her long nails impatiently on the work surface.

"Well, I'd appreciate some money soon, if possible. I need to buy some stamps. I'm sure we could all do with some cash, couldn't we girls?"

I smiled around at the others, optimistically, looking for some back up, but I was met with anxious faces. Everyone froze and eyeballs swivelled over to Kerry-Anne in anticipation of her reaction.

Her fingers stopped drumming.

"You will be paid when I think this show is up to scratch and, at the moment," she took a deep breath, "It stinks!!" she screamed, looking as though she would either cry or laugh like a maniac, I wasn't sure which. I was annoyed at the way she had made everyone jump with her outburst but held my temper. Nicole got up and went to her room and the rest of us sat, in uncomfortable silence, until it was broken by Helen, a slightly more experienced member of Stanley's company, jumping up and going over to the kettle,

"I think we should all have a nice cup of tea before bed. Thank you, Kerry-Anne, we'll look forward to an early start, won't we girls?"

I loved Helen and wondered to myself why she wasn't the dance captain. I nodded at her suggestion of a cup of tea, trying to keep my chin up. She was an interesting girl, not hugely glamorous, approaching her job as though she were a teacher. She was one of the longest standing members of Stanley's company and not, to date, one of his girlfriends although I was sure it wouldn't be long before curiosity got the better of him, and he went for a bit of Mary Poppins style action. I was sharing a room with Helen, and I wasn't sure how long I would be able to cope with her persistent Julie

Andrews approach, lovely as it was, at first. I mean, I was an optimist of the first degree, but her positive manner was slightly excessive, even to me. However, I was certainly not prepared to be bullied by Kerry-Ann for much longer, and decided to wait things out a bit, before taking action. After the disastrous kitchen meeting, we let the situation stew for a few days, hoping that Kerry-Ann would relax a little, after all the stress of the journey and opening night were over. I even suggested we accept some of the invitations that were being sent from the lovely bar staff, to go out to a local night club for a bit of karaoke with them. Singing on karaoke machines was the main form of entertainment in Japan at that time, very popular as a form of relaxation. It was to prove to be my saving grace in the weeks to come, although I was not aware of it at the time.

Nicole and I eventually managed to persuade all the girls to come out for an evening. It was the best thing we could have done because a few drinks and songs cheered us all up immensely, especially as Kerry-Ann was forced to be friendly in front of the Japanese staff who'd kindly invited us. The delicious dishes of seafood, exquisitely carved melon and exotic fruits that were brought to our table must have cost them a small fortune, but they wouldn't let us pay, just happy to reach out to us with their generous hospitality, very typical of their culture. The most popular drink in Japan at that time was water with ice and a dash of whisky in a large tumbler, which was a new one on me. I took to it with no trouble at all, of course, noticing that Nicole was telling the waiter not to worry about the water bit, just asking him for plenty of ice and to fill it to the top.

Amusingly, Kerry-Ann spent the entire evening singing karaoke songs as loud as she could and glaring at me with a clear message of hatred, demonstrating perfectly why she had been sacked as the singer, which after a few tumblers of whisky, Nicole and I began to find rather amusing. Unfortunately, though, the lovely night out failed to improve our outlook, and our troubles really reached a new level a couple of nights later, after a particularly stressful show that involved tears, on and off stage. Earlier that evening one of the girls had missed her cue, causing an outburst from Kerry-Anne in the dressing room that resulted in floods of tears from everyone which was not a good look for the Finale. Crying showgirls in a kick-line are somewhat unsettling for the audience, so I decided it was time to make a stand. I was starting to be really concerned for morale, including my own, and Nicole was getting near boiling point, so I didn't trust her with the sushi knives in the kitchen.

My relationship with Kerry-Ann had been strained from the start really. It had all kicked off during rehearsals in Sydney one sweltering afternoon, after hours of learning a French Can-Can routine in the studios. Stanley and Veronika had called us through to perform for them so they could tick the Can-Can off their list, as complete and ready to roll. I had noticed during the rehearsals, that everyone was performing the Can-Can in a very precise way, with rather serious faces and perfectly placed steps. Being from Europe, I had been taught the Can-Can in Paris by Guy Stranger, so I knew that it should be performed as a dance from the heart, with much emotion and merriment. The other girls had been going through the steps with a noticeably subdued approach that I had assumed was just for rehearsals, and that they were understandably saving any liveliness for real audiences.

The mood was somewhat tense that day as we all traipsed through to Stanley's studio in our beautiful velvet Can-Can frocks and bright pristine feathered head dresses. I caught sight of myself in the large studio mirror in my kingfisher blue bodice and red lipstick, feeling quite giddy with excitement as we prepared to show Stanley our work. Veronika was draped across his desk making sure she kept his full attention, despite the impressive view, and there were a couple of other girls from the five-star show sitting each side of him, preening their golden hair and adjusting their bra straps. I felt a pang of pity at this moment, for Kerry-Anne. I realised how daunting this was for her and, by the looks on their faces, the other dancers in our Can-Can show were pretty nervous too. I really didn't care a hoot because I love performing the Can-Can. It's my favourite dance in the world and no-one ever deters me, especially not puffed-up footballers like Stanley. We lined up while Offenbach's Can-Can Overture started up, igniting the usual emotion within, setting my heart racing as it always does before this dance takes off. It transports me to the Parisian music halls of the nineteenth century, when dancers risked their lives every night. Performing their kicks in full, frilly skirts near the naked flames of the torch lights, many a girl met her end in flames, it was just one of the risks of that time. The famous tune enveloped me instantly and I leapt into my dance, with vigour. With eyes flashing and legs flying, I let out hearty screams and hollers, cart-wheeling my way around the studio until it slowly dawned on me that rest of the group were performing just as we had in rehearsals, with fixed smiles and very precise footwork, calm as cucumbers. I approached Kerry-Anne as we prepared for our partner spin. This is when you hold another dancer by the waist, at the same time each holding one leg up over your head. Hopping and spinning around together as one, with Kerry-Anne, is not one of my treasured moments of the rehearsal period. I glanced nervously at her face, close up as we spun, her eyes like saucers on a very alarmed expression.

"What the fuck are you doing you idiot!" she hissed through a forced smile and gritted teeth.

I didn't have time to answer because only seconds later we were kicking for all we were worth in a straight line as we neared the finish. I decided that it would look more ridiculous if I suddenly stopped my Parisian approach to please Kerry-Anne, so I continued to enjoy myself. At the end, for the finale, we all threw ourselves into the splits on the floor, as is the tradition. Tadaaa!

The music stopped and the studio was silent.

I kept my head on my knee, panting, sweat trickling down my neck, but I knew I would have to look up at some point. I could eventually hear muffled snorts of laughter and disbelief from Nicole, whose head was buried in her skirt next to me. Slowly I peeped up at Stanley's desk in front of us before rolling over exhausted.

"Phwaar, that was great!" I announced, past caring anymore, preparing to be flown back to England. I decided to stay with the mood, not prepared to apologise for what, I felt, was actually a pretty impressive performance. I knew it was my big number and I was proud of it. As Kerry-Anne and the other girls gingerly lifted their heads, not a bead of sweat to be seen, Stanley suddenly threw his head back and started laughing while slowly clapping.

"Oh, my God! that was awesome Jane!"

As soon as his posse of spectators, sitting open mouthed, realised it was safe to smile, they all joined in the clapping, albeit reluctantly.

"See everyone, we have a European amongst us! I want everyone to do it like that." He came over and helped me up.

"Priceless darlin, good on yer! That was really French mate!! Do it again everyone," he ordered, "but like Jane did it."

He walked back towards a slightly sneering Veronika. "I love it, and so will the Japanese," he added, before sitting down again for the second performance.

If looks could kill I would have been struck down as I glanced briefly over at Kerry-Anne for any sign of forgiveness. She was fuming. Shit, this was not going to help me at all, and the re-run was quite challenging because I was exhausted from my earlier performance. It's very unusual to dance a full out Can-Can twice in a row. The rest of the group found it virtually impossible to be mad French women, so I felt a little bit guilty and sorry for them. Nicole mastered it pretty well although she was laughing hysterically throughout, but I could see I was going to have to hold extra rehearsals in Japan, to help them learn to let go, and be wild, sex crazed wenches. On the way back to our studio, Kerry-Anne grabbed my arm, her long nails digging into my sweaty skin.

"So, you're the favourite now sweetheart, aren't you? If you think we're doing that ridiculous exhibition of hideousness when we open the show, you can just forget it."

It felt like a scene from Neighbours.

So, as we stood in the kitchen in Japan, listening to Kerry-Anne's little sermon after Stanley's departure from the hotel and such a tearful start to our Japanese contract, I was furious. She was really on the warpath. I mean, who did she think she was, upsetting everyone like this?

For the first few weeks in Japan, we spent our free time relaxing. Without the luxury of internet, writing long letters home was the main activity. It was becoming clear that all the girls were miserable and tired of the relentless rehearsals every morning as it became obvious that Kerry Ann was determined to bring the show up to five-star standard by the time Stanley returned. Stanley was due back in a few weeks' time, to see how we were getting on and Kerry-Anne was clearly on a mission to impress him. I tried suggesting that we all rewarded ourselves for all our hard work with an afternoon exploring the area and taking some photos, but my suggestion had been met with anxious comments. I could see that, at this rate, if we didn't stand up for ourselves, we weren't even going to see any of Japan during our stay. How wrong could I have been?

Most of us have had to work with disagreeable characters at some point in our lives. My Granny used to say,

"In every workplace, there is always a disagreeable old cow and, in my office, it's me."

I have always found that it helps to try to look for a person's good points when they are proving to be disagreeable to work with. I try to put myself in their shoes and offer a bit of compassion, often shedding a new light on someone's reasons for being unbearable and offering a way forward. However, in the case of Kerry-Ann, although I had been sympathetic to the fact that Stanley Starsmore had humiliated her and treated her abominably, she just wasn't letting up, as we all tried so hard to win her round.

The apartment was rather quirky, and we had all been very amused that there was a bath installed in the kitchen, with a wooden board over it to double up as a dining table. It was such a tiny apartment, and the bath/table arrangement was obviously just a space saving measure. There was a shower room too, but I really do enjoy a good old soak, so one night, after a particularly stressful performance, craving some fun, I decided that it might be funny to fill the bath with bubbles and be sitting in it when the girls came back from the theatre at the end of the show. I wanted to make them laugh, cheer them up a bit, and break the tension that was mounting daily. I knew that a crazy night of singing, drinking and dancing had always worked for Susannah and I when things got tough on the tours with Guy, so believed it could help us now, here in Japan.

Earlier that evening I'd swapped a Fleetwood Mac cassette with Daichi, one of the barmen in the hotel, in exchange for a bottle of whiskey. I often stopped to chat and flirt with Daichi on my way to work, albeit with caution after my track record of bringing innocent men back to Britain with me. Daichi reminded me that there were still nice people in the world. I had gone past caring what Kerry-Ann did next, thinking that I would quite happily go home if she sacked me, so my party plan began developing with confidence. After the show, I slipped back to the apartment early, saying that I had to get some aspirin. Once there, I ran the bath, putting in extra bubbles so that they floated merrily around the kitchen. I found six little sake glasses in the cupboard and lined them up along the top of the fridge with my bottle of Jack Daniel's as it glowed invitingly. I was fed up with green tea and we hadn't had a proper drink since the karaoke night, so I couldn't wait to get stuck in. I giggled nervously and decided to pour myself a well-earned glass to enjoy while I waited for the others to arrive.

I had rigged up my little tape recorder next to the tumble drier and stripped down to my Iron Maiden knickers just as Tom Jones' *What's New Pussy Cat?* belted out of the speakers. My heart skipped a beat as I heard footsteps coming down the path. I poured myself a second drink before hopping into the gloriously hot water. After removing all my hair pins from the show, my hair was in the usual crazy bird's nest style, that comes from all the hairspray and back combing. My rosy face was only just visible above the bubbles. I started to laugh to myself in a slightly manic way as I peeled off my false eyelashes and stuck them on the wall. The whisky had gone straight to my head because we were not really being fed very much, and the weeks of anxiety were catching up with me. I hummed along with Tom until I heard the kitchen door open with a bang, as Kerry-Ann arrived. Her footsteps stopped.

"What the hell?" she exclaimed, throwing her bag down.

"What do you think you're playing at Missy?"

She looked down at me as though I were twelve years old. I sunk lower into the bath and took another slug of whisky from my glass. It tasted like heaven and crept into my vocal cords like a serpent, bringing me confidence that I had forgotten existed, there in the depths of my emotions.

"I'm having a bath, darling, won't you join me?" my voice sounded deep and velvety like an advert for indulgent chocolates on the TV. Fortunately, Nicole was right behind Kerry-Anne, surveying the scene with sheer delight, so I knew that if I was murdered, at least there would be a witness. All the pent-up emotion from the last few weeks was rising to the surface in the form of unstoppable laughter. Nicole took one look at this extraordinary scene, threw down her bag and ripped off her track suit.

"Move up, I'm comin' in!"

It was rather a squash when Nicole lowered her extraordinarily long legs into the bath enthusiastically, her spikey bleached hair completing the craziness of the scene. Accepting a glass of Jack Daniel's, she looked defiantly across at Kerry-Anne who, speechless for once, marched to her room and slammed the door with rage. Giggling nervously, we waited for the others to arrive at the party, which was only a matter of a few seconds. Helen took one look at the scene and went into schoolteacher mode, ushering the other dancers to their rooms.

"Girls, go to bed, I'll sort this out, these two are being very silly."

Nicole refilled her glass and raised it over her head,

"Cheers mate."

"Cheers darling!" I knocked another one back, feeling wonderful and quite pleased everyone was going to bed because I realised that I didn't really want to share the whiskey six ways anymore. Helen came and sat on the side of the bath like Sister Margaretta from The Sound of Music.

"Nicole ... Jane ..."

She paused and tried to smile at us, but it was one of those politician-smiles that isn't in the eyes or the heart, just the mouth.

"I know it hasn't been easy for us recently, but I really feel we should keep this show on the straight and narrow for the sake of Stanley's reputation."

Crikey! *I knew it!* She fancied Stanley Starsmore as well.

"Now have your fun," she attempted to laugh but it wasn't convincing.

"Have your fun, and tomorrow morning we will have a talk with Kerry-Anne, and maybe now is the time to call Stanley, and see what we can do about the unrest within our group."

This, we knew, of course, was the correct thing to do, but our mischievous silence indicated otherwise. Nicole and I beamed at each other as Helen went over to the sink and shuffled a few chopsticks on the draining board, waiting for us to agree with her. I knew she wanted us to pull the plug out and go to bed but unfortunately for her, Freddie Mercury had started to sing *We are the Champions* on the tape, and we couldn't help ourselves. I felt a little bit guilty as I heard her stifle a sob on her way to her room. We both agreed that it was a shame that Helen hadn't accepted a drink. She needed one.

"Let's fix her up with Daichi the barman," chuckled Nicole.

"Yeah good idea," I agreed, loving our newly discovered camaraderie. The whiskey was convincing us that we were so wise for our years.

"Look what you've done Janie girl, you are a scream. *Rule Britannia!* that's what I say!"

"Yeeah!" I agreed, laughing triumphantly, feeling like such a card.

"Oh, God I miss my family," I sighed.

"Yeah, me too ... I mean, I miss *my* family, I don't know yours!" another collapse of giggles as Nicole drained her glass.

"You've certainly cheered me up anyway, I don't think anyone else wants to join us."

I pulled the plug out and we hit the last chorus with Freddie.

"We are the champions my friends, and we'll keep on fighting till the end."

I drunkenly hoped that Kerry-Anne could hear us. Nicole was really good at loud burps and I was finding it hugely amusing.

"How childish!" I chortled.

We screamed with laughter and, realising that, sadly, no-one else was joining us, we took the bottle, and moved out on to the balcony that overlooked the back of the hotel and the main road into town. We sang a few more songs before settling down to drinking and chatting about our hopes and dreams, lighting up cigarettes as the whiskey really kicked in. Feeling better for a heart to heart, we sat in silence, not wanting the mood to change, before dropping off to sleep. When I awoke, it was getting light and Nicole was looking out at the stunning view of the yet, unvisited, Suruga Bay.

"I think I want to leave thish place Janie girl. I can't bear it anymore," she muttered.

"I know, we're trapped really," I agreed, "I'm dreading tomorrow, she'll kill ush in rehearsals, and we'll be hung-over."

Nicole got up and continued to observe the mountains over the railings of the balcony, her long naked body making a perfect silhouette against the glow of the sunrise. There was a twinkle in her eye as she swung around to look at me, slurring her words slightly with shining eyes.

"I think it's time for ush to leave. If you're up for it, we could get to Tokyo and find new jobs. Our working visas don't run out till October you know."

I suddenly loved the thought of leaving and held her gaze for a few seconds.

"Oh, my God you are joking, aren't you?"

"Nah! I know Tokyo really well," she was whispering now, "We would find modelling work shooo eashily. I could call my Japanese friends. They'd help ush out. They love Gaijins, we're such a novelty with our long noses."

I marvelled at this new information, as Nicole gazed into her glass.

"Whatsh a Gaijin?" I asked,

"Itsh Japanese for foreigner."

"Wow! thatsh amazing darling," I attempted to look down to admire my long nose but there were two of them.

Nicole leaned forwards, slipping off her elbow and spilling her drink.

"You and me are shpecial. They will love us, I promish,"

"What, like becaush we're Gaijins?"

"Yeah, exshactly, now, go and pack a few things … we can't take bloody everything though."

312

She waved her cigarette vaguely in the direction of our rooms, "and I'll go fetch our parshports from reception. Daichi is on night shift so it'll be no problem."

I pulled myself up from the floor with renewed enthusiasm.

"You better not go into resheption looking like that darling," I warned, regarding Nicole's naked body and little G string.

"Meet you back here in ten, I'm on my way."

I lurched through the kitchen, skidding all over the place, to my room. I found my smallest case but being rather drunk, it was difficult to decide what to take with me, but I knew I couldn't catch the train to Tokyo just in my wet Iron Maiden knickers and pink flip-flops.

Helen stirred in her troubled sleep.

"Are you ok now Jane?" she whispered.

"Oh, it's alright Helen, I'm jusht a bit drunk so Nicole and I are jusht going for a little walk to sober up."

"Oh, I am glad you've seen sense, I'll see you in the morning at breakfast, everything will be alright, nighty night."

She snuggled back under the quilt, her hair still scraped back in an annoying ponytail like a nun and I longed to snip it off before I left. I crammed as much as I could into my case in the dark, and threw on jeans and a jumper, knowing it was not the time to start deciding which bras to take with me.

Daichi had been quite happy to give Nicole our passports with no questions. She later told me with great hilarity, that she had remembered to put on a bathrobe before appearing in reception, thanking him for the passports with a long snog.

Once Nicole was packed and dressed, I met her on the balcony. We knocked back one more drink before throwing our cases over the top of the railings and slipping onto the grassy slope that led down to the road. Being drunk, we were completely confident that we would be able to hitch a lift into

313

town, somehow, and as we slid down the grassy bank, the excitement was exhilarating. I felt like Steve McQueen in The Great Escape. This was real adventure and I realised I was loving it and couldn't wait to take Tokyo by storm.

Halfway down the bank, Nicole grabbed my arm as I had started to roll a little bit too quickly. We hung on to the dewy grass catching our breath, laughing and snorting quite hysterically now. Nicole was signalling to be quiet, by holding her finger up to her nose. There was something worrying her as we sat panting for a moment in the fresh morning air. Voices, quite alarmed voices in fact, were not far away. Very slowly we turned our faces back up the slope where, to the left of our balcony was a fence. We had always wondered what was on the other side of it. There, in the morning light, stood a row of stark-naked guests, businessmen probably, although it was hard to decide when they were naked, enjoying the sunrise at the hot baths from the mountain spring water. They were obviously on a relaxing weekend away from their stressful office jobs in Tokyo, performing a steamy sun salutation in their birthday suits. I don't remember who was more shocked, them or us, but there was an embarrassing silence that seemed to last for about two days. Eventually, one of the men started to laugh and nod his head, his little dinkle bobbing in the breeze. Nicole still had a hold of me, frozen, and we must have looked like a scene from Scooby-Doo. The laughing man's colleagues caught on very fast to the amusing moment and we all erupted into joyful morning laughter.

"Thank you! So sorry! Good morning!" Nicole started calling to them in her best Japanese accent.

We reversed down the hill, bobbing, smiling and backward-rolling, as lady-likely as we could, until we presented ourselves on the tarmac outside the hotel laundry. It was a very busy time of day for the domestic staff and there was a large van waiting, while two little men heaved huge baskets of dirty sheets into the back. Quick as a flash Nicole waved at the driver and made the hitch-hiking thumb sign to him with a dazzling smile. A huge grin spread across his bored face and he pointed to some vacant seats in the back of his van next to two, very old, smiley grannies.

When we climbed in, the driver passed us our cases, and within minutes we were trundling down the mountain road towards the town. The two grannies started to chatter furiously, pointing and laughing at us as they clung to their seats while we bumped and swerved down the winding road. They had no teeth and were sucking on bits of dried fish which they passed over to us. It was a moment that I will always treasure. Real Japan.

Having spent so long imprisoned in the hotel and its grounds with Kerry-Anne, apart from the balcony view, this was the first time I had really seen the beauty of where we were staying. When we had arrived from Sydney it had been late at night, so I'd been unaware of the scenery until this moment. We passed little huts where the inhabitants were up early, busy working on their vegetable gardens, black silhouettes of knobbly trees on the skyline behind them like a silk painting. There were people walking up the hills, hunched right over, carrying bundles of firewood home on their backs. It was wonderful, beautiful and the first real taste of Japan for me. Real, rural, traditional Japan with the sun glinting on the sea and a stunning backdrop of the mountains. There were little islands dotted along the coast, with green trees growing out of them like pins poking out of a cushion. Added to which we were now laughing with two old Japanese ladies, who were smiling over at us in their kimonos.

It really didn't get more Japanese than this.

Nicole was rooting around in her bag now, not too fussed about the scenery, as we pulled into the town square by the train station. The sun was peeping through the trees and I started to wonder where this new day would take us. I thought of poor Helen waking up to find us gone and felt a pang of terrible guilt. It occurred to me uncomfortably, that I was making a habit of running away from situations. I prepared to suggest that we stay on the van until it delivered us back to the hotel on its return journey, so that we could have that well overdue talk with Kerry-Anne and Stanley.

Our bath party had been the highlight of my Japanese trip so far, but I was quite hungover and needed to take some aspirin and get into bed. I didn't have a yen to my name either, so I had no choice but to slope back to Kerry-Ann. I could just imagine her smug face waiting for me in my room.

"Come on sleepy head, the train leaves in five!"

Nicole woke me from my little daydream. She was standing on the pavement with all of the luggage and two tickets to Tokyo in her hand, courtesy of her credit card.

I scrambled over the baskets of damp sheets in the back of the van, nodding blearily to the driver, who I noticed had bought over two of his friends to have a look at me. Six-foot tall dancers from Britain didn't visit these parts very often and they certainly didn't settle into his laundry baskets for a morning kip amongst the wiffy sheets very often. As I staggered across to her, Nicole passed me a little cup of miso soup that she'd bought from a wagon by the ticket office.

"We'll be able to get amazing coffee in Tokyo Janie, you'll love it."

My bath party had allowed Nicole's true character to shine through. She had kept quite a low-profile during rehearsals

316

but now that she had found a partner in crime, she was on a roll. On the flight from Sydney, she had explained how she usually worked as an air hostess on domestic flights throughout Australia, but she took the odd contract with Stanley when she fancied a change of scenery. This would definitely be her last job for him, and I wondered what her family would say when she explained what she had done, let alone what she would say if she ever bumped into Stanley again. Being Nicole, I had a feeling she would think of some convincing explanation. I will never forget the delight on her face when she walked into that kitchen and saw me in the bath, at the end of my tether, confronting Kerry-Anne. A light had flicked on in her eyes as she found a willing accomplice to join her on a getaway.

My heart raced as I hauled my case along the platform, realising that there was no way now that I would persuade her to go back to the hotel. As I sobered up, I started to see the reality of our drunken idea. Obeying Nicole in my exhausted state, as she steered me down the carriage to our seats, I felt too exhausted and ill to resist. She chatted drunkenly away about her friends in Tokyo who would be so glad to see us. I was certainly convinced that I wouldn't see Kerry-Anne ever again, which was a great feeling, but there was a pang of guilt when I thought of the rest of the girls. Trying to put a show together that evening was not going to be easy with two, whopping, great dancers missing. I smiled as I realised that, at least, Kerry-Ann would get her singing solo back. These thoughts were almost too much for me to cope with though at this hung-over moment. I bumped and squeezed my way down the aisle to my seat. I had other more urgent issues to attend to.

"You do know I have no money at all Nicole, and that you are my chaperone, don't you?" I reminded her nervously.

"You'll have to find me a job with these friends of yours. I still have time to leap off this train if you don't want the hassle."

She didn't respond so I continued, "I will forgive you, and we'll still be life-long friends as long as Stanley doesn't kill me first."

I waited for an answer to what I thought was a very reasonable announcement, especially the being killed bit, but Nicole seemed to find it extremely amusing. She was fearless! I settled into my seat and closed my eyes, realising that there was no turning back now, as I felt the soft jolt of the train pulling away from the station. Nicole and I sipped our Miso soup and gazed at the trees as they flashed past, faster and faster. It felt like we were flying as the Shinkansen bullet train, sped out into the countryside and we sobered up, contemplating our next genius move. I felt exhausted and remorseful already.

"Relax darlin, you're spoilin' it!" Nicole squinted into the sunshine, looking out of the window at the horizon, "We're about to embark on a life experience."

She raised her cup of Miso soup as a toast, and I realised that she had very likely performed much more daring feats than this during her life. I raised my cup and knocked back the rest of my soup, even swallowing the sea-weedy bits in the bottom, knowing this was possibly the last meal I would eat for days and I needed to savour the nourishment. I tried to relax and look at the view that everyone else on the train was finding so thrilling. The Bullet Train experience was something people from Europe saved up for, for all of their lives, and should have been a beautiful moment, but I wasn't seeing any view, just my life flashing in front of me and an image of Stanley and Kerry-Ann in my mind. He was shouting and pointing at me from a courtroom like Mr Angry at the hotel reception in England. I was certainly good at upsetting handsome, scary men, and

I seemed to have started leaving a trail of destruction all over the world. What I wouldn't have given to be back behind that boring desk again at the hotel in London.

～

Nicole broke my dream.

"We're gonna suck Tokyo dry this summer!" she mused, staring out at the horizon.

Oh, my God, I wasn't sure I was up to life sucking, at this time. I was feeling sick, trying frantically to find a happy thought like Peter Pan. I knew that I should be taking in the breath-taking scenery as we belted through the countryside, but I was preoccupied with trying not to cry and bang my fists on the table. I imagined that Stanley was bound to take us to court, and we were definitely going to go to prison for breaking the contract. I could just picture us being led away in court, our parents weeping in the dock. Nicole started chatting about our Tokyo plans, convincing me slowly that we were in for a very successful Japanese jaunt, before returning to our families back home, loaded with yen. Stanley Starsmore was history to her now and I longed to feel her relaxed frame of mind. Eventually, my optimistic side, which is usually very reliable, started to slowly return as we studied the scruffy contracts we'd signed in Stanley's office.

"These don't look at all professional and they're definitely not equity contracts," I pointed out as we looked through the wording. I must have relaxed immediately, dropping off to sleep for a while, because I was woken up again by the clinking of ice cubes in glasses as Nicole poured gin and tonics. My poor liver.

For a moment, I was back in the kitchen bath at the apartment, waking from a horrendous dream, but no.

"Cheers beautiful." Nicole was holding a glass out to me, "Wakey wakey. Nearly there."

I accepted her offering, marvelling at her beautiful complexion and sparkling blue eyes, even after such an all-nighter, noticing out of the window that the scenery had changed quite dramatically. Blocks of flats were popping up every so often and we were getting further and further away from our Stanley Starsmore world. My stomach did a flip when I looked at my watch, realising that the other girls back at the apartment would now know that we had done a runner and be on the phone to Stanley. Judging from my groggy mood and the dribble from my mouth, I must have been asleep for quite a while because the bullet train had shot us pretty much all the way to Tokyo.

30

KAREN CARPENTER

I MANAGED A smile as I took a gulp of the huge gin and tonic, offered as breakfast from a grinning Nicole.

"Cheers Nicole," I said nervously.

We didn't have mobile phones or internet in the eighties, so until we arrived in Tokyo, I would have to take Nicole's word for it, that we would be able to walk straight into jobs and find somewhere affordable to live. At the back of my mind, I was also forming a Plan B.

I had a feeling that, in his rage, Stanley would definitely be tempted to call my parents to tell them some horrendous story of my whereabouts. Of course, the real story *was* horrendous, but better told by me, so I knew that when we arrived into the city I would have to phone home and tell my folks that I was changing my plans. If I could tell them that I had taken a new job in Tokyo and that I was fine, then they wouldn't worry. To tell them the exact truth was not a hugely popular option and, hopefully, wouldn't be necessary if I could find work quickly. I was proud to have never asked my parents for money and was hoping, with all my heart, to keep it that way. As it turned out, I later learnt that Stanley *had* rung Mum and Dad, telling them that I was travelling back to the UK on the back of a motorbike with a man I'd met in a night club. This reassured me that Stanley Starsmore was not a nice man and I'd been quite right to leave.

The passengers started getting luggage down from the racks and chatting excitedly as the view from the window became built up with skyscrapers, flashing neon signs and highways. We pulled into the train station and made our way out onto the chaotic platform. It was the first time in my life that everyone but me, seemed to know where they were going. There were people with names on signs at the ticket barrier and how I wished my name would pop up, but I knew there would be no chauffeur waiting for me today.

The most unsettling part of our arrival in Tokyo, were the Japanese symbols on all the signs, because for Nicole and I, they were impossible to make head or tail of. When in Europe you can usually get a rough idea of what signs say, but here, there was absolutely no way of knowing and, as Nicole marched confidently ahead, I knew she was putting on a bit of a show to keep my confidence up. Luckily, Nicole had a few coins in her pockets that took us on the subway to Roppongi, a district of Tokyo that she knew from a previous trip and, supposedly where her friends might be. Once out of the subway, Nicole led us to a little pink plastic phone on the street that reminded me of something from a toyshop. They are rare these days, I gather, but at that time, these little phones were dotted around the city of Tokyo for domestic calls only. I thought they were adorable. Nicole wasn't bothered about how adorable the phones were though, as she rifled through the back of her old diary, glaring angrily at the dog-eared pages as she hunted for numbers of old friends.

It soon became apparent, however, that everyone had moved away.

After several failed attempts, she slammed the phone down, looking tired, cross and a bit deflated.

"Shit! What 've I done?" she said angrily.

Fortunately, my mood had started to perk up, as it always does of its own accord. It hadn't even occurred to me to feel annoyed with her for leading me into this dilemma. I felt well and truly that we were in the mess together, and since I'd been so miserable working with Kerry-Ann anyway, I was slowly but surely adjusting to this new life of adventure, deciding it was rather gripping. Stanley seemed a world away already.

"What do you mean Nicole?" I asked honestly. "I'm loving this! Just think ... we're in Tokyo ... yeah!"

I did a little punch into the air and tried to look as though I was enjoying myself, but she stared at me, baffled, so I continued.

"C'mon, let's find that hostel you were talking about," I suggested with a jaunty nudge. "We need to get out and find a job ... tonight."

After walking through a maze of busy streets, I felt relieved to finally find the hostel. It was friendly and basic with many Europeans pottering in and out, either on holiday or visiting for business meetings. I'd been keen to sort out a few worries, the first, and most critical, being a roof over our heads and now secondly, I wanted to make a quick call home, half hoping my parents might come up with a solution. I felt quite envious when Nicole explained that she didn't need to call her parents and that if Stanley rang them, her Mum would tell him where to stuff it and carry on with her day. Since I didn't have any money, my only option was to reverse the charges to England. In those days, you could call an operator and ask for help, although I've no idea if these angels even exist anymore. They could make a call for you, or direct you expertly to anywhere you desired, asking the person on the receiving end, if they minded paying for the call. My heart skipped a beat as I heard the familiar ring tone of England and my Dad's voice,

"Butley 3728"

I wanted to cry as I heard the usual exchange with the operator, asking Dad if he would accept the charge before I spoke.

"Dad, it's me just to say I'm absolutely fine, so don't worry if you get a strange call from Stanley Starsmore."

My voice sounded really groggy and I felt an unexpected knot of home sickness, as I pictured him in the kitchen by the kettle, or sat at his desk, with the dulcet tones of Radio 4 drifting across his study. I could just imagine the lovely English rain that I usually complained about, trickling down the window, the dog in her basket with her head raised and tilted, as it did when there was a phone call, as though she could follow the conversation. I felt a lump in my throat.

"Who? Stanley who? What the dickens? Jane darling, you're not still in Japan, are you?" Dad quizzed.

"Yes Dad, but don't worry I'm absolutely fine," I sighed emotionally, not wanting to worry him, but then Dad's tone changed.

"Reversing the charges from Japan, are you out of your mind? This will be costing me a fortune. I'm putting the phone down now!"

The phone went dead so I replaced the receiver, staring at it in astonishment for a few seconds. Dad had heard me say that

I was fine, at least, and I knew he would tell Mum. He clearly hadn't realised that the situation was a little serious and had complete confidence in me.

Surprisingly though, I started to feel a slow surge of relief rising up from within.

"Hey ho. At least they know I'm safe," I smiled, reassured at least that I didn't need to dwell on that worry anymore. That had been the point of the call, hadn't it?

After the very brief chat with my Dad, I was delighted to feel a strange shift in my outlook on the current predicament. A huge weight was lifting from my hung-over shoulders as I was hit with a confidence that we *were* going to find our own way out of this mess. The brief conversation with Dad had given me the courage to do whatever I pleased, without having to explain my choices and decisions to anyone. I felt such a new sense of freedom and strength, it was extraordinary and boded well for the evening ahead. I looked over to see that Nicole had crossed the road from the hostel and was sat on a wall staring into space, smoking her last cigarette. She looked less buoyant than when we'd boarded the train that morning, having been devastated that her Japanese friends weren't around to help us out. It seemed to have knocked the wind out of her sails somewhat and worryingly, she had also confessed that we were just about at the credit limit on her Mastercard already. Seeing as I had no credit card of my own, I knew at that moment, that it was time to act. Taking a deep breath, I crossed the road to join her on the wall. Nicole squinted at me as she dragged the last bit of life out of her cigarette before squashing it underfoot.

"Come on you, let's go and find a job," I suggested as I took her hands and pulled her up. I just knew we were going to sort this mess out whatever it took, even considering, with surprising enthusiasm since the phone call home, that I might even become a striptease artist, although I'd never heard of striptease clubs in Japan.

"What about the Arabian knight you told me about from Cairo who's waiting for you, can't we call him, he's rich?" ventured Nicole quietly, adding, "Have you got his number?"

I snorted with a tired laugh as I imagined Babu hearing my desperate voice. I knew that calling him was out of the question.

"Oh, my God no, he would just love that. I would be forever beholden. Ask me again tomorrow."

I had found my second wind and enthusiasm seemed to be seeping out of every pore, which was just as well because Nicole seemed to be flagging big time. It was time to take over the reins of our crazy adventure and get into business mode immediately, so I swung around and grabbed her slumping shoulders.

"Nicole darling, we don't need a hand-out. We are fabulous women and we're going to dress up tonight and show Tokyo what we're made of."

She didn't respond to my outburst of enthusiasm, so I continued,

"I promise you that by midnight we will have a job, even if it's a shit one."

That last comment at least brought a smile to Nicole's face and pleasingly, her enthusiasm returned, showing how fragile the line between confidence and desperation can be.

"Yeah! Fuck it!" she took my hand and we marched back to our hostel room. Tipping the little luggage that we had from our drunken departure onto the bed, made us realise how plastered we'd been when we left. There was a tight black evening dress that actually hung off me like a sarong, I was becoming so thin, but fortunately, I'd thought to pack my high heels. Being a size nine, it would have been impossible to buy a new pair of heels in Tokyo, and evening wear would not have looked good with smelly trainers on. I'd packed a few other clothes, my address book, thankfully, and my wash and make-up bag, vital survival tools. I cringed briefly to myself when I thought of the things I'd left behind that included my camera. We set out into the evening with restored confidence though, and plenty of lip gloss, stopping on the way several times to taste the free food samples that seemed to be conveniently promoted outside the bright, colourful, mini supermarkets everywhere, knowing that this would be our only sustenance for the time being. Nicole spotted free sachets of shampoo at the chemist on offer too, so we took a few of those, delighted that we would have beautiful hair at least.

Roppongi is a district famous for its nightlife and there was quite a buzz in the air as we walked through the throng of young people on their way to the bars after work. Every now and then there was a Pachinko Parlour, a type of amusement arcade housing rows and rows of slot machines with men sitting transfixed, staring as they played. The tokens for the machines were little metal balls that, combined with the music and whacky voices blaring out from the games, created an ear-splitting sound as the winnings cascaded into the metal trays underneath. I was told that people went there to relax, which I found extraordinary. The cafés and restaurants of Roppongi were full of trendy Japanese artists, models, musicians and businessmen and women, all eating and drinking at little tables that were lit up with lamps. There were pretty girls coming in and out of tempting dress shops, with armfuls of little, designer boutique shopping bags, chatting furiously to each other, no doubt planning the evening ahead. Being the eighties, Europeans were a huge novelty in Japan so, now and then, we would notice people staring and smiling up at us as we made our way through the crowds. I've watched some footage of Roppongi recently and it looks like a different place altogether, much more built up and noisy with plenty of tourists everywhere. On that first evening with Nicole, I just felt envious of all these people with their jobs and their freedom to stop for drinks wherever they pleased. Having no money at all was a new experience to me and I felt lost, miserable and desperate, but the liveliness of Roppongi was bringing restored hope that, with a bit of luck, we might be invited to become part of this exciting city.

The challenge ahead was huge, so it was just as well I felt so determined because Nicole looked anxious, wandering along beside me. I was worried that I wouldn't be able to lift her mood before our first interview. Eventually I could bear the anticipation no longer, added to which I was getting a blister from my high heels.

"Come on Nicole, this looks like a cool place."

Opening the door to a cocktail bar on a lively corner, I steered her inside. We had to start somewhere, however humiliating it was, and it was becoming clear that no-one was going to stop us in the street and offer us a job. I could tell that it was going to be a case of presenting ourselves to as many establishments as we could before closing time and hoping for the best. Our first and biggest dilemma was the language barrier which hadn't even occurred to me until now. It was nerve-racking to realise that we would actually need to speak to people, let alone mix cocktails for them. I had only ever ordered and consumed cocktails from the customers' side of the bar, never wondering how to assemble them, let alone discuss them with others in Japanese, so I became nervous as hell.

As we ventured inside our first potential workplace, two very smiley young ladies in matching black and white suits popped up from behind the bar.

"Helloooo!," they sang in unison.

They seemed thrilled that we had chosen to enter their bar and giggled continuously as Nicole introduced us in, from what sounded to me, like perfect Japanese. Before we'd had a chance to broach the subject of employment opportunities, Ying and Yang had produced a little tea pot and four cups.

"Welcome, this ... is ... Japanese Tea!" offered Yang proudly passing us a cup each.

I accepted gratefully, terrified that we might have to pay for it, while feeling completely useless as I realised just how serious the language barrier was. How could I ever begin to learn such a tricky language? I felt a lump in my throat as I smiled and sipped, the conversation dwindling until we'd resorted to saying the names of American celebrities, whilst smiling and nodding desperately. I felt exhausted and it was only our first attempt.

"Nicole," I turned and smiled, "What is the Japanese for *Give us a job mate?*"

Nicole understood that I was keen to get this nightmare on the road and started gesticulating and, credit to her, somehow managed to explain that we were looking for work. I was starting to feel like her gormless sidekick. Phoning Babu became more and more appealing but I could imagine him insisting on flying us to Dubai before attempting to re-kindle the part-time relationship and marry Nicole off to a playboy.

Ying and Yang looked completely flabbergasted as they listened to Nicole and then, collapsing into giggles again, shook their heads apologetically. No way was there a job for us here. We drained our teacups and as politely as we could, shuffled out of the bar waving goodbye, managing not to throw ourselves on our knees begging for work.

When we got outside, I didn't stop to discuss this first failure, instead going into raptures about Nicole's impressive linguistic skills. I knew it was better to focus on the positive things at this stage, rather than dwell on the failed attempt at finding work. We tried several more bars with the same embarrassing results until, even *my* self-esteem started to seep away. I wasn't panicking yet though. I knew how quickly things can turn around if you keep trying, grateful that, with our track record, we were being served tea and not alcohol. I was just thinking how I really couldn't take in any more fluids when I spotted a little alleyway. On closer inspection, I could just make out a flashing neon leg at the far end of it. Up and down the leg went, outside what appeared to be a tiny theatre. I was disappointed it wasn't a public toilet as I was desperate for a pee but realised it could be the answer to our predicament.

"Hey Nicole, I think this might be our saviour. That looks like a striptease club to me."

She grabbed my arm, "What, are you kidding, have you completely lost it?"

By then I had already started marching down the alleyway in search of my new career, one that I never thought I would have the pleasure of pursuing. I didn't look to see if she was following me. I had already decided to go ahead with it if the opportunity arose. I was even thinking of which tune I would choose for my opening number.

"What's new Pussy Cat?" I hummed as I scurried along. I was hoping Nicole would join me to form a double act so we could be called The Leaping Lesbians or The Sparkling Sisters.

I had always been intrigued with professional strippers, really proper ones, and thought that Burlesque dancers were really beautiful. After the phone call to my Dad, I felt excused of any duty to behave myself as far as my parents were concerned, bringing tremendous freedom. I looked forward with renewed enthusiasm to a lucrative, sordid career in a corset.

On reaching the entrance of the club, I paused and realised, on looking back to the street, that Nicole hadn't come down the alley with me. She was loitering suspiciously on the main road.

"Come on Nicole, we're going to be strippers darling!" I called back merrily.

Nicole slowly crept towards me, her eyes like saucers, looking behind her every now and then as though her mother was going to pop out from a corner at any moment to tell her off. As we peered through the glass, we could make out a little bar and stage. There was a hat stand in the corner with a sparkly top hat on it. I felt quite envious of the owner of that hat.

"Oh, I love this place," I whispered, gazing in awe at the high ceiling and exquisite little cocktail bar. I was disappointed to realise it was closed.

"I wonder what time they open," Nicole murmured as we gazed up at a little trapeze in the rafters. I could just imagine myself spinning, upside down from it, topless, smiling down at my audience, although I did notice it was designed for a more petite, Japanese person. In reality, at six-feet tall I would probably drag over all the tables knocking drinks over. The door was locked and there was no-one to be seen.

"Well, we'll definitely have to come back later to introduce ourselves. It's obviously a late-night venue," I explained with glee.

Things were looking up, but Nicole couldn't get back to the bustle of the street quick enough. I made a mental note of the location for our return later.

We decided to try one more place before we moved on to networking tactics. Nicole had quite rightly suggested that we urgently needed to find English speaking people in the bars in order to try to get to know a few Europeans, Americans or Australians that could advise us. I wanted to have one more go at working in a club though. Eventually, we spotted a bright red sign with a guitar on it that stood out amongst a large group of signage at the base of one of the many tall buildings that housed little clubs and restaurants galore. The Japanese symbols were illegible to us, but I had a good feeling about this, knowing that music was something the Japanese gave Europeans a lot of credit for. We set off up about four flights of stairs to see what we could find.

"So, do you play the guitar then Janie, why are you so confident about this place?" called Nicole as we jogged up the stairs with renewed vigour.

I chuckled at the thought of me sitting on a stage in my black sparkly dress in the spotlight, strumming along as I sang *Go Tell Aunt Nancy The Old Grey Goose Is Dead*. This was the only tune I had ever mastered on the guitar, and I laughed to myself remembering my impromptu piano performance in Harrods. Singing however … well … that was something that I knew I could do well, so there was a little ray of hope in my heart. I was so excited about the possibility of becoming a stripper, that I seemed to have found renewed enthusiasm. The four flights of steps were no problem. Nicole, however, sat gasping for breath on the top step.

"God, I need a cigarette," she panted.

We spotted some lights around a door at the end of a corridor. We could just make out the guitar sign again and it was like being in one of those mystery houses at a fun fair, not knowing what you would find around each corner. After knocking at the door a few times and receiving no answer, we found that it was unlocked so we ventured inside. At the bar, stood the tallest man I had ever seen. I actually had to look up instead of down for a change as he polished glasses, bopping and humming to whatever was playing on his headphones. Unfortunately, we made him jump as he hadn't heard us enter. This caused a great deal of laughing and apologising from him, which is so typical of the Japanese. I would have been furious if someone had crept up on me and would definitely have bopped them one, but he happily introduced himself as Yuki the barman and we were so relieved to hear him speaking English. Out came the teapot again as we gazed longingly at the rows and rows of whiskey bottles along the shelves. They all had engraved silver labels hanging around them. Yuki explained that these were names of club members and that they each had their own personal bottle to enjoy at each visit. I longed for a bottle with my name on it.

The club was no larger than our living room at home, but there was a cosy warmth about the place and a feeling of comfort. I clocked a tiny stage and drum-kit in the corner. Nicole seemed to be relaxing a little more as we chatted to Yuki, and I really felt that this could be our winning club at last. I was very worn out, and the blister on my heel was giving me an interesting limp to go with my desperate, unemployed expression, which didn't bode well for my striptease audition later.

I could tell that Yuki liked us instantly.

"You hungry?" he asked, whipping out a tray of snacks which we tried not to stuff into our mouths like starving gannets.

"Starvin' mate!" Nicole bellowed, losing her polite little Japanese voice for a second.

"Ooh, don't mind if I do!" I gushed as I took one or two, feeling them melt on my tongue exquisitely.

My taste buds went into overdrive. I was so hungry but there were only enough rice crackers for a Barbie doll. Yuki soon realised that we were properly hungry and produced a plate of sushi from a little kitchen behind the bar. Nicole was looking through the kitchen door and I was worried that she might ask if there were any burgers available and push our luck too far. This man was proving to be a true hero and I was just deciding that I was falling in love with him, imagining what beautiful children we would produce, when Yuki broke my little dream.

"You wait, my Master come soon," he beamed at us, picking up the phone to call his boss.

Some very fast Japanese talking ensued and I stifled a giggle as I recognized the word *ladies* amongst it. I was at the tired stage where I could easily have collapsed into childish hysteria and ruined everything.

"Why is his boss called Master, is this Star Wars or something?" I giggled.

"No … you wally. That's what people call their boss here. You'll get used to it and if it's a woman it's Mama San." Nicole knew these things from previous visits to Tokyo and I was hugely impressed with her worldly wise-ness.

A few minutes later the door burst open and a short, athletic looking man, laden with gold medallions, marched through to join us. He wore a black silk shirt and his eyes glittered in amusement. His nose was a bit wonky which added character and we learnt later that the reason for this was that he was a retired boxer, quite well known in Tokyo. He had been in a lot of fights by the looks of it. Nicole and I leapt off our bar stools and I just managed to stop myself from curtseying. I was so desperate for Boxing Master to like me and more importantly employ me. While we all shook hands, Yuki poured him a cup of tea. Yuki and Nicole had to work quite hard on the conversational front as Master spoke virtually no English and I was totally useless, so we all smiled and nodded like mad. Master disappeared into a small office and just as I decided we were going to have to move on, to the next club, he leapt back into the bar and pointed at me.

"You!" His eyebrows had shot up into his black shiny hair and his eyes were bright. I tried hard not to stare at his spectacular display of assorted teeth, as he beamed at me in an ear-to-ear smile of yellow and gold.

"Aha! You are singer! Miss Karen Carpenter!"

I stepped back in surprise, catching my heel on the bar stool and knocking over a dish of Wasabi Peas with my elbow. There was a brief silence as everybody watched in anticipation.

I noticed a smile creeping over Nicole's face as she took in the scene. It had been said before that I looked rather similar to Karen, so I wondered if this likeness could be, somehow, useful at this moment. I was about to explain that I was actually Jane Hoggar from Ipswich when Nicole took over.

"Yeah Mate, she's Karen Carpenter!" she boomed, beaming at Master and casually throwing an arm around my shoulder. I could hear her business mind whirring around as I hopped back on my stool, casually swinging my leg over my knee and nodding modestly as though I'd just been found out. I even managed a little *Honto!* I wasn't sure what it meant, but I'd heard Nicole saying it a lot and felt that it suited the moment. Karen Carpenter was going to pay for our flights home, I could feel it. Over on the stage was an impressive arrangement of instruments as well as a karaoke machine. Master put his arm around my waist and steered me towards the microphone with glee.

"Now Miss Karen, you sing ... sit ... sit, welcome Karen... to my club," he patted my knee as I made myself comfortable on the stool.

Nicole remained seated at the bar looking rather concerned. Her last memory of me singing, was my drunken rendition of *We are the Champions*, in the bath, which wouldn't have filled her with confidence in me. Then I remembered I'd been singing *New York! New York!* in the show, which may have reassured her although, neither of those songs sounded anything like Karen Carpenter. I could understand her concern and I felt sick to my stomach thinking how much we needed this to work. It was getting late, and time was not on our side. I dug deep and remembered how Karen used to sing her songs, with a richness and occasional, seductive croak. I somehow managed to hear it in my head and felt everything would be alright if I really focused. My only worry was that Master clearly didn't know that she, Karen Carpenter - the chanteuse - had actually passed away five years previously, but I felt like she was right with me in spirit and would have found this whole scenario hilarious, so I went with it.

Yuki handed Nicole a cloth to help him polish the glasses and she hesitated. She clearly didn't look like anyone famous on this occasion, but I would much rather have been in her shoes than mine. I was relieved when she took the cloth and smiled up at Yuki instead of telling him where to stuff it. I think she fancied him a bit, which helped and anyway she spoke Japanese, so I didn't feel at all sorry for her. Seeing that our lives pretty much depended on my imminent performance though, having exhausted most other options of finding a job that we so desperately needed, I understood why she was blushing profusely with a mixture of dread and anticipation. Of course, there was the striptease possibility, but I was rather tired, and just wanted to stay at Master's club. As I sat amongst all the instruments on stage, trying frantically to remember the words to *Top of the World*, I thought how ironic the song would be, since it certainly didn't describe our mood on this particular evening. I knew that this was very likely our last chance of survival in Tokyo. I couldn't face calling my Dad again, just imagining the likely scene at the dinner table that evening, caused by my earlier call.

Mum: "What do you think of this casserole darling?"

Dad: "Oh lovely. By the way, Jane rang today, reversed the charges from Tokyo, the little minx, just to tell us not to worry because she was fine! Kids eh?"

I think he would have slowed down as he spoke, thinking it through, just as my mother's jaw hit the dining table. I reassured myself that, all being well, I should be able to call them later with the news that I was not a stripper, but Karen Carpenter, which would be much easier to tell their friends. I was woken from my little dream by a blast of music from the karaoke machine as Master had managed to find the Carpenters section in his catalogue. Sure enough, the introduction to *Top of the World* tumm-ti-tummed out of the speakers and with great relief the marvellous little screen was lit up with the words to the song in English. Halleluja! Karen wouldn't have needed the words. If the screen had only shown Japanese lyrics, then my secret would have been out. I didn't trust myself to make up my own words after the day we'd had, so I thanked Mr Sony for modern technology. Master leapt to the front of the stage, went down on one knee and threw his arms out to me,

"Sing! Beautiful Karen. Sing!"

I tried to focus, as my cue to start singing got nearer and nearer, glancing briefly over at the bar, to see Nicole and Yuki bopping happily away together to the music.

Karen Carpenter songs are very comfortable to sing as they stay in an easy range of middle notes rather than having to yell up at the top of the scale. I was just really thankful that Master didn't think I looked like Barbara Streisand or Whitney Houston. Their songs are much more challenging, and I may not have been very convincing. It was make or break time, singer or stripper. I smiled as I realised I wouldn't mind either job really. It was a *win-win* situation!

"Such a feelin's comin' over me," I crooned.

"There is wonder in most everything I see," I think I actually winked at Master at this point.

"Not a cloud in the sky, got the sun in my eye and I won't be surprised if it's a dream."

Relief flooded through me as Master went into raptures, applauding and running to the bar and then back to the stage, planning the career of his club's guest star. As I sang away, I looked over at the bar again and realised that Nicole's wild gesticulations were reaching the ridiculous. She really didn't need to give me the thumbs up, mouthing I Love You and blow me kisses, it was almost putting me off.

Master was doing a sort of Tango, Sumo-style dance with Yuki. It did look funny with their height difference and we all enjoyed the happiness in the room, although I wasn't sure where the happiness was leading.

During my debut, the door opened, and two very elegant, Japanese businessmen walked through to the bar. Oh, my word, guests were arriving and being led to their seats, not taking their eyes off me until beautiful Nicole arrived with their whiskey bottles on trays, welcoming them with much eyelash fluttering and impressive Japanese conversation. At the end of my song there was much enthusiastic applause and not just from Nicole. They loved me! I still wasn't sure if Master really thought I was Karen or not, but it didn't really matter anymore, because the room was so full of excitement and business.

I sang a few more songs and then Master called me over to sit at the bar with Yuki and Nicole while the guests had a little session on the karaoke themselves, absolutely murdering some Elvis songs. We continued to be part of the evening until the last guests had left at around midnight with much bowing and nodding. Nicole and I gathered our bags ready to leave, awkwardly waiting to see what Master was going to say.

"Karen, Nicole, you come tomorrow night, eight o'clock please," he demanded as he came out of his office with two huge wads of yen and stuffed them into our hands.

We bowed and bobbed our way out until we were out of sight. I will never forget descending those stairs with Nicole that night. We didn't speak until we got to street level in case Master heard us whooping, but when we got out onto the pavement we just collapsed into a big emotional hug. Euphoria is an understatement.

"I knew we could do it, Pommy!" Nicole squawked as she jumped up and down and squeezed my arms a bit too hard. We couldn't help but boast to each other of our wonderful performance with Nicole's linguistic skills and my Karen Carpenter impression. What a night!

"Right! Time to go to the strip club darling!" I cried.

Only when I grinned at Nicole did she realise that I was kidding, although I was actually still up for it if she was. Instead, we treated ourselves to a huge cocktail in one of the bars that we'd been into earlier, pausing at shop windows on the way, deciding which slinky evening dresses we would buy once we'd saved our flight fare home. It was glorious to be a happy customer again and after discreetly counting our wages while sipping our cocktails, we realised that Master really did rate us very highly and that we were going to get our flights home after all.

~

One of my fondest memories of Japan was the walk to and from the hostel each night with Nicole. On the way to work we would listen to *Gold* by Spandau Ballet. If I ever hear the song now, I always cry, transported straight back to Japan, where the song constantly inspired and encouraged me throughout the trials and tribulations that I faced. It makes me so proud of that time, surviving such an ordeal.

We would leave Master's club at midnight, bopping along the rainy pavements with our Sony Walkmans plugged in. Nicole loved *Never Too Much* by Luther Vandross and we would share her headphones and dance a merry dance as we walked to our hostel from the subway in the dark. With our pockets full of money, we had that great feeling that life was good again. Nowadays this song still makes me cry, because I've not been able to find Nicole on Facebook and I miss her.

The day after our debut at Master's club, I decided to call home again to explain that I had found a job. It was possible that the mood was a little tense by now at home, and I didn't want my mother to employ the S.A.S. to come and find me. This time I was able to pay for the call.

"Mum, it's me." I announced nervously.

"Oh, darling, where are you?" Mum sounded worried.

"I'm in Tokyo and I have a new job, I'll explain another time, but we had to leave the last one, I just wanted you to know I'm having a ball."

Mum laughed, "Oh well done. What a hoot! You'll *never* guess who's here darling," she continued merrily.

Oh, shit, I just imagined Stanley Starsmore and beautiful Veronika sitting on Mum's best sofa sipping sherry.

"Sheila and Bill from America! Do you want to speak to Sheila?" Mum was onto the next item already.

"No Mum! Just send them my love, bye!"

I put the phone down quickly, as soon as I knew they were happy, normal parents. I really didn't have the need to chat to Sheila and Bill if Mum wasn't in the slightest bit worried about me. Mum would make up her own version of what I was doing in Japan to keep everyone happy until my next call, and that suited me fine.

After our initial settling in period, Nicole and I found our way, moving to another hostel full of Europeans. Most of the girls that we lived with worked as hostesses in night clubs, earning exorbitant amounts of money by chatting to businessmen all evening, encouraging them to dance and buy champagne. They earned a fortune but sitting talking to strangers in this way sounded weird to me and never appealed. Knowing that I was going to be financially safe with my singing act, made me appreciate Master even more. It turned out that Yuki and Master were accomplished guitarists and could play any song I requested so I was in my element.

Getting back to the hostel in the early hours of the morning, the hostess girls would sleep all day, coming out of their rooms during the early evening to chat and decide what to wear as they discussed the dramas going on in their clubs, which were sometimes quite shocking. They would save and save their money and then leave, many of them for Thailand, where they would live very comfortably on the proceeds of their work, with their boyfriends, on the beaches for a whole year or more. One of the girls worked near to Master's club at a very traditional, Japanese place called Miwa's. Master always scowled if I mentioned the club. He often lost business to Miwa's, as his own was quite modern in décor with no Hostesses. Many tourists wanted a more typically Japanese experience and were often tempted to enter the traditional, wooden door of Miwa's older building, rather than entering the cool modern block that was Master's.

Miwa's club was in a time warp, run by a beautiful, little, old lady, called Miwa of course, who, I imagined, had once been a traditional Geisha Girl in her youth. If language hadn't been such a problem, I knew she would have had many wonderful tales to tell and it frustrated me often, that I couldn't hear more about her life. In full daylight, her little club room looked dusty and worn out, with threadbare velvet cushions, tatty silk pictures of garden scenes and faded pale pink and green paintwork on the walls. She always wore a silk patterned kimono and looked like one of those little dolls that you buy on holiday, in a clear box to take home as a souvenir. Her make-up was perfect and if I popped in before the club opened, she could be found curling her delicate black wig in the back room, at her ornate gold mirror with an exquisite tea set laid out at an ornate dressing table. She would be wailing away, as she fixed her hair, singing along to some traditional tune, that sounded like a cat being strangled on her crackly radio. Whenever she saw me, her face would light up. Beckoning me through to join her, we would have hilarious conversations, mainly in sign language, as she demanded to know if I had found a boyfriend in Tokyo. Over delicate cups of tea, she would show me pictures of her grandson in the mountains, dragging me over to look in her glass cabinet full of little frames of relatives.

Despite her sweet little face though, Miwa was a shrewd businesswoman. She fooled many American and European businessmen, as they called in looking for sex while they were in Tokyo, working away from their families back home. Miwa would invite these men in, to sit with her lovely ladies that she dotted around the room. The guests would be sung to and offered fruit, tea and whiskey with lots of small talk and giggling, until she kicked them out at midnight having rinsed them for every yen or dollar they had in their wallets. She took great care of her hostesses and paid them very well, making sure they all got straight into a taxi at the end of the evening. I used to pop in to see her often, before work, or on my way home, and she became rather a mother figure, always complaining if I looked pale, under-nourished or occasionally drunk. She would bring me concoctions of pumpkin mashed with mayonnaise and mustard or little mixes of mushy beans that I hated but ate just to be polite. At that time, the Japanese didn't really eat chocolate and sometimes I would be given a pretty little box of what looked like chocolates only to find, to my dismay on opening them, that they were more of the sweet mushy bean mixture shaped into squares and wrapped in beautifully patterned foil paper.

I was having such a ball in Tokyo that I rarely called home but making the effort one afternoon to catch up on any news,

I was alarmed to sense unusual tension in Mum's voice when she picked up.

"Hello darling. You'll never guess who's here?"

"Oh no, not again," I thought, rolling my eyes at Nicole as she watched through the phone box window.

"Not Sheila and Bill again," I snorted to myself, glad to be away from all that boring family stuff.

Then came the bombshell.

"Giovanni is here! He's waiting for you."

My heart skipped a beat as her words rang in my head,"

"Sorry Mum?"

I thought that maybe I had misheard her.

"Giovanni is HERE," she whispered. "What do you want me to do with him sweetheart?"

I felt my cheeks burning as I frantically planned in nano seconds what the hell to do and say.

Mum continued, matter-of-factly,

"He wants to wait for you here, I think, but we're not sure. Hang on love."

I heard Mum's footsteps clatter down the hall as she went to find Giovanni. I pictured him in the greenhouse with my Dad, comparing the taste of Italian tomatoes with our English ones. How they were communicating I couldn't imagine. Dad only knew how to say spaghetti and was probably calling him Dino. Giovanni spoke about three words of English, namely, darling, you and beautiful. After much shuffling and yelling down the garden, there was a pause until Giovanni came on the line.

"Darling! ... Darling? ... My Darling!"

After an awkward discussion in pidgin Italian about my situation in Japan, mixed with an extremely deep longing to see him again, my Mum interrupted, not being able to bear it any longer.

"Jane, shall I deal with this, or are you coming home?"

I heard her sending Giovanni back down the garden before she continued in a forced whisper.

"It's really not a problem. Just give me the word and I'll spell it out to him. He has a *child* in Italy and that's where he should be. Now get on with your trip and pretend we never had this conversation. Don't worry about a thing and leave it to me!"

She replaced the receiver. I later learnt that, in her usual way, Mum had dealt with the situation, filling Giovanni with ambition to be Italy's most famous chef and go home to be there for his daughter, rather than wasting time, waiting for hers to return from cavorting around the globe, causing havoc.

Knowing that I only had a few months before my working visa ran out, I made the decision to immerse myself into the lucrative world of work while I could, with a view to going back to Italy when I returned. Nicole had been right, there were so many opportunities presenting themselves on a daily basis. Keen to get back to Australia, it only took one photo shoot for a fashion magazine to earn Nicole the money for a flight home, so sadly we had to part, very emotionally, shortly after our arrival. As is the way with us though, our last night together was memorable.

We'd been drinking Long Island Iced Tea all evening in a club as a farewell treat and we were extremely merry. Coming out of the club in the early hours of the morning, singing *We are the Champions*, which had become our anthem since the great escape, we hailed a cab. We sang to the driver all the way back to the hostel and as we pulled up outside, Nicole opened her door and crawled out onto the pavement.

It was at that moment as I shuffled myself across the back seat to do the same, that the driver threw his seat back to the reclining position, with his little penis pointing up in the air. As I caught his begging expression looking up at me while I was scrambling out of the car, I let out a shriek of horror. His expression was worse than the sight of his penis and has stayed with me ever since. I'd never been flashed at before and assumed I would be traumatised if it ever happened, but fortunately I was with Nicole. She let out an almighty scream of amusement, dragging me out and slamming the door. When the driver realised we clearly weren't going to oblige him with a fondle, he zoomed away rapidly, leaving us rolling about on the pavement crying with laughter. Nicole pointed out that the funniest part was that, as he left, I was still looking in my bag for my purse, worried we hadn't paid him. It was certainly a night to remember and helped us smile the next morning as she set off to the airport.

"That was a blast Janie," she whispered as we hugged goodbye. I couldn't speak, holding on for ages until I pulled myself together.

"I'll miss you partner," I replied, managing to laugh as I waved her off without collapsing in sobs. It really wasn't going to be the same without her.

31

TOKYO LIFE

YUKI HAD GIVEN me his racing bike when Nicole left and I quickly worked out the different areas of Tokyo, discovering cafés and bars galore. In the trendy parts of town there was a hub of networking activity. Nicole had been right, European models and actors were highly regarded at that time and paid accordingly. I quickly accepted an exotic assortment of assignments, knowing that I should make the most of it. I would soon have to return to Britain where good modelling work was like gold dust.

My first day job was for a health magazine. I'd met a photographer at a party, and he had persuaded me to consider posing for an article he was working on about sex. I agreed to do it when he insisted there would, somehow, be no nudity. He gave me the details of the photographic studio and I cycled over the day before the shoot, incognito, just to check out the location. I was thrilled to find a state of the art, glass building with models and photographers coming and going from the busy reception area so felt that it would be safe. Not having internet, it was impossible to google these places and research their credibility, so one always had to be extra streetwise.

On my big day, the stylist scraped my hair back tightly so that I looked really stern. My face was then pasted with pale foundation as they marvelled, as usual, at my long European nose. I thought I looked horrible and rather ill, kitted out in black corset and French knickers, like a kinky, wicked witch, but all the team seemed to be nodding in approval as I was led through to a huge studio onto a vast open space of white floor and walls. Eric the German photographer was sitting with the crew, beaming at me with pride.

"Hi Babe!" he called over, probably hoping that they all thought we were an item.

"Oh, hi Eric," I replied rolling my eyes at the crew, so that they knew we definitely weren't.

The first set of photographs was very artistic although rather unsettling. I was sat on a chair with my ankles tied to the chair legs. I wouldn't let them actually tie them to the chair, much to their disappointment, because I'd seen too many horror films and didn't trust them. I couldn't bear the thought of having to escape in my French underwear through the streets of Tokyo, still tied to the chair like one of those nightmares where everyone is pointing at you and you can't get away. After a full morning of posing seductively around the set, I discretely looked at my watch, wondering how long this was going to take as I was feeling rather chilly.

Eric sidled over, "Hi honey, you're doink great my darlink. They just loff you to beets!"

"Thanks Eric, yeah they're really nice." I murmured, becoming suspicious.

"Now for siss next shot, it's a bit more exciting. Zey vant you to dreenk a glass off meeelk very qvickly, but they will photograph it all pouring over your naked breasts!" He stood back to await my response with an excited smile.

I nearly slapped him. "No way Eric!" I yelled furiously, glancing briefly over at the camera crew and bringing my voice down to an angry whisper. Their anxious faces blinked across at me from the other side of the studio.

"I told you, no nude scenes, and you knew that," I snapped.

"Yes, baby but you're looking so fabulous, they begged me," Eric explained.

"Eric! Will you stop calling me baby for goodness sake?" I marched off to my chair in a huff, which felt funny in my French knickers, but it was clear to me that Eric had known all along that this was required.

I made it clear that I wasn't going to be swayed into it. Eric was instantly cross that his cunning little plan hadn't worked, promptly losing his chirpy demeanour. Leaving the studio for a few minutes, he returned, smugly, with a tiny woman who burst through the door of the studio, her shock of red hair tumbling around her shoulders and down her back. Within minutes she had stripped off completely before leaping and cartwheeling around the studio, warming up apparently, proudly parading her minge and boobs for all to see.

"What a girl!" I thought to myself as I changed into my tracksuit, glad that I wouldn't have to pour milk everywhere and stink all the way home. I bid Eric farewell and he was surprisingly very pleasant about the situation.

"You see my darlink, Kristina has no problem vith beink nudey, und she ist very rich too!" he rasped as he stuffed very generous wages into my hand. I didn't care about Kristina, I had my money and felt proud of myself for keeping my modesty. The only disappointment I felt was a few weeks later, when I bought the magazine, to see my photograph, I was horrified to find that they had cut my head off the picture. They'd only wanted me for my body after all.

Fortunately for me, after my sexy photo shoot, I met an agent who was to provide a constant stream of daytime work that would keep me busy until I left Japan. I started teaching aerobics and English for her, to rich Japanese housewives and their beautiful children. Things really picked up though, when I managed to pass an audition to dance in an advertisement for a Brazilian coffee company that was to be shown on Japanese TV. Amongst the dozens of hopeful dancers at the audition was a real Brazilian lady, quite sure that she would be offered the part. I had to agree with her because she was the epitome of Brazilian womanliness, with her locks of chocolate brown hair and voluptuous figure, but I waited for my turn, deciding that it would be good experience to audition anyway, knowing from past experience, that companies sometimes earmark you for another role when they see you. They were shooting an ad for those little cans of ready-made coffee that you can buy from vending machines in Japan. Having discovered them, I've never understood why we don't have them in England because they're absolutely gorgeous. You simply put a coin in the machine and a ready heated can of coffee rolls out. Fantastic.

As it turned out, after a few high kicks and a couple of Oi Lambadas in the audition, much to my surprise, the job was mine.

On filming day, I was sprayed top to toe, in fake tan. My costume was based on Carman Miranda, with sparkling fruit piled on top of a glittering turban, teamed with a long, red, full skirt and golden bikini top. I felt wonderful as the stylist showed me through to a fabulous studio. On a circular stage, sat a very handsome, Japanese man poised under a spotlight, ready to play the guitar. The stylist placed me strategically just behind his shoulder.

"OK Jane. When music play, you dance!!" called the director, waving from behind the cameras. The lighting man was taking ages to adjust the spotlights so I couldn't resist a little natter with the handsome guitar man. He asked me where I was from, and realising that he spoke English, I chatted politely with small talk, asking him if he did many adverts or if he was in a band, that sort of thing.

"Oh! If my friends could see me now!" I chuckled to myself as I gyrated around to the music in my fruity hat.

At the end of the shoot, I said farewell to the agent, pocketing a very fat envelope of yen.

"You call me soon Janie!" she called out as I left.

I headed towards the big studio gates where I'd left my racing bike, locked to the railings. The beautiful bike from Yuki was giving me the freedom to get myself wherever I needed to be at the drop of a hat, and I was extremely grateful. Walking down the drive towards the gates, I spotted handsome guitar man and decided he was rather hot. Wishing I could share a cab with him, I regretted having my bicycle with me. Unfortunately, he seemed rather pre-occupied though and as I chatted away about my hopes for more work on TV, he scanned the horizon, looking for someone. He was just being polite on set, I could tell. I had to accept that he didn't fancy me, which I found unbelievable as I shimmied along at his side in my Brazilian costume.

As we approached the gates, I could hear screaming and lots of girls crying out,

"Masatoshi!"

There was a huge car waiting nearby, not far from my bike and, as we got nearer, it dawned on me that Handsome was famous!

"OMG I'm such a plonker," I cringed to myself with embarrassment, remembering I'd asked him earlier if he was in a band. He clearly was! The girls pushed passed me as we left the safety of the gates. I was sort of trampled out of the way as I watched him signing autographs and smiling for the flashing of cameras. I sidled up to the open window of his chauffeur driven car, having retrieved my bike from the railings.

"So, what's his name then, he must be famous?" I jauntily but casually asked the chauffeur. He looked at me in amazement. It wasn't often that a Brazilian lady with sparkling fruit on her head poked her face into his car, particularly one straddling a racing bike. He also seemed staggered that I'd never heard of Handsome.

"Masatoshi Nakamura is very successful madam, as you can see," he stifled a snort of laughter.

I chanted his name to myself all the way back to Roppongi on my bicycle, weaving my way through the rush hour traffic. This was tricky in my Brazilian costume until I stopped to tuck the red skirt into my knickers, so it didn't get caught in the bike chain. The TV company hadn't asked for the costume back at the end of the shoot as I'd wandered out with Masatoshi, so I'd just kept walking, jeans and T-shirt scrunched up in my little rucksack. I planned to burst into Miwa's club, for a laugh, in all my finery before wearing it at Master's, to sing my Carpenter songs. People stopped and waved as I made my way and I wondered if they thought I was Karen Carpenter on her way to a fancy-dress party.

When I got to Miwa's club it was early so there was no-one around. As I collapsed onto one of her little sofas, I could hear her singing to the radio in her back room. I peeled off my silver sandals and inspected my blisters, appreciating how exhausting Brazilian dancing was.

"Miwa!" I called out, excited to describe what I'd been up to all day.

"Me-sing-sing-with-Masaotoshi-Nakamura today!" I cried. I was so excited to tell her about my day, knowing she would be ecstatic. The radio stopped and she rushed through to the lounge.

"Noooo! Masatoshi! Hontoooooo?" she went quite pink, almost the same colour as her kimono, clapping her hands with joy while I explained, as best as I could, the events of the day. She beamed across at me as she poured the tea before commencing her daily polishing of the glass counter. Switching on the glowing, dusty old lamps around her lounge area, she transformed it from drab to twinkling, in an instant. Eventually, she signalled to the phone where she proceeded to call her sister in the mountains to tell her all about my fame, not taking her eyes off me as she chatted, inspecting the workmanship of my costume from across the room.

I told Yuki and Master to look out for me on TV and they promised they would, smiling politely I could tell they didn't believe me. Someone had finally broken the news to them that Karen Carpenter had passed away, so they understandably didn't trust me with my extraordinary tales. I reassured myself that they loved me all the same though, because we were making a fortune with our Karen Show. Unfortunately, I never saw the advert, but despite this, I was hugely proud that, for one day, Masatoshi Nakamura and I had worked together to create a beautiful piece of coffee advertising and I added it to my C.V. with pride.

The following day my blister seemed to have doubled in size and looked infected. Having no medical insurance, I knew I had to fix it before my leg became gangrenous and dropped off. Limping along the street near my hostel, early the next morning, I found what looked like a pharmacy. The lady inside beckoned me in as I peered through the glass door. One look at my foot and she marched me through to a treatment room and laid me on a bed that wasn't long enough for me. She dragged a chair over to support my feet and before I knew it, a dozen little women in white aprons were gathered around, inspecting my blister with great interest. They were fascinated with the fact that I didn't fit on the bed, and as usual, the enormity of my feet and length of my nose caused much amusement and wonder. After a long discussion, one of the ladies nodded over to her colleague who went to a drawer and pulled out a huge bolt of gauze bandage. It was then that I had a vague recollection of the Asian tradition of binding women's feet to make them look smaller. In fact, as I watched them gathering around the end of the bed, I started to worry that I had wandered into a foot binding clinic. Maybe they were going to break my feet and bind them down to a size six and I couldn't decide if that was good or bad. I mean, it would be much easier to buy shoes. Fortunately, as the gaggle of ladies filed out of the room, my carer snipped a small piece of bandage, soaked it in a bright orange alcohol solution before covering the blister and bandaging it up neatly. The relief was immense, but she spent another twenty minutes calling more colleagues through to look at this giant stranger that had appeared from nowhere. The establishment turned out to be an old people's home but that hadn't stopped them from helping me, with no charge, so typical of the kind Japanese people I met.

Since Nicole had returned to Australia, I'd become more friendly with Yuki the barman and his social circle. I missed Nicole but these charming locals regularly invited me out to places that no tourist would ever manage to find, which I'd learnt in the past was a perfect way to get to know a country and its people.

When the night clubs closed, Yuki and I would often tour the city and its suburbs in the early hours on his huge motorbike, stopping at the harbour to meet with his friends, where we would drink sake and feast on raw fish, fresh off the boat, as the sun came up and the fishermen hauled in their catch. Yuki and I were good mates, but there was no spark there, romantically, just a shared sense of humour. So, it was particularly funny, therefore, to spend a night at a Love Hotel with him when it was absolutely pouring with torrential rain one night.

We had attempted to set off from the harbour, after a midnight feast at a café, but the motorbike wouldn't start and the queue for taxis was horrendously long. With no taxis in sight and feeling tired, cold and rather pissed on rice wine, I just wanted to get indoors. We were a long way out of town, and I pointed out that, by the look of the queue, a taxi would take ages, and cost far more than one night in the slightly seedy looking Love Hotel that I had spotted by the taxi rank.

Love Hotels are very cheap quirky places for couples wanting to have rampant sex. I've never seen or heard of them anywhere else in the world. Yuki was finding the whole idea absolutely hilarious, but I had made it clear there would be no sex, and that he was never to tell anyone that we had stayed there together. I just wanted to be warm and dry and go to sleep. On arrival, we were shown to a pink room with fluffy carpet and condom machine on the wall. There was a pink heart-shaped bed next to a pink bath that I promptly filled, telling Yuki to watch TV where he couldn't see me, chatting away in my drunken manner as I sank into the heavenly bubbles. It reminded me of the last luxury bubble bath I had taken, in the kitchen at the mountain hotel with Nicole, and I chuckled to myself with happiness that I had survived that ordeal. Watching a weird game show, Yuki poured whiskey from the mini bar, which ensured that we had a glorious sleep until morning.

I felt so smug as I sat in the bright sunlight of a street-side café, sipping green tea, watching Yuki fix his bike before he raced us back to the city centre. I was starting to feel like a local. As Yuki and I sped along the highway, I felt there was surely little left to experience in Japan. I was soon proved wrong however, when my agent sent me to a large supermarket in a suburb of Tokyo to promote American steak.

Show biz skills really know no bounds in the working world. Grateful for the work, I set off in my American Girl themed, denim skirt, white shirt and polka dot neckerchief, ready to sell steaks from a barbeque in a large supermarket. I was feeling quite adrenalised as I made my way across town on my racing bike, waving to amused strangers as they stopped to stare at the giant rodeo queen sailing past. After being led through to my workstation by the store manager, I was presented with a griddle, a fridge full of fresh steaks chopped up into bite sized pieces and a tape recorder playing Johnny Cash music. After a few minutes, it was apparent that I was going to have to really work the shop floor to make any sales. People were smiling enthusiastically before skirting around me as though I might lasso them into tasting my wares. I decided there was nothing for it but to crank up the performance.

"American Meat-o!!" I called in my best Japanese/American twang, turning up the music, slapping my thigh and throwing in a few yee-haa's! This tactic helped immensely, and sales immediately improved, as ladies timidly came over to add packs of steak to their trolley. I'd managed to eat quite an impressive amount of the little steaks by mid-morning, so when the manager came to see how I was doing later on, he congratulated me on how much had gone. I did realise later, when I went to the loo and checked myself out in the mirror, that I did have a little bit of sauce around my mouth, which was rather a giveaway, and when I smiled, the chargrilled bits in my teeth made me look like the wicked witch of the west.

I was just looking at my watch, adjusting my little American flags and wondering when it would be acceptable to pack up and go back into town, when there was a loud rumble, and I was thrown to the floor. I thought it was a thunderstorm at first, until all the customers started screaming. Women were jumping into freezers as though they were preparing to fight for bargains at a crazy, special offer sale. It turned out, however, that we were experiencing a minor earthquake and although it's never any less terrifying when it happens, Japanese people are used to it and know what to do. The frightful possibility of a major earthquake is something that they have to live with, day to day. It's a most unusual sensation, happening quickly with no warning. Having nothing to hold on to when the ground and walls were all moving at once and not always in the same direction, gravity takes you down, and sometimes half the building with you.

It quickly turned very quiet in the supermarket and as I blinked and looked around me, I could see there was rubble all over the floor and also in my frying pan, which annoyed me. Some people were nursing cuts, with dust in their hair and some were climbing out of hiding places. I've been told since, that it is advised to run for frames and structures, like doorways and shelving that will protect your head in an earthquake, which explained the freezer diving. I was grateful to be in one piece considering I had just laid still, holding a fork with a piece of steak on the end of it, throughout most of the ordeal. I only had a bit of shock and dust to deal with. Deciding that no-one would fancy anymore American steak that day, especially as it had become rather gritty, I switched off my cooker that was still merrily burning away, just as the manager appeared with a dented tin of peas. He handed them to me with a sweet smile, glad that I was alright. I was tempted to ask if the earth had moved for him, but decided against it, although this thought, and the dented tin of peas, sent me into convulsions of nervous laughter. On my way back into town, I began to appreciate how much of a fuss we make in England about the awful weather because, cycling away from the supermarket, taking in the frightening scenes of crashed cars and lamp posts bent over like a horror film set, I saw another level of nature that I will never forget. There didn't seem to be so much damage further away from the supermarket's district, so I knew I must have been in a particularly badly affected part of town. By the time I arrived in Roppongi, there seemed to be no evidence of trouble at all.

I had to go straight to Master's Club that evening as my shift as an American cowgirl, followed by an earthquake, had finished only an hour before Karen Carpenter was due to sing her first ditty of the evening. When I arrived, I realised that they hadn't even heard about the tremor and were shocked at my news, although highly amused by my costume. Having no internet, news took longer to reach people then and, as we poured the tea, dishevelled guests started arriving at the club in need of their whiskey, having spent the whole day being evacuated from high rise office blocks, after warnings of tremors. These guests were certainly ready for a party after running up and down, sometimes endless flights of stairs, the lifts being out of action, as is the rule during tremors.

Seeing an opportunity, Master wasted no time in finding songs like *Country Roads*, to match my cowgirl outfit and it was while I was halfway through singing *Stand By Your Man*, that the door opened, and in walked Harrison Ford's double. He was all alone and his face lit up when he saw me, as though I were an old friend, as was sometimes the way when you spotted someone that wasn't Japanese. I winked at him in my best American way and sang the remainder of the song directly to him alone.

As this alluring, new guest took a seat at the bar, Master and Yuki beamed and nodded furiously at me, sensing the mutual attraction. The day had been tiring and Master allowed me to talk at the bar until closing time, to this charming man, who turned out to be an American from New York, called Andy. He had such a handsome, kind face with twinkling eyes that accentuated an endearing smile. Sitting dressed as an American Belle, I chatted away about my life and adventures, amused that I had met him on the same day that I'd been selling Texan steak, instantly wondering naively, if it was a sign that I had met my match.

When Master's bar closed, Andy and I strolled to a popular 24-hour café, The Pink Almond, on the crossroads of Roppongi, where we chatted further into the night. Eventually Andy called a cab, horrified when I pointed out my shiny racing bike locked to a lamp post by the club. I must have looked funny waving goodbye as he stood on the crossroads, mesmerised as I sailed on my trusty steed along the empty street, in my colourful cowgirl costume. Impressed that he hadn't suggested we go back to his place for a bit of rodeo action, I'd promised to meet up with him again for a late Sunday lunch the following day, feeling rather thrilled with this rapidly developing romance.

32

TIME TO GO HOME

ANDY SWIFTLY BECAME part of my life and, keen to spend my free time with my new beau, I started to refuse work. Andy and I spent most of our time at his elegant apartment together, before I went out to be Karen Carpenter each night. Eventually he gave me a door key so I could enjoy the luxury of his penthouse when he was at his office. We drifted through the warm summer days enjoying each other's company as we took in the exciting sights of Tokyo, eating at authentic restaurants and picnicking in the sunny parks under the cherry trees. Swept off my feet with the comfortable lifestyle, after living in my humble little hostel for so long, I was blissfully happy. It was lovely to be with someone I could chat to at length in English, not having to explain myself in my best Japanese, that wasn't improving by any means.

Reluctant to burst my bubble of love, I ignored the fact that Andy sometimes disappeared with no warning. I would call him, only to be met by his answer machine explaining that he was in the States for a week, sometimes two, and I was to leave a message. Finding the flat quiet, there would be a note on the kitchen counter to say that he was away and to make myself at home. I reminded myself that he was a businessman, having to make countless trips to and from the States. It was something I would have to get used to, but he never gave any explanation for these absences, skirting around my questions when I brought it up, and not wanting to be annoying, I let it go.

"Sounds dodgy to me," warned Fiona, one of the girls at my hostel. "They're all the same these men away from home. It's like their 'other life'."

I'd confided in Fiona, hoping for reassurance but her comment made me feel sick with doubt, because Fiona had been a club hostess for years and had seen it all so many times before.

Busy with my job at Master's club, combined with the intermittent fun with Andy, I ignored my anxieties, not wanting to see the situation as it was. I loved the excitement when he returned from his trips, throwing his case onto the hall floor and chasing me into the bedroom, where I would shriek with delight that we were together again.

One evening, on my Sunday night off work, Andy mentioned that Doug, a colleague from his office, was joining us for dinner. This casual remark gave me a strong feeling that Andy might finally be attempting to bring me into his life more permanently and as usual, my imagination ran riot.

"Maybe this is it," I wondered as I made my way up to the apartment, "he wants to introduce me to his friends and family at last."

I padded down the hall to where Andy lay, stretched out on the sofa. He nodded to a pretty box on the table.

"Hey beautiful, something to wear for our dinner tonight. Doug's looking forward to meeting you."

I opened the box to find, amongst the luxurious tissue, a delicate silk dress in the softest mocha. It took my breath away.

"Well go on dear, put it on," Andy smiled over at me, watching my delighted expression with pride. Overjoyed, I hurried to the bedroom to change, slipping the dress over my head until it fell perfectly around my body like a second skin. I felt divine as I glanced in the mirror before walking through to the lounge where a pair of soft, caramel suede heels were waiting on the deep pile carpet next to Andy. The shoes, unusually, slipped on effortlessly and Andy jumped up and twirled me around, before pulling me towards him in a warm embrace.

"You my lady, look stunning," he whispered into my ear before we kissed. I felt like a million dollars as we stepped out of the lobby of the apartment and into a waiting taxi.

I was whisked out to a stunning hotel, where Andy's colleague of many years, Doug, joined us to celebrate a business deal they'd achieved earlier in the week. Doug talked business for much of the evening, but I loved just being there, as Andy's partner. We were sipping coffee after dessert when, to my delight, Doug turned the conversation to my career plans.

"Ooh," I thought, "he wants to know if I'm serious about Andy, I can tell."

Andy and I did make a very attractive couple, and I was loving every minute of it. He had mentioned his parents in the States on occasions and hinted a few times that we should travel over to meet them, but this hadn't yet been followed up, so I started to hope that things were accelerating at last.

"So, Jane, what are your plans? I hear you have to renew your visa and go see your folks in Europe pretty soon right?" Doug enquired as he signalled to the waiter to refill my glass.

Thrilled to be invited into the conversation more, I launched into an animated explanation of my ambition to become a Bluebell Girl in Paris, before retiring, and hopefully settling down somewhere. I glanced at Andy at this point, *Hint, hint.* I hoped my description would impress Doug more than my plan B which was to continue to be Karen Carpenter for another six months, if I could just swing it at immigration, renewing my working visa in Tokyo.

"Jeez! Now that *is* fascinating," he remarked, pausing to smile at Andy and then back at me, before continuing.

"The girls dance topless in Paris, right?" he asked with a leering grin.

I sat up in alarm.

"No! ... Well ... not exactly, I mean, the Lido is a fantastic, well-respected show as a matter of fact. The costumes are revealing, yes, but it's one of the most famous cabarets in the world. It's very sophisticated I can assure you." I tried to smile but felt flustered and reached for my wine, adding defensively, "I'd be proud to work for Miss Bluebell. It's somewhere I've always promised myself I will dance one day. She's a fascinating woman."

I looked across at Andy, disappointed that he wasn't defending me at all while Doug roared with laughter until there was an awkward silence. Andy scowled, looked at his watch and then signalled to the waiter for the bill while Doug sat grinning across the table at me, making me dreadfully self-conscious. I excused myself and went to the ladies' room, pleased to see, on my return, they were shaking hands to leave.

It was well after midnight when the cab slowed outside Andy's and he was so subdued that I wasn't sure whether, or not, to carry on to my hostel. I started to need the company of my lovely girlfriends around the kitchen table, knowing they would be instantly on my side, reassuring me when I recounted the awful end to the evening. Andy took my hand to get out of the car, so I followed him to the lift wondering if, maybe, I was being oversensitive.

"Sorry if I said something wrong tonight," I lied, thinking it would be better to get the ball rolling if there was a problem, because I've never been one to stew over disagreements.

He was silent until we got to his door, then turned and glared at me, "You didn't have to tell Doug that you're a stripper."

It felt like a slap in the face. He marched down the hall and out onto the balcony, but as he stormed away I felt a wave of anger and marched after him.

"How *dare* you say that to me, you ... horrible man," I hesitated, knowing I should have said bastard, but I've never been very good at swearing.

Andy had turned his back on me to stare angrily out at the stunning, night-time view of Tokyo. I was just considering swinging him round and slapping him when it occurred to me, that this was just like a scene from an old black and white movie and stifled a welcome snort of laughter. I had a flash back to the evening that Nicole and I had actually considered becoming strippers, not so long ago and a little smile crept over my lips. I bit the insides of my cheeks in a desperate attempt to make the smile go away, wondering what Doug would have made of our plans to become The Sparkling Sisters or possibly The Leaping Lesbians of Tokyo. Pleased to realise this whole charade seemed to be bringing me a surge of amusement and confidence, I went with it, with gusto.

"Right, that's enough of this," I announced, marching back inside. "How *dare* you call me a stripper," I shouted through to him as I changed back into my jeans in the bedroom, throwing the silly posh dress on the big bed. I flung the shoes across the room too, glad to take them off. They were killing me.

"I'm leaving, because I have better things to do than sit here being insulted," I hollered.

I'd always wanted to say that to someone, and it felt great. When I looked up, Andy was standing in the doorway looking irresistible, but unusually, it just fuelled my anger even more.

He held out his hand.

"Sorry honey, I didn't mean it that way, come here," he beckoned, pulling me towards him. Miraculously, I resisted and pushed past. Perching myself defiantly on the edge of the sofa, I zipped up my bag and prepared to leave. He hesitated, before heading for the kitchen, calling back,

"I know, why don't I make some coffee while you call your family. How would you like that?"

I couldn't actually think of anything worse.

"Whatever makes you think I'd want to call home *now*?" I retorted as he reappeared at the door. He looked sad.

"Please don't leave, I'm sorry I over reacted."

I had actually started thinking about my lovely flight home. It was booked for a few weeks' time and after the last few hours, the thought of Paris became more and more appealing.

Andy waited, looking really concerned. I softened and put down my bag.

"It's sweet of you Andy. I write to my family though, thanks. They're probably asleep now anyway," I explained, knowing I would cry if I heard my Mum's voice after all this fiasco.

Unfortunately, Andy was insistent though.

"No, it's Sunday morning in England honey, perfect time."

He handed me the phone, smiling, with a sleepiness that made me swoon, pulling me into the soft cushions of the sofa. I dialled, exhausted, not caring anymore what happened next. Phoning Mum wouldn't help the situation at all though, I knew that much. Sure enough, after the usual greetings, Mum announced that she had visitors. The familiar sound of home brought me down to earth with a bump.

"It's an amazing coincidence that you've phoned *now*. It's a *sign* … isn't it girls?" she exulted.

There was a chorus of agreement that made Andy's face light up, as I recoiled into the sofa realising that Mum's friends were there for the weekend, and that they'd very likely been on the Breakfast Bucks Fizz.

"Marge is here with Joyce. We were just wondering how you were, when she suddenly gets a message from the spirits didn't you Joyce?"

Andy poured me a glass of brandy just in time for them all to burst out together, in chorus,

"And then you *rang!*"

I nearly died as they all dissolved into a fit of giggles. This was going to be hugely embarrassing and there was nothing I could do about it. I frantically looked for the button to turn them off loudspeaker, but there didn't seem to be one.

"Out of the blue it was, wasn't it Joyce?" Marge added excitedly.

Joyce often came to visit our house with her sister, Marge, and halfway through the visit, she would usually grip the arm of her chair and announce that some long-lost relative was trying to contact her from 'The Other Side'.

"It's Albert and Grace from Billericay!" she would whisper, frozen in her seat, causing Mum to dive for her jotter, ready to take notes in shorthand, being absolutely obsessed with mediums. I realised that I should warn Mum that I wasn't alone because, of course, I didn't trust where this conversation was leading at all.

"Mum, I'm with a friend and we're both listening in," I began, hoping to avoid any further embarrassment. It was too late though, because she'd put Joyce on the line, and it was clear that they were on a roll.

"Jane, you rang, I knew you would. I came today because I *knew* you would call your mother. I've had messages and you need to know about them." Joyce was in full swing, but Mum cut in.

"You should've seen Joyce when she got her messages. Her voice sort of changes slightly and we hear what the spirits are saying, *through Joyce*! I've told them all about Giovanni and Dino, and how I sent them home, so don't you go bringing any more back." They all fell about in hysterics and then the corker came.

"I don't like the sound of this latest one. Joyce says he's married, don't you Joyce? That's why Albert and Grace from Billericay got in contact you see, they're worried about you."

I slammed the phone down.

"Enough!" I collapsed on the sofa, burying my head in the cushions not knowing where to look, but hoping Andy would be laughing merrily by the time I peeped out.

Silence.

When I felt him quietly get up and go to the kitchen to get the coffee, I just knew. Slowly, I stood up and walked to the bedroom to collect my things, leaving the beautiful dress and shoes on the bed. I didn't want to talk anymore, I needed to get away.

I had no trouble ignoring the constant phone messages left at my hostel from Andy, because none of them said that Joyce had been wrong, only that we needed to talk, and he would explain everything. He didn't come to the club and I was relieved about that because, once Yuki and Master knew I had been hurt by the big, bad American, they suggested with a menacing look in their eyes, that I invite him over. I declined this generous offer, but Yuki and Master made it clear that they were going to cheer me up by giving me a great send-off before I went back to Europe. This was welcome news because I needed friends urgently, to help me enjoy the last days of my Japanese adventure, because apart from the heartache of Andy, I'd had the time of my life.

The grand farewell dinner, courtesy of Yuki and Master, turned out to be an experience that, by that time, I could probably have managed without.

We went to a tiny restaurant in a back street, belonging to a friend of Master's. On entering, I was delighted to see that it was an authentic Japanese home, converted into a tiny restaurant, with a smell of home cooking, so divine that I knew we were in for a real treat.

There were just a few rooms with low tables on beautiful rugs, so we sat on the floor, while a very smiley lady bought us a tray of warm sake in tiny cups. I felt like Gulliver as usual, with my rather long legs folded several times around themselves under the table. Japanese people are built naturally for sitting all night cross legged, but I had cramp within ten minutes and Lord knows how Yuki managed. Fortunately, after a few cups of the sake, I didn't mind, and plates of truly authentic Japanese food had started to arrive in droves. I'd been suffering with the loss of appetite that comes with emotional angst but being with these friends relaxed me and I made up for lost time with a meal that was the best I had tasted on the whole trip. I felt very privileged to be somewhere that was clearly not for tourists, the food being cooked by a local family. There were little dishes of tofu in garlic, so light and delicate I looked forward hungrily to the next dish, a little cup of the sweetest chicken pieces, succulent and delicious making you ravenous for more until a plate of the softest tastiest noodles would appear, delighting the taste buds further. Dish after dish of endless delectations of rice, prawns, octopus and squid and of course soft-shell crabs that were eaten whole, continued to arrive, washed down with sake, much raucous sign language and a fair amount of reminiscing about my time at the club.

When Master signalled to leave, my legs were numb from sitting like a grasshopper for two hours. Master and Yuki steered me down the street until we came to a small door with a flashing sign over it, and I was thrilled to realise that we were going dancing. We were shown to a table as the whiskey arrived on a beautiful tray and before I knew it, Master, Yuki and I were strutting our stuff with wild abandon to *Le Freak*, by Chic on a little dance floor.

The dancing developed into quite a frenzy of activity and, being rather inebriated, we became quite adventurous in our dance moves, finding ourselves a small corner of the club where we could really boogie inconspicuously to our hearts content. Unfortunately, things, as they do, got out of hand when Master decided to get acrobatic with a few boxing moves. Yuki joined him with an impressive show of walking on his hands across the floor to the beat. This caused much hilarity until he lost his balance and crashed into the table of some very beautiful ladies, knocking their drinks over as he went. The boyfriends of these guests were watching the whole display from the bar.

Looking for trouble, they decided that Master and Yuki were going to get the ball rolling.

The next few minutes were ghastly, and I remember helping Master up and smiling at the ladies apologetically just before we were set upon. Apologies clearly weren't enough, and Yuki was pinned to the table amongst the broken glass, while Master, outnumbered, was forced to partake gleefully in a full-blown boxing match, much to his delight. I don't think he'd had a good punch-up in ages. When I saw a knife glinting in the hand of one of the villains holding Yuki down, I ran to the bar begging them to call the police. It all happened in slow motion as, to my horror, the bar staff seemed to ignore the whole situation. They refused to call the police because, I later learnt, the villains were part of the Japanese equivalent of the Italian mafia, called Yakuza. Apparently, intervention would have put the club at risk if anyone was charged. I fled outside onto the street to seek help, but a passer-by informed me that to call the emergency services from a phone box, you had to have a ten-yen coin. Ten yen is the equivalent of about one pence, and if you time how long it takes to find a one pence coin in an emergency, you'll be surprised. I imagine many Japanese people have expired whilst looking for ten yen to call the ambulance.

I rushed frantically up and down the street, calling, "Ten yen! Ten yen! Ten yen!" This made it quite clear to people staring at me inquisitively, that I didn't have a fucking ten-yen coin because my bag was sitting on a seat, amongst a group of gangsters that were murdering my friends. I needed assistance desperately. Mobile phones were not in use in 1988 and none of the onlookers seemed to have a ten-yen coin either as they rummaged in pockets and purses. The welcome sound of a police siren lifted my spirits. Someone else must have made a call because a line of four policemen with little truncheons trotted past. They seemed very young, and certainly didn't look like they would be able to take on the baddies, but I knew it was better than nothing and followed them inside, praying that Yuki hadn't been killed. Eventually, a very crumpled and blood-stained Master and Yuki were marched out of the club, stuffed into a little van and driven away. The gangsters were nowhere to be seen. I was warned by the night club owner to leave, before the police asked for my details, which would lead to complications on my visa. I insisted on going to retrieve my handbag first though. It was stuffed with money and my passport. This was a good example of how safe, in some respects but obviously not others, Tokyo was at that time. My little bag was still on the seat, open with its contents in view, untouched. The barman was convinced I was a troublemaker and ushered me out swiftly as though he thought I would want to stay on, have a drink and a laugh about what had just happened. I didn't care about him though, because Yuki and Master were out of danger, so I leapt into a cab and tried not to dissolve into tears as I gave my address to the taxi driver.

The following evening, I hurried to work, anxious to see if my boys were all right. What followed was a perfect example of the different approach of the Japanese to situations like this, compared to us British. As I entered the bar I could see Yuki precariously but calmly polishing his whiskey glasses as usual. There was a bandage around his head and his arm was in a sling.

"Good Evening Miss Jane, would you mind pouring the tea tonight please?" he asked, smiling, as I rushed over.

"Yuki! I've been so worried about you, Oh, my God are you Ok, where is Master?" I gushed, attempting to hug him.

He looked surprised and steered me to a barstool,

"Yes of course everything is ok. Master will arrive soon, and we have many guests tonight."

He clearly didn't want to discuss our misadventure, so I was forced to go about my evening duties of setting up my microphone and maracas with no questions. Master arrived later looking absolutely ridiculous with a Trilby hat tilted jauntily over his purple eye, a huge pair of sunglasses for good measure and his arm in plaster. As he limped over to his karaoke machine, I poured him some tea as though nothing was wrong, doing my best to act normally. Sure enough, as the guests started to arrive, none of them said a word about it, so realising quickly that we weren't to mention our night out, I threw myself into a very animated evening, managing to take the attention away from the boys. I somehow managed to hand around canapés and drinks, while singing *Only Yesterday*, with great feeling, and I could tell that Master appreciated my efforts tremendously. He and Yuki kept a low profile behind the bar until closing time, when they staggered home.

My last days in Tokyo were rather a time for reflection. I had experienced so many things and appreciated that it was, yet again, the sort of adventures only dreams are made of. I was a different person, that was for sure, to the girl who'd arrived in Tokyo on the bullet train all those months ago. With this in mind, when a bouquet the size of a house arrived from Andy, to Master's club one evening during my last week in Tokyo, I was calm. I hadn't let my disappointment surface since Joyce's spiritual revelation, looking only to the future as I gathered my thoughts, packed my case and hoped for more of an honest explanation from him ... but it never came.

Flowers could have meant all manner of things and I reassured myself that Master had my contact details, so if Andy came to the club looking for me when I left, although I wouldn't have put it passed him to swing a left hook at Andy, I knew he wouldn't dare withhold my English phone number. I longed desperately to see Andy's face one more time, and would scan the crowds hopefully, on my way to work during my last week, but didn't allow myself the temptation of calling him. I knew I just had to wait and see.

One evening though, the sad truth was made very clear. My flight was booked, and I had finished working for Master with a vague promise that Karen Carpenter would be back in the coming months after some time with family in England. With a few weeks to myself in Tokyo I had been packing and enjoying some time to say goodbye to all my friends, knowing secretly that it was possible that I wouldn't be returning to Japan if another new adventure appeared in The Stage newspaper. Miwa had insisted that I continue to join her for tea as usual, during the early evenings at her club, until her hostesses arrived and settled down to entertain her guests.

Hostessing in Japan originates from the early traditions of Geisha Girls. These ladies are an important part of Japanese cultural history dating as far back as the 7th century, providing hospitality with tea ceremonies and entertainment for gentlemen in the form of music, conversation and dance. I actually think most women around the world do this unwittingly anyway. We all know that if women didn't organise dinner parties and family gatherings, they wouldn't happen. There are many different interpretations of hostessing these days. Still being very much a part of hospitality in clubs all over the cities of Japan, their role is to serve drinks and make the guests of the club at ease, so a knowledge of the Japanese language is an advantage. Most clubs also have European girls working as hostesses to entertain the English spoken guests. Karaoke is popular, so a good singing voice is held in high esteem. Miwa employed mainly Japanese girls, but she often invited me to join her club, trying to entice me to make lots of money from the European guests. I would have accepted her offer if the job didn't look so boring. I knew there was no prostitution going on, but I feared I would quickly offend her guests with my caustic sense of humour. From what I could gather, the conversations were rather superficial. If I don't agree with something, I make my point, but I suspected that hostesses were supposed to agree with everything the men said, which I knew I would never manage to do. There was a perfect example of this on my last week in Tokyo when I was sat with Miwa at her little bar, when a group of European men walked in. As they stooped to fit into the little seats, the hostesses leapt into action bringing beers and whiskey to their table. I agreed to sing a complementary song for them at Miwa's request, taking to the microphone with a bit of Gloria Estefan that seemed to go down well. I took a bow and went back to sit at Miwa's table when one of the guests came over. He looked agitated.

"I don't understand why you are in a place like this. What would your family back home say if they knew?" he demanded sternly.

I smiled and waited a moment, rather astonished. These men were obviously over on a business trip and I was sure they wouldn't mention their outing to Miwa's club in their descriptions of Tokyo, to their wives on their return. I was rather angry that he was preaching to a twenty-year old, singleton like me, who had no strings attached or responsibilities to consider.

"I beg your pardon!" I laughed, "I think you should ask yourself the same question if you don't mind."

He scuttled back to his seat, guilt ridden, and I was just tittering to myself at the absurdity of the conversation when the wind was knocked out of my sails. There, at the bar with his back to me was Andy. Miwa was smiling broadly as she guided him over to sit at a table. Eventually he noticed me standing there, speechless, and his face went ashen before breaking into an awkward smile. To Miwa's delight, I went straight over to greet him with a tentative hug.

"It's so good to see you," he offered shiftily as we sat down.

"Thank you for the flowers. I've missed you so much," I breathed, searching his eyes for some sort of response, assuming he'd been looking for me, but he seemed troubled and lost for words.

Miwa brought us two glasses of whiskey, making it clear that it was not being counted as a social visit, placing the glasses with great ceremony on the table. I was about to ask how he knew I might be at Miwa's, when it dawned on me that he hadn't been looking for me at all, and my heart sank. He was just in need of female company. Once I woke up to the awful truth, I drained my glass and gazed at his face, confused what to say. We rose from our seats.

Another awkward embrace followed before Miwa, realising who he was, ambushed him with a huge bill as he headed for the door. While Andy was parting with a ridiculous amount of money for two drinks and a short conversation with me, I left the room and hovered by the lift outside, hoping desperately that he might prove me wrong by declaring undying love. To my dismay, he came storming out, snapping his wallet shut in fury. His face reminded me of his mood on the fateful night out with Doug. Miwa had definitely guessed who he was and taken all his money.

"That woman is a cunt," he barked unattractively, stuffing his empty wallet into his back pocket.

I reeled back in horror as the lift doors closed between us, and I announced, "No Andy, you are."

I never saw him again.

33

PARIS

I WAS RELIEVED to board my flight home because, in Nicole's words, I really had sucked Tokyo dry. Gazing into the inky night during the flight, I went over and over the last few weeks of my relationship with Andy, struggling to accept that it was definitely the end.

I'd been offered a very reasonably priced flight home from Tokyo, if I didn't mind landing in Paris. Convinced that Joyce the fortune teller would have told me this was *a sign*, of what was planned and *meant to be*, I grabbed it. Landing at Charles de Gaulle airport, I called Susannah. I knew she was living in Paris so, after grappling with my scruffy address book in a stuffy phone box, I'd called her mother in England to ask for her new number. Our mothers were used to these calls and loved them, but by the time I eventually got through to Susannah, after a full question-and-answer session with her Mum in Surrey, jetlag had started to kick in.

"Stay there, woman I'm on my way, why didn't you tell me you were coming, I could have been out and missed you for God's sake? Wait in Arrivals by the Tabac, darling!" Susannah instructed frantically before slamming down the phone. Since working on the world cruise with me, she had married a rather charismatic sound technician, who she had met on board. Wasting no time in setting up home in the suburbs of Paris with him, she was living in a quaint little apartment in domestic bliss. There had been an extravagant wedding that, unfortunately, I'd missed while I'd been in Japan.

Within half an hour, Susannah was shouting to me through the crowds at Arrivals, leading the way to the parking area.

"So, tell me about Japan, I'm so jealous."

Having missed the wedding, I felt that we had some serious catching up to do. More importantly though, I was particularly curious to hear all about her new employment as a dancer at Le Moulin Rouge in Pigalle.

"Oh, my God it's tough. I mean I have to see the osteopath all the time, but I love it," she laughed, catapulting us into the rush hour traffic in her Renault 5.

It felt strange to suddenly be in her world, so far away from Master and the adventures in Tokyo of only hours before. As she pottered about, showing me all her new storage units and domestic arrangements, it gradually sank in, that my Japanese trip was over. After all the dramas that had occurred whilst I'd been in Japan, Susannah and her Parisian life was a welcome distraction.

Over the next few days, thoughts of Andy became less frequent. Susannah and I chatted over huge coffees in the bistros of Pigalle and indulged ourselves with long lunches by the Seine, Susannah keen to hear about Andy.

"Sounds too tricky to me," she reassured me, filling my glass with more wine. "Move here and work with me. Paris is wonderful. Phillipe has some very handsome friends!"

Her enthusiasm was welcome, convincing me that there would be no better time to explore the city and look for a job. Susannah had become quite the French girl, I noticed, since signing up for the show at the Moulin Rouge. She chatted away fluently to the locals as we strolled around her neighbourhood and I was hugely inspired, quickly taken with the idea of doing the same.

～

It was 1988, and the Moulin Rouge show where Susannah had been working ever since we'd left the world cruise, was still managed and choreographed by Doris Haug, a German lady who had started performing the Can-Can there in 1952. Eventually retiring from performing, Doris had gone on to create her own troupe, Les Doriss Girls, sending them on tour all over the world, for many successful years. Eventually, in 1961, she was offered the role of manager of a new Can-Can show for the Moulin Rouge. Doris had become an instant success, managing the show there ever since, and Susannah wasted no time in taking me to meet her. I was delighted at the kindness and sweet nature of both Miss Doris, and later Miss Bluebell, when I met them. Being accustomed to the tough approach of the principal of our college and then the captains of many of my previous dance engagements, the gracious disposition of these ladies was a welcome surprise. Susannah knew there was a new contract becoming available in the near future and kindly recommended me to Miss Doris immediately.

Auditions were held onstage at the Moulin Rouge during the late afternoon, and as the concierge showed us through the dark entrance hall of the theatre on my audition day, I was reminded how much I loved the atmosphere of a theatre out of hours. It was a bit like Miwa's club in Tokyo with a drab, dusty appearance that would be transformed after dark, with romantic lighting, evocative music and the imminent arrival of the excited guests, bringing with them the anticipation of the evening ahead. There was always the sound of rehearsals going on at this time of day. Kick lines were being perfected, and you could hear the stomp of leather boots on the stage, thumping in time to the counts from the dance captain, making sure everyone turned perfect cartwheels for the show that night. The bustle of costumiers passing with armfuls of brightly coloured feathers and corsets, all added to my excitement as I popped into the dressing room with Susannah to change for my audition. The nostalgic smell of Leichner stage make-up lured me back instantly.

"I've missed this darling!" I hugged Susannah as we waited backstage for Miss Doris to appear.

"I've missed *you!*" she cried, delightedly fussing over my hair.

She handed me a lipstick from her dressing table, where I was touched to see a photo of the two of us on the ship laughing, in the sunshine, on the deck. As I applied the obligatory red mouth though, I realised I was dreading the audition because I hadn't taken dance classes while I'd been in Tokyo. I felt very stiff and rusty. Taking in the traditional surroundings, something told me I wasn't going to get away with a Karen Carpenter impression or a piano recital on this occasion. However, as soon as I went out onto the stage to warm up, I felt like I had come home as I watched the girls making their way to the dressing rooms after their rehearsal.

They all waved and wished me luck before going to put on their make-up for the first show of the night. Susannah went with them.

The Moulin Rouge is one of the most famous theatres in the world and standing on the stage, waiting for Miss Doris in the silence, I looked out at the empty seats and pretty tables with their little lamps, that had stood there for so many decades. These tables had heard thousands of intimate conversations, held between 19th century courtesans and their aristocratic lovers. Characters like the dancers, Jane Avril and the notorious La Goulue, had performed on this same stage during the 19th century, as painted by Toulouse Lautrec at the weekly Grande Fête and Bal of Montmartre. These dancers had a powerful influence on artists and poets at that time. I love this piece of writing by Paul Leclercq, a friend of the artist, Henri Toulouse-Lautrec,

> In the midst of the crowd, there was a stir, and a line of people started to form: Jane Avril was dancing, twirling, gracefully, lightly, a little madly; pale, skinny, thoroughbred, she twirled and reversed, weightless, fed on flowers; Lautrec was shouting out his admiration.

In the very early days of the Moulin Rouge, there was a garden at the back of the theatre, with seating for guests to enjoy drinking, dancing, fortune telling and even donkey rides. A huge model elephant, containing a ballroom of its own, housed a boisterous orchestra where the raucous laundry ladies invented the famous Can-Can, making the garden bohemian and exotic. Now this is all gone, replaced by new buildings, with just the original theatre remaining. That evening, knowing the history of the place, I felt extremely privileged to be part of a private world that the tourists never experienced. These moments alone on the stage before my audition with Miss Doris, as I waited in the calm before the storm, were haunting and unforgettable. The air seemed hung with history as the waiters quietly set tables with white linen, champagne flutes and silver ice buckets. In just a few hours, the peace would be disrupted as American and Japanese tourists arrived in droves, ticking another item off their holiday list. Waiters would dash to and fro, champagne bottles popping as hundreds of people felt the thrill of the Moulin Rouge, drinking in the atmosphere to take home with them, a precious memory for life.

The fact that I hadn't been to dance class for a while, became rather apparent during the audition for the Can-Can, with its fast and furious pace. I had to accept that it was going to be too strenuous for me to manage two shows every night, for a few days, let alone a whole year as the contract offered. Crashing my six-foot frame onto the floor innumerable times each night as I leapt into the splits and threw my body across the stage into cartwheels made me nervous. I was struggling to keep up with the music. Miss Doris had auditioned many girls over the decades and sensed my apprehension immediately. Seeing my concern, she offered me a role with Les Danseuses Nude.

Backstage, Susannah explained hurriedly to me, that this was not quite as it sounded.

"It's not nude! You just glide around the stage displaying the large feathers, diamantes and the heavy head dresses. Look, you'll see tonight at the show, they're stunning," she reassured me cheerfully, explaining anxiously that the nude bit was because your breasts were slightly exposed through the diamante jewellery. I agreed to watch the show and decide for myself, remembering Doug's revolting smirk in Tokyo, when I'd described the shows in Paris to him with such pride.

I went to see Susannah perform that night and was, of course, thrilled with the excitement and beauty of such a traditional performance, deciding immediately to consider it. As soon as the professionally trained dancers appear on the stage of Le Moulin Rouge, you see their sense of confidence, pride and finesse. They perform with great skill and sophistication, presenting something memorable and beautiful on a tremendously, large scale.

Being a dancer, I am very confident about the body that the fine tuning of ballet training has given me. I have the bust line of an athlete. Dancing on a vast stage, clad in beautiful, revealing costumes, with sixty other confident performers, the focus is really on the show as a whole, and not the fact that our bodies are barely covered.

Dancers of Le Moulin Rouge have been performing their shows for over a hundred years and The Bluebell Girls of Le Lido and MGM in Vegas have entertained millions for almost as long. Portraying only elegance and refinement, these shows in Paris have hosted celebrities such as Mistinguett, Maurice Chevalier, Josephine Baker and, more recently, Lisa Minelli, Gene Kelly and Shirley MacLaine. I feel nothing but pride for my contribution to this theatre history, a particularly vital part of the magic of Paris. Most people around the world, especially the French, celebrate the beauty of sexuality and their world-famous cabaret shows are seen as an art form. They are drawn from the history of La Belle Époque, the period before the First World War, when peace and happiness was spread to people by the ladies of the day wearing colourful multi-layered dresses as they sang and danced all over Paris. The time between the wars in France was also a time of hope, some prosperity and cultural exuberance. The Can-Can was seen by some as being decadent, to others though, it was a cheery hoot of a dance to lift your spirits. Unfortunately for us, many British and American people, generally, have strange reservations about sex, especially the female form whereas the French, Spanish and Italians celebrate it.

One of my friends, Emma, came to watch the Lido show whilst on a business trip to Paris with her boss. He had insisted on taking her out during their visit, so she didn't hesitate in suggesting the Lido.

"I had been telling him all about you throughout the week. 'We have to see my friend Jane, she dances at the Lido', I'd told him, several times."

They waited with anticipation after their beautiful meal and, as the lights dimmed, the Bluebell Girls appeared.

"There's Jane! Isn't she wonderful?" she exclaimed when she saw me. "Gosh! There's *all* of Jane!" she'd added as he nodded politely at our revealing costumes.

Susannah and I chatted excitedly in the taxi on the way home from the Moulin Rouge on that magical night, euphoric with the possibility that I might be joining the ranks and becoming a Parisienne at last. I knew I needed to go back to England though, just to have a break and ponder the permutations. Feeling exhausted after my journey from Tokyo, it felt like a huge commitment to join Miss Doris within a day or two of my return. I didn't sign a contract after the audition, and she was happy for me to have a week to think about my plans. At the back of my mind, I could still see Master waving me off in Tokyo, happy with my promise to bring Karen Carpenter back to his club for the following year, so my nerves were rather frayed, and my head was in a whirl with the turn of events.

~

I had really hit the ground running this time so getting home to Suffolk restored inner calm as always. As soon as I was in Mum's little red Ford, hearing about the local gossip as we sped home from the train station, it felt as though I'd never been away. Mum always made me feel that I could conquer the world and I will always love her for that. Added to this, the local gossip, delightful as it was, didn't excite me enough to cancel my plans in Paris.

Back home, Mum and I were just having a cup of tea by the fire with the dog, when Dad and Granny burst in.

"Darling! You're back!!!" they cried excitedly.

It was wonderful to see them, Granny holding my face in her hands and giving me the usual big smacker on each cheek. "My Bluebell." She beamed.

"Well ... give us a song Karen!" Dad laughed, before turning to look at me from the kettle, deeply serious suddenly.

"Now, before I forget, you had a call from Suzie, Suzannah ... Stephanie? and she says there is a job going at the Lydow... Lido... Lie-dowe?"

He went through to his desk in the study and rustled about, humming. When he returned, he handed me a nature magazine with my friend Stephanie's phone number scribbled on it. Things were developing rather quickly, and I realised that my stop-off in Paris had possibly alerted the dancer's jungle drums. We girls always looked out for each other and Steph, one of my long-standing college buddies and dance mates, was putting me forward to Miss Bluebell at Le Lido de Paris, on the Avenue des Champs-Élysées.

My heart thumped in my chest.

"There we are! I told you!" Granny piped up from the conservatory. She was enjoying a crafty fag while surveying the garden, gleefully blowing smoke out of the conservatory window. "That Stephanie's been ringin' all this week. It's all about to kick off!" she shrilled.

After asking casually if there had been a call from Andy, which there hadn't, I rang Stephanie straight away.

After an excited catch up, she explained that there was an audition for me if I wanted it, with Miss Bluebell herself.

I decided to go straight back to Paris.

As I re-packed my bags, I appreciated the serenity of my bedroom, realising then, with dismay, how much luggage I'd left in Japan during the escape with Nicole, from Stanley Starsmore Productions. "One of the drawbacks of absconding, I suppose," I muttered as I inspected a few scruffy leotards and concocted some sort of audition outfit. Laying my dance gear out on the bed, I noticed the usual pile of post that had gathered while I'd been away. Mum always chucked it in my room for when I got back so I rifled through it, hastily checking for something from Andy. There was nothing from Japan or America, but with great joy I found a quality, Basildon Bond style envelope with Duke and Son's printed in the corner.

"Well, I never!" I exclaimed with excitement, diving on the bed to rip it open.

Hilda and Molly had written me a beautiful update on life at the jewellers, in their hallmark violet ink, demanding to know where I was. I could just picture Molly at the little bureau with her spectacles perched on her nose and her sherry on the side. On closer inspection, though, my heart sank as I realised it was a letter from only Hilda, to say that Molly had passed away, added to which the letter had been written in the summer, so I'd missed her funeral. Sadness descended as I imagined Hilda coping without her side-kick. I made a decision to go to see her on my way to Victoria coach station, on the return journey to France.

There were also other letters, from all my accumulating men, which made me feel rather common. What did I think I was doing, careering around the world falling in love everywhere? Curling up to the dog who'd wandered in, I reassured myself that my dilemma was only because I kept choosing complicated, or unavailable men. I tried falling into a little snooze, to ponder the 'Andy situation' but annoyingly, Mr Angry at the jewellers kept appearing in my mind. I hauled myself up and reached for the remaining post. There was a postcard from Phillip the croupier at the flat in London demanding to know where I was. It cemented my decision to stop in London for a spot of visiting on my way to Paris. I was disappointed that Phillip hadn't taken my advice to go to work in the cruise ship casinos. I needed an update so promptly gave him a call, agreeing to visit on my way through.

Before I set off again, I had a day in Ipswich with Mum. I didn't let her buy me any smart clothes this time and smiled to myself, remembering the anxious weeks leading up to my trip to Madrid, years before, with the purchase of the famous blue mackintosh, which had since become Granny's pride and joy. As I replenished my supplies of make-up and essentials in Superdrug, I marvelled to myself at how much water had past under the bridge since that time. With no computers, we had to do our banking in person, usually with a bag full of cash. I often went to exchange my foreign currency on returning from my escapades abroad. On this occasion, I was loaded with Japanese yen that I exchanged at the little branch of Abbey National in Ipswich. Counting all the money was always intriguing for the cashier, who probably thought I was a drug dealer or something dodgy. I was *that girl* who swanned in occasionally, sporting a tan, a foreign boyfriend and different currency on each visit.

A few days later, packed and ready to go off again, I was back in the car with Mum, ready to jump out at the train station with my suitcase, as she dropped me off on her way to work. I did my usual check through my handbag as we belted into town, while mum gave me a motivational lecture.

"You didn't bring a man back with you this time, so it'll all be so much easier for everybody," she kindly pointed out, offering me an extra strong mint before continuing her speech. "Thank goodness for Joyce and her spirits, that's what I say, or we'd have some American to deal with, on top of everything else. Please tell me *he* won't show up like Giovanni, will he?"

I wasn't listening because, as we'd come to a standstill in the traffic jam, on the approach to Ipswich train station, a drastic thought had suddenly occurred to me.

"Master! Oh, my God! what will Master say if I don't go back?" I gasped.

Mum switched Terry Wogan off and leaned over to study my alarmed expression.

"What are you talking about darling? This is all getting to you again isn't it! Reminds me of when you nearly went to Damascus. Look how pale you are."

She pulled down the mirror on the sun visor flap and glared at me. "Are you pining for the yank?"

"No! Mum you don't understand. I have a return ticket to Tokyo in my bag, and Master is expecting me back in a few weeks. I forgot I was supposed to call him."

With all the Parisian excitement, I had let Tokyo become a distant memory.

"Good God!" Mum yelped, accelerating away as the traffic took off again. "I didn't know you had a flight to Tokyo booked!" she exclaimed in delight. I grabbed my handbag from the footwell.

"Well, it was almost the same price as a single, and I was planning to, possibly, go back after a few weeks. That's not going to happen now though. I'm pretty set on Paris, so I'll just have to call Master and explain," I announced, calming down.

I dreaded the thought of the phone call, as I knew how frowned upon it was to break a promise in Japan. Master would be all woebegone, making sure I knew I had been deceitful in every way, letting him down like that. I was beginning to feel weighed down with guilt from all my indecisiveness, in all directions of the globe but Mum was enthralled and speechless, a rare moment. After a bit of frowning, and grinning at the same time, she resumed the discussion with immense seriousness.

"Don't worry darling, I'll go. I need a change."

I restrained a smile as I could see she was really considering it, as she studied the road ahead. I rifled around in my passport case and pulled out the crumpled ticket. Everything was paper in those days. With no internet or mobile phones, you had to look after things much more carefully. I reached for her bag in the foot-well.

"There you go Mum. I'll put it in your handbag, so I'm not tempted, and you can think about it. You've got a week to decide, I believe, although I don't know if you're allowed to change the person named on the ticket, so don't get too excited."

Mum continued to drive, but she was so deep in thought that she was oblivious to my comments. I could see, this new idea was causing havoc on her way to the office. I could just imagine her taking her friend, Joan, for a coffee to share her exciting secret. I continued to talk as I prepared to leap out at the station.

"You'll have to be Dusty Springfield or Sandie Shaw though, I mean, no offence, but you may be a bit o"

"Alright darling, call me tonight!!" she cut in, pushing me and my suitcase out and slamming the door.

I stood and waved goodbye as she shot back into the rush hour traffic.

I lugged my case onto the platform at the station, squinting up at the sun, deciding where to sit and wait for the London train. I sat myself down on a bench and started to relax. I was on my way at last, quite relieved to get rid of the Tokyo thoughts and, in her current mood, Mum, actually. We were so close, that we always became anxious with the lead up to another farewell. As I watched the people arriving through the barrier ready for their day, I realised it was half term.

"Oh no, the train's going to be packed," I thought, as I opened a bag of Monster Munch.

It was then that I saw him.

Before delving into the crisp bag, I lifted my gaze to check the time on the station clock, and there he was.

Mark. Mark from The Purple Shop. Mark the teacher. *My Mark*. I'd dreaded this moment over the years, at the same time, hoping it would happen, and now that it had, I wanted to hide, but it was too late. Unfortunately, he'd seen me, his face breaking into that beautiful grin, as he hitched up his rucksack and came over. My heart leapt into my mouth and I thanked the Lord that I had lippy on, and that I was sitting down.

"Mark! How amazing to see you!" I stammered, my cheeks burning as I shoved the bag of Monster Munch behind my back. I was glad I hadn't just crammed a handful into my mouth, especially as they were spring onion flavour. Could this week get any more bizarre, I wondered? I was beginning to wish I'd stayed in Japan with Andy, or married Salvino, Dino, Giovanni, or Babu.

Gosh, when I said it like that I felt rather cheap. Mark could tell I was embarrassed and came straight in for a hug.

"So, young lady, what have you been up to since school, my girl?"

I stood for a few bewildered moments, thinking of the age gap between us, after his stress on *young* lady and *girl* ...

"Yeah alright, no need to rub it in," I thought to myself as I pondered how to describe what I'd been up to. I mean, where to start really ...?

I opted for the straightforward, "Oh this 'n that. You know, keeping busy." I mean, I didn't want to sound like one of those people at a reunion, trying to sound amazing, with descriptions of endless extraordinary adventures. He would have thought I was making it up, and definitely felt sorry for me. He would've missed his train as well, unless he'd walked off, leaving me there spouting off my list of different countries and boyfriends, like a crazy person.

I felt myself nodding too much, and as we chatted politely, it slowly began to dawn on me that there was no spark igniting within. My smile broadened as, I realised that I was feeling ... nothing.

That stomach flip that I used to feel in assembly when our eyes met, had gone, leaving just happiness for Mark and happiness for me and my travel adventures (not so proud of my list of boyfriends) that were releasing me from the grip of teenage angst, that used to hound me constantly. I realised how much I had experienced in life since he'd dropped me home in his sports car, that extraordinary day after the bus stop incident, probably six or seven years previously. I was elated to feel confident and completely comfortable, reassured that things had changed, and I had moved on. I was also hugely relieved when he explained that he had just arrived *from* London and was on his way home. I knew I wasn't relaxed enough to sit and talk to him all the way to Liverpool Street, actually feeling quite exhausted after just these few minutes on the platform together.

Once we'd waved goodbye, I spent my whole journey just gazing out of the train window, in astonished wonder at what had just occurred. I was so elated that I didn't even listen to my Walkman, which was completely unheard of.

I snapped out of my reverie as the train pulled into London, making my way to the taxi rank with renewed vigour for the next adventure. I had arranged to stop off at the flat for the night to catch up with Phillip the croupier, and although I was cross he hadn't taken my advice of applying for any of the cruise ship casinos, I was desperate for a heart to heart about men, which was his forte, keen to hear his own latest boyfriend dramas.

First though, I went to Duke and Sons where I found Viv replacing a velvet tray in the window display as my taxi pulled up outside. Her face lit up when she saw me staggering over to the door with my case, but I became quite tearful when Hilda came out to greet me without little Molly. Leading me straight into the back office, she sat me down to tea with sweet sherry on the side. We gazed momentarily over at Molly's empty armchair in the corner, but Hilda was surprisingly matter of fact about things, and certainly not in the mood for sadness.

"It's alright, Molly was older than you think darling," she explained as she passed me a Mr Kipling before lighting up a cigarette, theatrically blowing the smoke up to the ceiling.

"Trouble is, we all live so bloody long these days, it's exhausting. Molly was tired of being old, you know, every day was an effort," she sighed.

We sat in silence for a moment until she brightened,

"So, come on! How are you, pray tell, and where have you been dear child?"

She poured more tea as I attempted a potted history of Japan, but it's never easy summing up my exploits in a quick chat. I covered a fair bit of ground, describing my mad escapade in Tokyo, Viv popping in to join us in the parlour every now and then, to hoot with laughter. Hilda was most excited about the prospect of auditioning for Miss Bluebell in Paris.

"Well, Molly would have loved that. I think Viv and I may have to make a trip to see you."

As I drained my teacup and prepared to go, she leaned over and squeezed my arm. "Now, I've just remembered what I wanted to tell you," she chuckled.

"That nice chap that came in. Viv told me all about him. He's been back a few times. He always asks if we've heard from you," she winked at me, "I think he's rather smitten." I stared at Hilda, trying to think of which nice chap. I really didn't need another one.

"Mr Angry!" shouted Viv from the shop floor, "he's gorgeous ... and he's not angry and those red roses were from him."

"He's actually called Steven," corrected Hilda, as I sat bolt upright, shocked.

She looked amused, "You've got him all wrong dear," she stated, simply. "He stays at the hotel whenever he has to give a lecture at the university. Such a *good* man. Mathematician you know. He's become rather a friend since Molly died. So *kind*."

She took my hand as we walked through to the shop.

"I'd say he's rather a catch!"

34

LIDO LIFE

LEAVING HILDA, I made my way to Phillip the croupier, as he waited in the flat with a bottle and two glasses as though I'd never been away.

"Paris honey! How fab is that?" he exclaimed as he pottered around the kitchen, emptying bags of nuts into a bowl. He plonked himself next to me and opened the wine.

"Now, I know you're cross with me for still living in this dump, I've put you on the sofa tonight by the way, but I've met *the one*, so I couldn't possibly mess things up by travelling to the back of beyond, could I?"

At that moment, an Adonis in boxer shorts entered the kitchen, making Phillip blush with pride. Demanding details of my colourful love life, they clapped their hands with glee when I explained that Hilda had befriended Mr Angry.

"I think it's time you called him Steven," he declared, "and if he was the sender of those roses, well, I would certainly give him a chance darling."

It was all good, everyone was happy and by the time I hopped on the coach to Paris the next day, I was eager to get to my audition at the Lido with Miss Bluebell. Anxiety crept over me slightly as I sat on the long ferry crossing, wishing there was a fast train that would magically zap me across the sea. Little did I know then that someone, somewhere, was designing Eurostar. Dreading how I was about to throw myself into yet another life, with yet more people, I was relieved to see the familiar face of Stephanie waiting to greet me from the steps of the Paris Metro by the Champs-Élysées.

Walking excitedly along the boulevard to the theatre, she explained that I would be meeting the dance director at the Lido, Monsieur Pierre Rambert. Pierre was overseeing my audition that afternoon and I tried not to be disappointed that it wasn't going to be Miss Bluebell after all.

Stephanie sensed this, "You'll meet Bluebell later, don't worry, she often watches the show. Pierre is lovely and he manages things these days."

We entered the theatre by the elegant main entrance of the Lido, and I admired Stephanie's confident manner as she chatted to the people we passed. Lavishly furnished with vast, shimmering chandeliers, the walk along the plush carpet of the entrance hall to the Lido is tantalising. Music from the show tinkles from the speakers in the walls where video footage of the dancers is shown behind glass cases. Luxury designer gifts at the little boutique, also tempt you inside. At that time, there were two Lido shows each evening, one at 9.30pm with the option of arriving earlier for French cuisine, champagne and dancing to the orchestra. The second show was at midnight with just champagne, an impressive wine list and the show. Stephanie and I caught a glimpse of the afternoon rehearsals that were taking place on the stage, as we made our way through the auditorium. There were groups of acrobats, jugglers and pas de deux couples running through their most dare devil moves and lifts. It was truly thrilling to see, but Stephanie was used to it and bustled passed, taking us down to the dressing rooms to change.

"Miss Bluebell comes to say hello sometimes, but she is retired now, only popping in to keep an eye on us occasionally," she explained as we scuttled along corridors and down endless flights of steps into the basement. Having danced a principal role in the show for several years, Stephanie was very familiar with the Lido building. I was beside myself with excitement, and so grateful to have been invited for an audition, although a little anxious.

I gazed around me at the walls, laden with stunning costumes and props. The long-mirrored dressing tables were heaving with make-up, family photos, hair products, long, glossy wigs and tiaras on stands. Shelves below this, housed rows of different shoes, golden heels, flat pumps, red tap shoes, silver sandals and turquoise boots, all waiting to be matched with different costumes throughout the night. There were huge bottles of Christian Dior make up and large sponges at each place, next to boxes of false eyelashes and the same uniform shade of red lipstick, provided by the Lido, for every dancer.

"We have to cover ourselves every night with this stuff," Steph explained, rolling her eyes and showing me a huge bottle of body make-up. "Everyone from England has lily white skin and it's a nightmare to get off in the shower!" she laughed.

Stephanie had a separate dressing room with five other dancers. These ladies were called Belles and were chosen especially, by Miss Bluebell, to lead the show with their immaculate line, incorporating solos and routines choreographed just for them. To be invited into the Belle line was a huge compliment and meant you had 'arrived'.

Meanwhile, my audition was for 'Danseuses Nudes' again, and fortunately, having learnt from the Moulin Rouge visit that this term didn't mean leaping around naked, as the expression suggested, I was completely at ease during the audition with Pierre, the director of the show. Pierre Rambert was the epitome of Parisian elegance in his beautifully tailored clothes, enhanced by his sylph-like silhouette, maintained by coffee, cigarettes and the customary frazzled nerves of dance directors.

I was taught the opening number of the show, by one of the dancers while Pierre watched, with Steph, from the auditorium. I was required to glide across the vast stage in what was to be a large formation with dozens of other girls, taking giant steps in order to reach my positions on time. The show in 1988 was called Panache, a spectacular visual experience, with approximately sixty dancers, men and women, clad in stunning couture, presented under the spotlights with a burlesque feel. The show opened with the exciting introduction from The Kelly Boys, Miss Bluebells twenty male dancers, their title taken from her birth name of Margaret Kelly. In their striking white top hats and tails, these dashing young men presented The Bluebell Girls as they emerged, clad in white fur and diamonds, parading downstage towards the auditorium for the opening number, played by a full orchestra. The thought of becoming a part of this prestigious performance was exhilarating and I felt eager to embrace my long yearned for role of Bluebell Girl of Paris. I was delighted when, after my audition, Pierre cautiously offered me a six-month contract to sign, on the promise that I would accept the complimentary gym membership, offered to all Bluebell's dancers, encouraging me to get back into training. This was no surprise to me at all, knowing that my weakness for local cuisine was becoming evident. Thrilled with the style of the choreography at the Lido, I felt happy to decline the show at the Moulin Rouge and accept Pierre's exciting offer instead, feeling glad that all the years of feeling tall and awkward at school had been worth it.

When I signed the contract for Miss Bluebell, Susannah and I were disappointed that we wouldn't be working together at the Moulin Rouge after all, but thrilled that, at least, I was going to be in Paris for a while, giving us a chance to spend some time together again. In fact, looking back, I saw very little of her during my time in Paris, as nothing had prepared me for the long hours required of me at my new engagement.

Miss Bluebell's insistence of the height requirement of five feet and ten inches for her dancers, originated when a visiting American group, called The Buddy Bradley Girls, performed at the Folies Bergère show during the 30's. Bluebell had noticed that much of their elegance was due to their height and decided to adopt the same style for her own dancers, phasing in the new rule when she was invited to manage the Lido show in 1947. The taller dancers seemed to enable the heavy swathes of costume fabric to move more elegantly and effortlessly across the stage, showcasing them at their best. Inviting dancers of exceptional height and beauty to audition for the Lido, girls travelled over from Britain, delighted with the irresistible passport to adventure, especially during the 50's when foreign travel was rare. These girls ensured an unrivalled elegance to their performance, making Miss Bluebell's show world famous for its style and finesse.

There was a well-known wall in Miss Bluebell's office, backstage at the Lido, where the measuring process took place before any audition could begin. I was pleased to pass that test although later, I shared a dressing room with a girl called Gale, from Vegas, who had a funny story to tell. She had been recommended to Pierre, by another dancer at Miss Bluebell's show at MGM in Las Vegas. Gale was both pretty and elegant and very keen to visit Paris, but not quite tall enough to be a Bluebell. After fibbing slightly about her height on her application form, not wanting to miss out on an opportunity of a life-time, she managed to arrange a contract in Paris.

"I couldn't think what difference just one or two, incy, little inches could make as I typed out my C.V. to send to Pierre!" she recalled. "When I arrived though, it was awful, I mean it was just so noticeable that I was so short in the line-up. I was terrified because my little exaggeration about my height was much more obvious than I had anticipated. I just hadn't realised how gargantuan the girls from England, Australia and the Netherlands were going to be. I'd never seen dancers like it," she laughed.

Considering Gale had been flown all the way from the States, Pierre Rambert arranged to have some extortionately expensive shoes made especially for her, with in-built platforms to give her an extra two inches in height. It was precarious enough walking about on the stage, with its varying levels, tricky steps and ledges and I'd always noticed Gale taking extra care with her footing. This had tempted me to ask her about it one evening in the wings. As we stood with the camels, in our golden thongs, waiting to go on for The Legend of the Ancient Egyptians, she sent me into fits of giggles, recounting her tale.

I've since learnt that there is a famous cobbler at a place called Maison Clairvoy, near the Moulin Rouge on Rue Pierre Fontaine. It is an unassuming shop front, nestled between a kebab shop, massage parlour and scruffy fabric supplier. Despite its shabby exterior, the shop, established in 1945, is a gem of Parisian history. For over seventy years, shoes have been carefully moulded in this traditional workshop, before being sent out to stars of stage and screen, and of course the Moulin Rouge and Lido dancers. Shoes are made to measure, giving a perfect fit, enabling performers to dance at their best. I just love the thought of the hundreds of beautiful, pristine shoes and Can-Can boots in rows at the launch of a new production. I assumed this was where Gale's groovy platforms were fashioned. I would have been in my element in this little boutique, that reminded me so much of Sinora Porselli, the lady that measured me for my pointe shoes years before. Unfortunately for me, I was the exact size of the girl I was replacing at the Lido, so was given all her shoes.

At the very back of the auditorium at the Lido, there is a glazed VIP box that the girls called The Fish Tank. If you ever heard the words, "Bluebell's in tonight," while putting on your make-up, you would know that Miss Bluebell was watching the show with Pierre, from this viewing point, adding a frisson of excitement as you danced. Miss Bluebell and Pierre would often watch the show, the ends of their cigarettes glinting in the dark as they discussed the choreography. I felt excited to have been invited to watch the show with Pierre on the evening of my successful audition. It was just another example of how Miss Bluebell's dancer's welfare were always her priority, as were the complimentary taxi's home for all her girls after every show. She didn't join us that evening, but as I was served a glass of champagne, and the show began, I felt like I'd come home. I became rather emotional as I sat in The Fish Tank with Pierre and another new dancer, because I hadn't seen Stephanie dance since the world cruise with Guy. When she stepped out onto the stage that night, I was mesmerised. While I'd been gallivanting around Yugoslavia and Japan, she had clearly been working her way to the very top of the showgirl tree and went on to work for Miss Bluebell at the Lido for ten years.

∼

Rehearsals started almost straight away, and I loved every minute of it. The stage sets were so dramatic, and the costumes were designed on a scale that I had never seen before. My favourite moment of the show was when ten of us sat on enormous rocking chairs that sailed back and forth as the entire floor of the stage opened, and we rose up from the basement. My favourite costume was an enormous framework of orange feathers, fitted with an electrical circuit that lit up during a blackout when we reached for a hidden switch in the costume, creating a magical, glowing, carousel effect as we waltzed across the stage.

My new job at the Lido threw me instantly into Parisian life, overnight. Many of the dancers lived in the suburbs, in modern apartments, but Stephanie came up trumps yet again, making me an offer I couldn't refuse. She was moving out of a bijou little flat, right in the throng of Pigalle, Montmartre, and needed someone to take over the tenancy. One call to her landlord and it was mine. Looking out at the rooftops from the bedroom window, on my first evening, Montmartre twinkled up at me, just waiting to be explored. I couldn't believe my luck, marvelling at the fact that I was living right in the neighbourhood of the famous dancer, Jane Avril, amongst the streets and bars that she had frequented with her good friend, the artist, Henri Toulouse-Lautrec, one hundred years previously. Situated on the top floor of a tall thin ancient building, my flat reminded me of the hostel in Madrid, with its swirling bannister, beautiful tiling and creaky wooden steps.

My neighbour was a very elderly lady by the name of Delphine and from what I gathered, she had lived in her little flat for most of her life. She was delighted to have a new neighbour, so I was often invited in for a chat and a piece of mouldy cake, accompanied by a glass of brandy that made my throat burn. Delphine had no trouble with hers, raising her glass with gnarled old fingers before knocking the firewater back with a grin. There were photographs of ladies in 1920's and 30's dress on her mantelpiece. I longed to know who they were, and what had happened to Delphine during the war, but she had severe memory loss and would just smile when I asked her, gazing at the photographs, mystified. One morning I came back from the boulangerie to find her prodding a tramp who'd somehow managed to get through the coded entrance door, settling across the step to my flat for a sleep.

As I'd climbed the stairs, I'd been alarmed to hear Delphine shouting, "Debout s'il vous plait!" as she poked him with her walking stick.

She was furious that someone was trespassing on our little landing. I calmed her down and we went to a lady on a lower floor to use the phone. The gendarmes arrived swiftly, giving Delphine a wonderful excuse to get the brandy out while they removed the unwelcome visitor. She rarely ventured outside, finding the stairs difficult, so the visit from the gendarmes caused great excitement.

Night after night, Le Lido de Paris offers the thrill of an awards ceremony with guests gathering on the red carpet of its glamorous entrance, hours before curtain up. Dressed in their finery, assembling on the Champs-Élysées, tourists from all over the world chatter excitedly, waiting to be escorted to their seats. People wandering by, pause curiously, to watch the elegant doormen, escorting glittering guests through the long entrance hall to the theatre. The lights dim, the champagne is poured and at last, the wait is over. Everyone is seated and the orchestra erupts with the cascade of an overture as the auditorium moves, mechanically, repositioning the seating to ensure that each and every member of the audience has a spectacular view of the stage.

The photographs of my family and their friends, drinking wine on the Champs-Élysées on that first evening are precious. Their excited faces shine out at the camera, as they raise their glasses to me, on my opening night, at a café near the Lido. It was to be an evening they had looked forward to, after many years of encouraging me to audition for Bluebell, since I'd been forced to give up any hope of becoming a ballerina, so we were all feeling quite pleased with ourselves.

"We knew what we were talking about pet!" Granny chortled as Dad led them up the glamorous entrance hall of the Lido in their best frocks, clutching their tickets. It was such a joy to watch them, so pleased they would see the famous show at last.

Flowers and cards had started arriving, in celebration of my opening night, as we put on our make-up in the dressing room that evening.

Welcome to the madhouse! Stephanie X
Keep your vest on! Mum and Dad X
I knew you could do it! Granny XX

But then, to my astonishment.

> Molly would have been so proud! Come to our
> hotel tomorrow at noon darling. Love from Hilda,
> Viv and our chaperone

I stared in disbelief at this last card, noting the five-star hotel note paper.

"Hilda!" I gasped, chuffed but astonished.

I'd recently written to tell her all about my debut, knowing she would want to know every detail, but I never dreamt that she would manage a trip to Paris to share the occasion.

"Who could the chaperone be?" I wondered. Since my last visit to Hilda, I suspected she had enlisted her new acquaintance, Mr Angry, the man I had hoped never to cross paths with again, to bring her and Viv to Paris. She *had* been busy!

"Whoever is that card from, you look like you've seen a ghost?" Diana, one of the girls, was watching me in the mirror, as I stared at the card in amazement. While we applied our eye-lashes, I recounted the terrifying tales of the hotel and jewellery shop, with a description of Mr Angry, our rather awkward relationship and the red roses he'd sent to me on Valentine's Day. This last detail sent all the girls into raptures of excitement as we pinned our wigs and tiaras in place. They found it extremely amusing.

"We want to meet this terrible man!" exclaimed Gale as she fluffed out her curls.

"I think Hilda is playing Cupid,' announced Diana excitedly.

It's a surprise to many people when they hear that Bluebell Girls and Kelly Boys have little social life outside of the Lido, due to the long hours involved in putting on the two shows, for six nights, every week of the year. Any suggestion of potential romance was always hugely intriguing, but I chose not to look out for my surprise guests in the audience that night. The thought of Mr Angry and I making eye contact as I sailed across the stage, didn't bear thinking about. Mainly though, I had too much else to remember on my debut for Bluebell, so didn't have time to dwell on this new development for long.

"Have you seen him yet darling?" yelled Paul, one of the boys, as we climbed the steps of the vast waterfall, to our places for The Polynesian. News travelled fast backstage. Miss Bluebell's Kelly Boys loved a bit of gossip.

"Bring him to our dressing room for a drink!" suggested Paul excitedly.

Every now and then, at the end of the show, some of The Kelly Boys would slip into their favourite cocktail dresses to enjoy a glass of champagne and a few laughs in the dressing rooms before heading home or going to a club. It was always a treat to pop in for a natter. I knew Hilda would have loved to be introduced to these flamboyant characters, as would my family, but it was just too much for me to contemplate with everything else going on. The inevitable thorough interrogation from Granny about the gay scene in Paris also made me nervous.

Hilda and Viv had informed me, on my last visit to the jewellery shop, that Mr Angry was in fact, called Steven, and was rather an admirer. I reassured myself that he was just a man that I had met once or twice, in rather awkward circumstances I had to admit, but none the less, there was absolutely nothing to be alarmed about. I reminded myself, as I walked across the stage in my orange plumes for the finale that evening, that he had sent roses to me at the jewellers, so he was hardly the enemy. Could it be that he had been charmed by my outrageous selling skills and receptionist manner at the hotel? As the night progressed, I became rather intrigued to meet Steven at Hilda's luncheon the next day, remembering his dashing smile as he'd left the shop on that fateful afternoon. I pictured his grin, the last time I'd seen him and felt rather a surprising shiver of excitement.

After the first performance on my opening night, I had said farewell to the visiting family, before going back to perform the second show, relieved that they were leaving on the coach, very early the next morning. We'd already enjoyed two exhausting afternoons of sight-seeing, so Mum and Granny agreed I should rest.

"There's no need to get up to see us off. You get some shut-eye darling, you've got to do it all again tomorrow!" Granny had insisted, admiringly.

Performing two shows at the Lido in one evening, meant that there was never enough time in between, to meet visitors for a drink. After the first show, my guests would go back to the flat or their hotel, while I did a repeat performance until two in the morning. I wasn't looking my best therefore, as I made my way to meet Hilda and Viv at their hotel the next day. Having entertained the family and their friends, giving them a complete tour of Paris before opening night, followed by a second performance, I was weary to say the least. By the time I arrived at Hilda's hotel, it was a relief to be getting on with our rendezvous at last. Exhausted as I was, I felt keen to get back to normal, lusting after a day in the flat where I could drink tea and snooze at my leisure.

As I sat dazed, in a taxi, I started to imagine endless ridiculous outcomes to the imminent meeting with Hilda, Viv and Mr Angry.

"Bless Hilda though," I thought, climbing the elegant steps of her hotel, realising what a big deal it must have been for her to make this trip. Hilda looked tiny in the grand lobby, teetering across to greet me as emotion took over.

"Oh, my star!! You were wonderful sweetheart, the show was super!" she exclaimed, hugging me tightly, tears popping out of her bright eyes. We were both thinking of Molly. Viv was close behind, gazing around the breathtakingly beautiful, hotel reception. Hilda never did things by halves. Together we made our way to a lovely table in the window, that overlooked the elegant square. It felt funny to be in Paris with them, having never seen them outside of the jewellery shop. Hilda signalled to the waiter to pour our champagne and then beamed across at the man himself, Mr Angry.

"This is Steven, the most attentive escort a lady could ask for," Hilda giggled as Mr Angry stood up to shake my hand.

Hilda and I had become quite emotional by this time and I surprised myself by hugging Steven and thanking him for bringing my friends to see me. I was startled at how confident and relaxed I felt. I didn't feel like a blithering idiot at all.

Lunch was a feast of Fruit de Mer, served on towering plates by attentive waiters, while Hilda updated us on life at the jewellers and quizzed me for descriptions of Paris. Eventually Hilda and Viv excused themselves, with a very obvious wink, setting off across the foyer to powder their noses. Thankfully, Steven spoke first.

"Well, you certainly have variety in your working life that's for sure!" he joked with a knowing grin as he refilled my glass. There was a kindness about him that was most welcome, taking me by surprise as he waited for my response. By the time Hilda and Viv came back, Steven and I were chuckling about my extraordinary selling techniques at Duke and Sons and my lively receptionist skills at the hotel, not forgetting his little tantrum when I gave him the wrong room key.

"Last night was unforgettable. I think the Lido is definitely a more suitable career. You were wonderful," he declared, holding my gaze for a second, creating a very noticeable tingle of excitement. "I'd like to apologise for my rudeness at the hotel. Apparently, I'm known as Mr Angry." He stifled a smirk as I cringed.

Hilda returned, moving us all over to the lounge area for delectable coffee. Relaxing into the comfort of the hotel, she described the last time she'd been to Paris, not long after the war, and I only wished Miss Bluebell could have joined us. The lights started to flicker outside, and I knew it wouldn't be long before I would have to leave for the theatre. Hilda sensed this, as I looked discretely at my watch. After promising to visit them when I was next home, I hugged Hilda and Viv before they promptly set off to visit the Chanel boutique down the street.

"Won't be long, Steven!" they twittered, leaving us alone, yet again, as they made their way through the lobby.

"I ought to get going really," I explained reluctantly, as I was offered another coffee.

Walking me to the taxi rank, Steven opened the car door and paid the driver.

"Sorry you have to leave. I hope we can meet again," he said quietly.

I had a bizarre feeling we would.

～

All my work schedules before I joined the Lido, had been short, between the hours of nine and midnight. The Lido shows however, were performed twice nightly, meaning that the last show ended at around 1.30am. The shows were long and so, by the time my Lido taxi driver had delivered me to my little flat at 2am each morning, I was ready to sleep until well after lunchtime the following day.

After completing a few chores in the flat, I would usually set off towards the Champs-Élysées at around four o'clock in the afternoon. The walk took me along the tree lined pavements of Boulevard de Clichy, past the red windmill of the Moulin Rouge at Blanche, before descending down the hill to L'Opera. Watching the world go by, I would stop for coffee and croissant, just to enjoy the hustle and bustle of Paris, sometimes meeting a friend from the show for a spot of shopping and some early dinner, before we disappeared into the theatre for most of the night. It was a really long walk to the Lido from my flat, taking over an hour, but it brought fresh air and normality to my day. I remember those times most fondly. As a Parisian dancer, your day begins when most people are thinking of going home after a long day at work in offices and shops. As the city lights were beginning to flicker and the aroma of roasting garlic floated across the streets from the restaurants, it was tempting to stop, for a plate of Mussels or a colourful bowl of salad at the street-side tables of pretty bistros and cafés. This was my time to breath in the atmosphere and really feel part of the city, before we dancers would bid each other "Good Morning!" at the stage door, launching ourselves into the shows for the night.

This extract from Jane Avril of the Moulin Rouge, by Jose Shercliff, published in 1954, sums up Paris, in the early evening pretty well.

It is the hour between work and play, when a hundred thousand chefs are casting succulent spells in steaming kitchens; when precious liquids bubble bright coloured into glasses; when the air is exciting with the smell of life - the rich, lovely nostalgic odour of Paris- hot croissant and chicory, sawdust, rum and anise at the open bistro door, pungent smoking hams in the charcutiers window, sweet herbs and flowers and women's perfume around Madeleine. For a while Jeanne wandered in the dying light. It was a pale September evening in the year 1881, one of those evenings when the sun sets behind the Champs-Élysées in a veil of rose and silver light, and even the narrow, twisted streets of old Montmartre hold magic in their dusky maze.

~

Paris in the late afternoon was my private time. Proud that I had a salary and a rented apartment, I felt truly a part of this unique city, steeped in history with a character and style of its own. Admiring the well-preserved delicate cast iron balconies, wooden shutters and elegant doorways, I enjoyed time to explore the intricate street formations that lead to the grand avenues connecting all the world-famous monuments and parks of the city. I often visited the Musée du Louvre to take in a few rooms of paintings on my way to work, having purchased a membership card enabling me to come and go as I pleased. Later I would enjoy walking across Place du Concorde and through Jardin des Tuileries, before strolling up the Avenue des Champs-Élysées where the designer boutiques were a hive of activity. Here, restaurants enticed tourists to their tables, heaving with shellfish, champagne and charcuterie at exorbitant prices along the magnificent boulevard. With its stunning view of the vast Arc de Triomphe at the top, the Champs-Elysees never ceased to thrill me. Looking up the avenue, before turning down Rue Washington, on my way to the stage door of the Lido, I was proud to join the dancers as they arrived, preparing to transform from thin, pale girls into dazzling enchantresses for the night.

I met many interesting people at the Lido, making some of my closest friends whilst waiting to go on stage from the wings. Diana, from New Zealand, was next to me for the opening number and before setting off in our velvet, fur and diamonds for L'Ouverture each evening, we would plan where to meet the next day at different locations all over the city, for lunch and a stroll. Diana worked as an I.T. whizz in Auckland, when she wasn't being a showgirl. She had been at the end of a back-packing holiday in Europe with her boyfriend when Pierre had offered her a place at the Lido. Keen to stay longer in Paris, she had strolled into the theatre one afternoon, and auditioned for the show. Being much taller than average height, and classically trained in ballet, even in her scruffy shorts and T-shirt, Pierre had offered her a contract there and then. Waving her poor boyfriend off as he left for the airport, Diana grabbed this golden opportunity to experience real Parisian life. Her boyfriend Paul has since explained that he can take the credit for her success at the audition because they had been starving themselves on their trek around Greece due to lack of funds.

"She was looking particularly fabulous with her tan and skinny figure because we hadn't eaten for several weeks."

Gale, from Las Vegas, turned out to be a professional sightseer. A bright girl, who went on to work in law when she eventually returned to the States, constantly enticed me out on tours of Paris. I've always taken Europe for granted, but these two girls always reminded me how the British seldom take advantage of the European history on our doorstep. With this in mind, we made sure we explored every inch of the city. I'm pleased to report that Diana returned to her boyfriend eventually, and they now live happily together in Australia with their son. I will always be grateful to these sassy women though, for making sure that we took in as much of Paris as we could. My phone would often leap off its hook at noon, when Gale would entice me out with her alluring American drawl.

"Jane we're down the street in that cute little patisserie near Jean-Pierre's and would love for you to join us honey. We've bought so many pastries. Let's do the Eiffel Tower today."

I would stagger down the street to join them, yawning in my dark glasses, before spending the day on the River Seine aboard Les Bateaux-Mouches gazing in awe at The Eiffel Tower, or listening to jazz as we ate late lunch in the Latin Quarter.

Just as I loved hearing Gale's stories of the shows in Vegas, she loved hearing my tales of countries that I'd worked in, especially the world cruise for Guy on the French cruise-line. She would grill me for details of that particular trip, where we, the dancers, were looked after so beautifully with silver service, cocktails by the pool and five-star treatment while we floated around tropical islands on our luxury ship.

"That's what I wanna do next," she would say dreamily as we watched the world go by, from cafés and bistros during our lazy afternoons. I knew she would make it happen sooner or later on her quest to see the world.

It was Diana though, who arranged the most memorable afternoon of my entire stay in Paris. Diana lived in one of Miss Bluebell's apartments and noticing how interested in Bluebell I was, after buying copies of her memoir, she had suggested that we took them to be signed by the lady herself.

Miss Bluebell lived in a chic apartment near Avenue Foch, one of the grand avenues that leads off L'Arc du Triomphe. Many of these elegant buildings had been occupied by the

Nazis during the war and having closed her show at the Folies Bergère during that time, refusing to open the theatre to the Gestapo, Bluebell had been constantly interrogated. It was awe inspiring to see her sitting in such comfort, after learning of the battles she had faced, to save herself and her loved ones. Hiding her Jewish husband in an attic directly opposite Police buildings, the Germans had never managed to discover her daring secret.

As she rose from her tea table to greet us, dainty in twinset and pearls, it became more apparent how petite she was. Bluebell only introduced the height requirement for her dancers after her own retirement from performing, and with her Parisian haircut shining in the sunlight that streamed through the window, she looked delightedly up at us, genuinely thrilled to welcome us into her home. She seemed flattered that we were so proud to be part of her show and, as with Miss Doris at the Moulin Rouge, I found this hugely endearing.

"So, my dears, how are you enjoying your time with us in Paris?" she asked signalling to us to sit down on her traditionally British looking armchairs.

Miss Bluebell passed us strong tea in delicate china cups as we perched on the edge of the immaculate furniture of her bright, sunny home of many years. As we described our new lives in Paris, my mind raced, keen to hear about her own life, which I knew was far more exciting. She was delighted when I asked her how she had started her career and perhaps, being used to visits from inquisitive dancers, she treated us to a wonderful account, as though she were telling her story for the first time.

"I was rather frail as a child, so the doctor in Dublin, where I was born, recommended that I attend ballet class to improve my health. He used to call me Bluebell because my eyes looked so big and blue on my tiny face and the name stuck really."

Bluebell sat, poised and calm. Having had such an eventful life, she was used to recounting her experiences to people at interviews or socially.

"I first discovered my love of dance from Madame Cummings in Liverpool when I moved there from Ireland, with Mary Murphy, my guardian. I'm an orphan you see, and Mary was so good to me, making sure I had everything I needed."

Surrounded by her treasured, framed photographs, in the peace of her elegant sitting room, we listened intently, taking in her every word as she described her early life.

"I started working at fourteen, dancing with The Five Hot Jocks around the music halls of Scotland but my first job abroad, was for Alfred Jackson in 1926. He was looking for dancers for his show at La Scala Theatre in Berlin. I'd been along to a rehearsal hall in Liverpool to support a friend, Effie, as she auditioned for his company. Alfred had insisted that I too should audition, so dear Effie lent me her leotard and we were both successful. It was a very exciting time for us because we were offered a very good wage. I wasn't keen to leave home but Mary, my guardian, encouraged me to grab the opportunity to earn a good living. Girls started work at a very young age then and I had to earn my keep somehow. I decided to take the chance and I'm glad I did."

Bluebell's eyes lit up as she described the glamorous shows in Berlin and Paris during the twenties and thirties. These assignments were an exciting passport to travel for her then, just as the shows I'd performed in had been for me, during the eighties. However, the different decades had brought very dangerous challenges to her that made my own adventures pale into insignificance. Diana and I sat, transfixed, as Bluebell described her time in Paris during the war and it occurred to me then, that Bluebell had been dancing in Berlin during the same period of the Kit Kat Girls and Sally Bowles from Cabaret. Although Cabaret was fictional, I knew it was based on the many night clubs of that time, when people were in denial that a war was brewing, preferring to lose themselves in the magic of fantasy and entertainment.

"By the time the war broke out in 1939, I'd moved to Paris and started managing a very successful show at the Folies Bergère. Of course, most of my dancers were sent home to Britain when Hitler arrived, but eventually after a great deal of trouble, I managed to convince the authorities that, being Irish, I should be allowed to remain in Paris. I was married to a Polish musician by the name of Marcel by then. Being a Jew, we feared for his life and we'd started a family, so I wouldn't leave him. Marcel was soon taken by the Nazis and sent to an internment camp in Gurs."

Bluebell went on to describe how Marcel had managed to escape from Gurs, and returning to Paris, he had found a hiding place, through a friend, in an attic in Rue Berthollet. Bluebell hid Marcel there for two and a half years, knowing that they would both have been shot by the Gestapo if he'd been discovered.

"I was never scared of them," Bluebell smiled defiantly, "I would look them straight in the eye. I'd learnt to speak German during my years in Berlin at the Scala show, you see, and that really helped me to outwit them. Never for one moment did I think they would win the war."

Bluebell smiled over to us triumphantly as we gazed, reeling from her descriptions that made our own adventures seem so trivial. Having been threatened and humiliated by the Nazis, witnessing violence and disappearances in her community, it

415

must have felt hugely satisfying for Bluebell to have claimed her freedom back and be living in an area that had been occupied by the enemy, during those frightening years. She had good reason to smile and tell her tale so willingly, but I knew there had also been some tragedies along the way. Although she was used to telling her story to dancers, and her Irish eyes were sparkling, I could see she was weary and so we prepared to leave.

"Thank you, I can't wait to read the full story," I said, clutching my Bluebell book and not wanting to outstay our welcome. Thanking us for buying her book, Bluebell signed our copies with a flourish.

"You're welcome dears, it was lovely to meet you. Look after yourselves and I'm so glad you're enjoying your time with us at the Lido."

∼

The months flew by and in no time at all, new Lido contracts were due to be signed. This time, the contract was for a whole year and, to my joy, Pierre invited me to stay. This was welcome news. However, a new romance had developed since opening night, tempting me away from my career path. I was gradually warming to the idea of returning to England to hang up my dance shoes.

35

A CHANGE OF HEART

BACKSTAGE AT THE Lido, the conversations were mainly about the imminent, new contract.

"Are you signing for another year with us here at Le Lido, ma petite fleure?" quizzed my wardrobe assistant, Isobel, frowning one evening as she helped me force the zip of my costume together.

"I fink you need to do a little aerobics Cherie!" she puffed as she stood back to look at me. I had been busy entertaining my constant stream of visitors from Suffolk with sumptuous feasts, since my contract had begun, and it was starting to show. All my devoted friends and family in England, not to mention my Mum's work colleagues, had been arriving in coach loads on a regular basis. Taking full advantage of the opportunity to see me in action at last, I'd inadvertently found myself running a kind of holiday company. Their visits were accompanied by mammoth tours of Paris and, where most retired dancers from the Lido probably have beautiful photograph albums of themselves in their stunning costumes backstage, to show their grandchildren, I just have drunken snaps of my visitors on my lounge floor opening another bottle of red or waving on the back seats of the open topped bus.

One evening, as I tip-toed into the dressing room with the supplies for my next group of visitors, packets of croissants and bottles of wine peeping out of my grocery bags, I collided with Pierre Rambert.

"Bon appetit!" he smiled, laughing merrily.

I was so embarrassed because we were supposed to be dancers, not holiday reps.

"Ah oui! Merci Pierre," I laughed nervously, wishing the stairs would swallow me up. In addition to this, there were my indulgent days out with Gale and Diana when fine dining and tourism were becoming more of a priority than the show. I knew this life-style was very wrong if you were a dancer, but I had started to admit, it felt right. Seeing the principal dancers arriving from the gym, making the most of their prestigious role in the show, I felt confused knowing I should be doing the same. I'd also started to listen to BBC World Service in my flat and on a good day I could even find Radio Four while I baked and pottered, inviting the girls over for roast dinners, reluctant to leave for the theatre when it was time to set off.

If the homely comforts had been the only distractions to life in Paris though, I knew I could have considered putting down a deposit on my own flat, creating a real home that I could have balanced alongside my work for Miss Bluebell. Many dancers did just that. There was another more discernible reason playing on my mind though. Since meeting Steven, after opening night, he'd started to call me occasionally to see how the show was going, and I'd started looking forward to our chats more and more. The dancers at work found this hugely exciting.

"He's not as angry as you thought," teased Gale.

Past experiences led me to expect something was bound to eventually rear its head to spoil things. I tried not to be too pessimistic and as the weeks passed and our Lido contract drew to a close, the pressure was on to renew, and I knew I needed to make a decision.

Our wardrobe mistress, Isobel, always enjoyed little chats with me throughout the evening at her workstation by the stairs. She'd become a good friend and I decided to confide in her about my reservations for committing to the show for another year. It seemed such a long time and she knew all about my budding relationship with Steven. Repairing and adjusting costumes and reminding people when they had forgotten their feathers, crowns or tiaras, was Isobel's main responsibility, so I'd got to know her well over the months. She often stopped me at the bottom of the steps so she could give me a once over, just before I raced up three flights and onto the stage, warning me, "Your fevver iz missing again on your 'ed-dress Cherie," or, "Those are ze wrong shoes for ze snow scene."

The snow costume was Isobel's biggest concern, being constructed of sleeves with long poles attached to them with silver strings of tiny white pom-poms dangling off them like snowflakes. These usually entwined themselves around the pom-poms of the girl next to you if you weren't extremely careful. Poor Isobel often had to untangle people just before they set off to the stage, with seconds to spare, which must have been very stressful for her. During the ice-skating performance towards the finale, we would grace the stage in our pom-poms, as an ice rink rose up, out of the floor, to reveal a world-class skating couple, spinning in preparation for their opening sequence. One particular move gave me a funny turn every night when the man swung his wife around several times by her feet, her head missing the ice by a whisker. This always caused the audience to wince and gasp as we smiled out at them, confident that nothing would go wrong. It was our job, as the rink ascended, to teeter around the perimeter of the stage, arms raised over our heads, without falling down the forty foot drop onto the ice. Smiling gracefully from our viewing points, poised, elegant and beaming out to all, with no blood flow to our arms, we held them high until the skaters were finished and we reversed the process.

We had just managed to remove my snowflake arms one evening when Isobel pulled out a chair for me. It was becoming my favourite part of the show, where I had a good twenty minutes to wait for the next number, so we usually had a little natter and a swig out of her hip flask before I went to change for the finale. This particular night she could tell I was pre-occupied with thoughts of the contract renewal.

"Oh, Isobel, I just want a husband and lots of children really," I sighed.

"Me too!" she giggled, sewing on yet another diamante bead that had popped off my turquoise harem pants. Her smile faded though, becoming serious,

"Can I warn you, if that is really what you want, then I fink you will not find it ere in Le Lido Cherie?"

Isobel had been working for Miss Bluebell for many years, so she really was a voice of experience and, as she looked intently at me through a cloud of turquoise organza, her dark eyes piercing mine as she sewed, I knew she was right. There were occasionally successful relationships amongst the Lido cast and hospitality staff, but it was rare. I thought of Sherri-Lee, the beauty from Lancashire, who graced the Panache sign each night for the opening number, breath-taking under the spot-lights, living every girl's dream. The truth beneath the vision of splendour was that she was pining for her childhood sweetheart back home in Wigan. He had given up waiting for her and married someone else.

I made my decision to leave.

~

I'd started to warm to the idea of returning to England, with a view to spending more time with Steven, especially after my chats with Isobel. My plans wavered one evening though, when we heard on the dressing room grapevine, that there was a three-month, world cruise cabaret opportunity available, beginning just weeks after our last show at the Lido. Gale and Diana were ecstatic, insisting we all applied.

"This would be a perfect end to our time in Europe and we *have* to do it together," Gale announced, as we scrubbed our make-up off that evening.

I saw her point, but felt confused, especially when Steven urged me to accept it.

"You can't turn down a trip like that!" he'd laughed, his relaxed approach making me more and more keen to throw myself on the ferry to England.

I was anxious that he didn't seem to care if I went away, and immediately started to worry that he was just like all the others. Since his visit with Hilda, we'd started chatting regularly on the phone. This had led to a date with him, during a short trip home to visit family, that had ended in an extremely passionate kiss at the train station, leaving me weak at the knees and very reluctant to board the train.

Diana helped me on this occasion, reminding me of her long-term partner back in Australia that she'd abandoned during their back-packing holiday together.

"Paul is waiting for me in Melbourne. He knows that if he complains, I'll resent it for the rest of our lives. I'm sure we'll end up together. Listen, if a man is serious, he won't give up."

When I confessed my anxieties to Steven on the phone, he suggested he came over immediately to discuss it and my heart soared. We strolled around the Louvre, climbed the steps to admire the view at Sacré-Coeur and walked along the Seine, watching the world go by from bistros and restaurants. Sitting on a bench by the river on a rare night off, we surveyed the boats on the shimmering water in the quiet evening. Eventually, people started turning in for the night and as we watched the last of the party revellers swaying across the bridge, we turned our gaze to the large full moon that reflected beautifully on the river. There were moths humming around the streetlamp above our heads and Steven pointed them out.

"They're like you. Nocturnal, drawn to the spotlight, and if I try to catch you, mid-flight, or hold you down, you might disintegrate ... I'll wait ..."

I was speechless for a change, as he looked intently into my eyes.

"Go and have some fun on the ship with Gale and Diana, and then come back to me."

I was hooked.

36

END OF AN ERA

KNOWING WHAT A sad farewell it was going to be when Gale and Diana headed home, to the other side of the world, we agreed that the cruise would be a wonderful adventure before we all went our separate ways. Declining the Lido contract, we signed up immediately to sail the seas, reassured that we would be returning home within a few months. Gale was planning to finish her training at law school in America, Diana was keen to return to her boyfriend in Australia, and I had started to fantasize about domestic bliss. Astounded that the cruise had coincided so perfectly for us all though, we had decided it was meant to be.

Our cruise contract was offered purely on the basis that we were Bluebell Girls, reminding us that we were leaving a very prestigious post at the Lido, throwing caution to the wind with this little-known company.

Cruise rehearsals had over-lapped with our final week at the Lido, so we'd had to endure frantic hours of learning new routines in a stuffy studio in Pigalle, before throwing ourselves into the showers ready to perform for Bluebell until 2am at the Lido. Added to this, we'd been for travel vaccinations during the last week and trying to smile, exhausted as we forced our aching arms up for the opening number, was challenging to say the least.

Working in the theatre, we were all used to farewells at the end of contracts, taking the familiar, emotional hugs in our stride on our last night. It was a normal part of cabaret life to swap addresses at the end of each contract and wish each other luck in our next jobs. It was just how it was.

~

Christophe, our French dance captain for the cruise show, stubbed out his ciggie and hit the CD player.

"Ok girrrls, let's warm up!"

I didn't dare catch Diana's eye as Christophe started Le Jogging without taking his eyes off his reflection in the huge mirror on the wall. What he lacked in bulk, he certainly made up for in pizzazz in his brightly coloured lycra. His teeth gleamed and he had beautiful blue eyes that he flashed out to his imaginary audience as he strutted his stuff to his warm-up music which, on that particular morning was *I'm So Excited* sung by The Pointer Sisters. We all seemed to fall into the same way of dancing, excited for our upcoming cruise. Before long, he had us all beaming out at the mirror in the same way, keen to impress him on our first day.

"I'm so looking forward to settling into my cabin on board," Gale murmured as we waited for the Metro, later that day.

We were missing our chauffeur from the Lido. Not being used to public transport, we were keen to set sail, away from the crowded city, out to the fresh air of the ocean.

"All this hard slog will be worth it when we are being served local cuisine around the world," Gale continued dreamily.

I prayed that Christophe had it all under control.

~

It was on departure day that I started to feel a real sense of unease. As we set off on the train to Genoa in Italy to join our ship, Christophe explained that we were actually starting with a three-week tour of the Mediterranean before the world cruise really began. When he muttered something about waiting for our visas to come through, alarm bells rang. Added to this, I knew the weather could be unpredictable on the Mediterranean in March and April. Knowing that holiday firms often ran low budget trips until the weather improved on these waters, I feared ours was one of them, but I said nothing. We were on our way. It was too late to back out and we would have to make the best of the situation. I knew Gale had no idea about seasonal weather, being from Vegas. I remembered that once, she had booked a long weekend tour of Ireland in January, wondering why it wasn't green, sunny and colourful like the brochure.

I decided to do my utmost to keep everyone buoyant.

"Listen guys, once we get on the ship you'll relax, and we'll just have a wonderful time wherever they take us. Think of all the wonderful cuisine and wine-tasting," I reassured them.

Seeing as Gale had been encouraged by inspiring stories from my previous, five-star cruise experience to all corners of the globe for Olivier Briac, I felt rather responsible for the success of the trip.

Whilst waiting to join our ship, standing by the staff gang plank at the harbour in Genoa, we noticed that the staff disembarking for their day off, all looked rather tired and fed up. I didn't let it worry me overly at that stage.

"Why are we standing over here? I thought we would be greeted by the captain at the main entrance with the guests," Gale whispered, surveying the scene nervously.

When I squinted into the distance, noticing the new guests arriving excitedly for their holiday, I realised that this was not going to be anything like the cruise I had described to Gale and my heart sank. There were families with squabbling children clambering up the steps, eager to find their cabins, ignoring the captain as he stood smoking and chatting to some of the deck hands, in a rather crumpled uniform. This certainly wasn't the standard of voyage that Gale was expecting, more of a bargain cruise that was clearly not planning on going around the world at all. Christophe looked sheepish as I took in the scene, so I turned to Gale with a big smile.

"Don't worry, I'm sure it'll be great when we get going."

"I'm not so sure," Diana muttered as we noticed the previous cabaret artists climbing down from the luggage area, dragging their big trunks full of costumes. They looked exhausted and I noticed two of them cheering as they left. Sure enough, when we eventually were led to our cabins we realised, as we went further and further down into the depths of the ship, that we were going to be living in the basement.

"Oh, my Gaard, get me *off* this boat," Gale moaned, hurling her case into her cabin.

It was then that I saw a different side to Christophe as he sneered at her, "Well what did you expect Cherie, ze QE2?" he laughed mockingly before disappearing into his cabin.

"Girls, upstairs, now," Diana instructed as she grabbed my arm. After lobbing our cases into our cabins, we went back upstairs along the corridors of brightly patterned carpet, probably fitted, especially to disguise the patches of sick.

"I don't think Christophe realises who he's dealing with here," she whispered, "but I know we need a beer."

Guests were milling around the lounge area as we wove our way to the bar. I noticed a beautiful girl in floods of tears, and when she saw us, she made her way hurriedly over, eyes wide, chin trembling.

"Are you the new dancers?" she asked, gaping at us anxiously, barely audible.

Gale had started explaining a very complicated cocktail that she wanted, to a rather baffled barman, while Diana ordered some beers for us, so I signalled to her for an extra one and sat the poor girl down. Her name was Karen, one of the dancers from the previous show and she was supposed to be leaving that day. She had fallen in love with one of the waiters and, since he was on a permanent contract, he wasn't due to leave the ship with her. She was distraught, leaving it as late as possible before they would be forced to say their farewells. Hearing her tale of woe, Gale seized the moment, her legal mind whirring into action. Confident that she was completely within her rights to leave, she nestled in beside Karen.

"It's your lucky day honey, there is no way I am staying on this boat and I think you might be my passport out of here," she explained, then hesitated, "This is just not quite what I'd had in mind, lovely as it is ..." she added, grimacing as the waiter passed her what looked like a glass of orange squash.

I realised that Gale was about to show Christophe, that she wasn't just a pretty face. Sensing trouble, he had swiftly followed us back upstairs, where he was sat earwigging, while filling in forms for our cruise passes. Karen sat on a bar stool and leaned over to listen carefully as Gale explained her plan.

"Listen, if you wanna stay with your man, you can replace me. I'm not staying on this boat because it's not the quality world cruise that we were promised in the contract. If I teach you the dance numbers, you can take my place and I can leave at one of the next ports. Are you ready to work hard?" She held Karen's gaze, before turning to Christophe, who was pretending not to listen, anxiously taking in her every word, with no choice but to accept her decision.

Karen nodded, mesmerized, her tears drying and hope glowing in her eyes. Gale pointed out to Christophe, that it would be in his best interests to go along with her plan if he didn't want his company's reputation permanently ruined.

"I think we understand each other Christophe, don't we?" she demanded, still fuming.

Grabbing an itinerary programme from a passing holiday rep, Gale inspected the map of our route, planning where to get off and how long she would have, to teach Karen the entire show. There followed a mad dash to the office to sort out Karen's extension on board before the ship left the dock. Karen was ecstatic, looking like she had won the lottery, although her boyfriend, the handsome waiter, looked somewhat befuddled. She had cheered up immensely since hauling her suitcase into Gale's cabin and resuming her position on the top bunk, insisting Gale rested in bed.

"Have a rest Gale and we can start rehearsals in a few hours," she suggested, clapping her hands together with joy.

Chatting away later, as we followed her through the sparkling curtains onto the stage, Karen showed us around the theatre. Christophe came with us, realising he needed to be nice to us if his show was to survive.

"It's a bit of a squash but it's not the lack of space that's a problem, it's the rough sea that's a nightmare this time of year on the Med. You'll need to find your sea legs," she laughed merrily.

I had noticed that we were rocking about a bit already but had decided not to mention it on top of everything else we were dealing with. The hairdressers in the salon were struggling too and we could hear the head stylist, David from Liverpool, complaining as he sat with his legs crossed and arms folded stroppily. Karen took us in to meet him.

"Darlings, you don't realise the dangers that we face day to day in these storms, we're using *very* sharp instruments," he complained, "I mean it would be awful to take someone's ear off. We were thrown from pillar to post yesterday weren't we girls?"

He took out his manicure set and started filing his nails furiously as his ladies nodded in agreement. The cruise director was having his hair cut by one of the stylists and joined the conversation.

"Well, yes I appreciate your dilemma Monsieur Davide. Hopefully this weather will pass," he looked nervously out to sea and I wondered if anyone would actually know what to do if the ship ran into real difficulties. Christophe was looking rather green around the gills as we traipsed back to our cabins to unpack. The boat was rocking moderately, as it left the harbour, so we popped in to check on Gale.

"Oh, Lord please get me off this boat," she whispered as we peeped into her dark cabin where she laid on her bunk, listening to her relaxing pan pipe cassette, that played sea shanties. She'd ordered it especially for the cruise and the delightful sound of *Blow The Man Down* floated across the room from her tape recorder.

Over the next few days, Gale taught Karen most of the show and very soon, we found ourselves tearfully waving her off at a little train station on the Italian coast as she made her way back to Paris. As she leaned out of the window, the old train pulled away and I marvelled at her professionalism.

"See you in Vegas darling!" I sobbed, knowing it was unlikely. It was a very sad moment.

"Now don't take any nonsense from Christophe girls, I think you should finish on the boat and get home. This has been outrageous!" she ordered as her voice trailed off and the train slipped away.

It was, actually, to be thirty years before I saw her again.

After waving Gale off, Diana and I stopped at a bar for lunch at the harbour.

"See! It's not that bad, is it?" I said, as Diana looked up at the waiter. He was pouring her a tall beer into a cold glass while his colleague arrived with a steaming bowl of mussels in creamy garlic sauce. I gazed up the street at the pretty little shops and cafés, agreeing that although it was raining, it was a nice way to earn a living.

As is always my way, I just enjoyed the moment.

"How bad can it be?" I laughed.

We were about to find out.

∾

Christophe eventually confessed that the route was not further than the Mediterranean, but rather than being angry, we reminded ourselves that, coming from New Zealand, it was still a wonderful opportunity for Diana to see these places, feeling glad we hadn't panicked and fled.

I've always admired head strong, brave people that speak their mind when things are not right or fair. I appreciated Gale's business approach as she refused to stay on. We should really have gone back to Paris with her when the route was unfairly changed, however, we had developed a fear of missing out. We decided to persevere with Christophe's Cruise, being suckers for adventure, clinging on to the last few weeks that he had up his sleeve.

After a few weeks and I have to say, some marvellous meals along the coast of France and Italy, we all found ourselves on a train to Milan where Christophe insisted he had booked our show into a prestigious club, the cruise having been mysteriously cancelled. He finally admitted that he had fibbed a bit about the route of the ship in desperation to find dancers in Paris.

Apparently, the Porta D'Oro nightclub in Milan of today, is very slick but in 1989 it was in dire need of a re-vamp. As I stood singing *I will Survive* to an audience of six shifty looking men sat at tables with equally shady looking ladies, on our opening night, I knew it was definitely time for us to go home.

Diana and I agreed that evening, that although we were ready to leave, Gale would never forgive us if we left without our overdue wages that fortunately, were due to be paid the next morning. Early the next day, we popped out to the train station and purchased two tickets to Paris, for the lunchtime train. Returning to the hostel reception, we were relieved to find Christophe, reluctantly counting out our wages into envelopes.

"Pah! You two are out early!" he remarked, regarding us suspiciously as he handed over our money.

"Oh yes, we're determined to see all of Milan while we're here Christophe," I gushed.

The other girls went rushing off to the shops with their pay, while Diana and I went back to our room to wait for Christophe to leave, so we could slip away to freedom.

Sitting on our beds we reviewed our situation.

"That was the moment, just now, when we should have explained to Christophe that we're leaving," confessed Diana sheepishly.

"I know, I don't have the balls, do you?" I replied, as I tip-toed over to look through the key-hole at Christophe.

After putting away all his paperwork, I could just see him lighting up a cigarette and accepting a coffee from Carmella, the land lady of our hostel.

"Oh no! He's staying for coffee! We'll miss our train if we don't get going," I whispered frantically.

Knowing that our train from Milan to Paris was booked for midday, and was not going to wait for us, we started to panic slightly. A terrible drama would ensue if we strolled out with all our luggage, casually announcing that we were leaving. Terrified of confrontation, I thought long and hard about what the girls at St Claire's would do in an Enid Blyton novel.

Realising that Christophe and Carmella were settling in for the morning, I knew we had to take drastic action immediately. I wanted to go home so badly now, and I could see Diana was feeling miserable.

"OK, I tell you what we're going to do darling. We're going to put *all* our clothes on and walk out."

Diana stared at me, aghast.

I realised that fortunately, having left our big cases at Stephanie's flat in Paris, we only had soft nylon holdalls with us. If we filled them moderately with wash bags and shoes, we could wear layers of all our clothes, leaving nothing in the room but the keys and the rent on the bed. It was ridiculous, but our only hope and so, fifteen minutes later, we waddled out of our rooms, waving casually up the hallway to Christophe and Carmella. They stopped talking and glared across at us inquisitively.

"Just off to the shops!" we trilled, looking like we should really have been on our way to Weight Watchers.

Once on the main road, we chased a bus that was just leaving. Thankfully the driver saw us, slowing down again so we could leap on.

"Where's this bus even going?" Diana called out as I clambered up the steps with my bags,

"I don't care!" I yelled, "Quick! Get on, Christophe's coming!"

Leaving the hostel, we'd pretended not to hear Christophe shouting down the stairwell after us, our pace quickening rapidly as we'd bounced down the endless flights of stairs like Teletubbies. It was so obvious that we were up to something, and Christophe's clogs had clattered down the stairs after us, fortunately slowing him down.

It was about one hundred degrees on the bus and our hearts pumped with fear as we looked out of the back window anxiously, beads of sweat gathering on our foreheads. Just before the bus turned the corner, we saw Christophe burst out of the hostel door onto the street, looking up and down the road in search of his absconding Two Ton Tessies.

Once safely out of sight, the hideousness of the situation and the relief that we were free at last, struck me, setting me off into a fit of giggles. An elderly lady on the bus had been thoroughly enjoying the drama, fascinated as Diana and I collapsed into our seats. Realising that the bus was going in completely the wrong direction for the train station, I panicked slightly. Glancing at my watch, I rang the bell for the next stop. To the elderly ladies' delight, and the driver's annoyance, we bounced off again, miraculously straight into the path of an available taxi that whisked us to the railway station. Throwing ourselves gleefully onto our train to Paris, just minutes before it left, we collapsed onto the waiting seats with joy.

The journey to Paris was going to be long but we didn't care. We were free.

"I can't do this anymore. I'm tired of adventures," I sighed as we watched the Swiss Alps passing by, sipping large, welcome beers from the buffet car.

Diana snorted with laughter, "I loved the last few weeks though. Wouldn't have missed it for the world!"

On our return to Paris, we were thrilled to learn that Gale had immediately found work that she couldn't resist with Miss Doris at the casino in Monte Carlo. She was already in rehearsals. For Diana, recent events had made her rather homesick, so she promptly booked a flight home, much to the joy of her boyfriend.

For me, I knew it was time to get Angry, and I just hoped that he was still waiting patiently, but that's another story.

THE END

ABOUT THE AUTHOR

After hanging up her silver dancing shoes for the last time, Jane enjoyed a teaching career alongside her role as mother to Holly and William. Now busy writing and gardening in a rural part of Suffolk, she lives with her husband ... the one and only ... you'll have to read the book!

FURTHER READING

Chemo Summer by Jane Hoggar

In Chemo Summer, Jane takes the reader through a light-hearted and informative account of her discovery of breast cancer in 2014.

Cancer of any description has the capacity to chill those it affects, and their loved ones. But for Jane, early discovery and diagnosis provided for a satisfactory resolution. All side issues are covered in this book, effects of chemo and radiotherapy, hair loss, wigs, changes in diet and exercise, making Chemo Summer a valuable and engaging look into a serious and often frightening subject.

Available on Amazon
or
www.austinmacauley.com

Further photographs of Jane's travels and more recent events can be found @janehoggar
Facebook and Instagram

BV - #0013 - 150621 - C0 - 216/140/24 - PB - 9781913425975 - Gloss Lamination